*Civil Engineering and
Engineering Mechanics Series*

N. M. Newmark and W. J. Hall, Editors

ELASTICITY IN ENGINEERING MECHANICS, by Arthur P. Boresi
ELEMENTARY STRUCTURAL MECHANICS, by Tung Au
FOUNDATION DESIGN, by Wayne C. Teng
STRUCTURE IN ARCHITECTURE, by Mario G. Salvadori
THEORY OF PRESTRESSED CONCRETE, by Michael Chi and Frank A. Biberstein

PRENTICE-HALL INTERNATIONAL, INC., *London*
PRENTICE-HALL OF AUSTRALIA, PTY., LTD., *Sydney*
PRENTICE-HALL OF CANADA, LTD., *Toronto*
PRENTICE-HALL OF INDIA (PRIVATE) LTD., *New Delhi*
PRENTICE-HALL OF JAPAN, INC., *Tokyo*

*ELASTICITY IN
ENGINEERING MECHANICS*

Civil Engineering and
Engineering Mechanics Series

N. M. Newmark and W. J. Hall, Editors

ELASTICITY IN
ENGINEERING MECHANICS

Arthur P. Boresi

Professor of Theoretical and Applied Mechanics
University of Illinois

Prentice-Hall, Inc.

Englewood Cliffs, New Jersey

Library of Congress Catalog Card Number 65–15093

Printed in the United States of America
24691—C

To Henry Louis Langhaar
Teacher and Friend

PREFACE

The material presented here is intended to prepare the student for a critical study of the fundamentals of several branches of solid mechanics. In Chapter 1, some preliminary requisite mathematics is presented. Chapter 2 presents the theory of stress, while Chapter 3 discusses the theory of strain. These theories are separated purposely to emphasize their independence of one another and also to emphasize the striking similarities between them. Furthermore, by examining them separately one can more easily illustrate their general nature; that is, they depend only on the approximations entailed by a continuous medium model, and they are independent of material properties. Certain parts of Chapter 3 follow closely the theory of deformation presented in *Theory of Shells* (class notes) by H. L. Langhaar. The general theory of strain is treated (in contrast to the classical small-displacement theory of strain), making it easily possible to examine the approximations entailed in the classical theory of elasticity. Furthermore, in the theories of shells and stability (buckling), general strain theory is required, so that Chapter 3 serves as preliminary theory for a rigorous study of shells and buckling.

In Chapter 4, the theories of stress and strain are united for elastic media which obey the generalized Hooke law. General results are specialized for isotropic homogeneous linearly elastic materials. However, some emphasis also is placed on anisotropic elastic materials.

In Chapters 2, 3, and 4, general three-dimensional theory is presented for rectangular cartesian coordinates (x, y, z). The general three-dimensional results are specialized for plane isotropic elasticity theory with respect to rectangular cartesian coordinates (x, y) in Chapter 5 and with respect to polar coordinates (r, θ) in Chapter 6. In Chapter 7, the problem of a

prismatic bar subjected to end load is treated; while Chapter 8 gives an introduction to the theory of thermal stress. The basic elasticity equations in three dimensions are expressed in orthogonal curvilinear coordinates in Appendix A; a brief discussion of certain numerical methods is presented in Appendix B.

A novel feature of the text is the inclusion of Appendices to Chapters 2, 3, and 4 in which the basic elasticity equations are presented in index notation. Hence, after studying the concepts of index notation presented in Chapter 1 the reader may, if he desires, develop the subsequent theory in index notation. Alternatively, he may study these Appendices after studying the text proper, thus gradually acquiring a working knowledge of index notation by using it to summarize principal results. Another feature of the text is the inclusion of a number of exercises whereby the student may test his understanding of basic concepts.

The material presented here and the order of presentation have been evolved by the author in the process of teaching to engineering students an introductory course in elasticity; the course also served as a prerequisite for further study in the mechanics of solids (theory of shells, buckling, etc.). Experience has shown the material to be suitable for senior undergraduate students in the Engineering Mechanics curriculum at the University of Illinois as well as for first-year graduate students in engineering.

The author is indebted to Professor H. L. Langhaar for many stimulating discussions on ways to present an introductory course in mechanics of deformable bodies, with emphasis on elasticity. The organization of the book and the topics treated reflect this indebtedness. A number of the problems were contributed by Dr. R. E. Miller. The author also wishes to express his thanks to Mrs. Hertha Vandiver, who expertly and cheerfully typed the manuscript. Finally, thanks are due Professor N. M. Newmark for his encouragement and counsel and to the publishers for their cooperation and help.

Urbana, Illinois   ARTHUR P. BORESI

CONTENTS

1 PRELIMINARY MATHEMATICS   1

1–1 Brief Summary of Vector Algebra, 1.   1–2 Scalar Point
Functions, 4.   1–3 Vector Fields, 6.   1–4 Differentiation
of Vectors, 7.   1–5 Differentiation of a Scalar Field, 8.
1–6 Differentiation of a Vector Field, 9.   1–7 Curl of a
Vector Field, 9.   1–8 Eulerian Continuity Equation for
Fluids, 10.   1–9 Divergence Theorem, 11.   1–10 Diver-
gence Theorem in Two Dimensions, 13.   1–11 Line and
Surface Integrals (Application of Scalar Product), 14.   1–12
Stokes' Theorem, 15.   1–13 Exact Differential, 15.   1–14
Orthogonal Curvilinear Coordinates in Three-dimensional
Space, 16.   1–15 Expression for Differential Length in Or-
thogonal Curvilinear Coordinates, 17.   1–16 The Gradient
and the Laplacian in Orthogonal Curvilinear Coordinates, 18.
1–17 Index Notation: Summation Convention, 21.   1–18
Transformation of Tensors under Change of Rectangular
Cartesian Coordinate System, 24.   1–19 Symmetric and
Antisymmetric Parts of a Tensor, 29.   1–20 The Symbols
δ_{ij} and ε_{ijk}, 30.   1–21 Homogeneous Quadratic Forms, 32.

2 THEORY OF STRESS FOR CONTINUOUS MEDIA   35

2–1 Definition of Stress, 35.   2–2 Stress Notation, 37.
2–3 Equilibrium of Moments. Stress on an Oblique Plane,
39.   2–4 Tensor Character of Stress. Transformation of
Stress Components under Change of Coordinate System, 43.
2–5 Principal Stresses. Stress Invariants. Extremum Values,
44.   2 6 Mean and Deviator Stress Tensor. Octahedral
Stress, 50.   2–7 Plane Stress, 52.   2–8 Differential Equations of Motion of a Deformable Body, 56.   Appendix:
Theory of Stress in Index Notation, 59.   A2–1 Stress Notation. Stress Formulas, 59.   A2–2 Transformation of Stress
Components under Change of Coordinate System, 60.
A2–3 Principal Stress. Principal Directions, 60.   A2–4
Equations of Motion, 61.

3 THEORY OF DEFORMATION FOR CONTINUOUS MEDIA 63

3–1 Rigid-body Displacements, 63. 3–2 Deformation of a
Continuous Body, 64. 3–3 Strain of Any Line Element,
67. 3–4 Definition of Strain, 71. 3–5 Final Direction of
a Deformed Line Element, 72. 3–6 Shearing Strain, 74.
3–7 The Strain Tensor, 75. 3–8 Principal Strains, 76.
3–9 Volumetric Strain, 78. 3–10 Mean and Deviator Strain
Tensor. Octahedral Strain, 79. 3–11 Rotation of a Volume
Element, 81. 3–12 Strain Components in Terms of (ω_x, ω_y,
ω_z). Small Displacement Theory, 83. 3–13 Special Types
of Strain, 87. 3–14 Compatibility Conditions of the Classical Theory of Small Displacements, 90. Appendix: Theory
of Strain in Index Notation, 92. A3–1 Strain of Any Line
Element. Strain Components, 92. A3–2 Definition of
Shearing Strain, 94. A3–3 Tensor Character of $\varepsilon_{\alpha\beta}$. The
Strain Tensor, 96. A3–4 Determination of Principal
Strains. Principal Axes, 97.

4 STRESS-STRAIN RELATIONS OF ELASTICITY 102

4–1 Concept of Elasticity, 102. 4–2 Strain Energy Density Function, 103. 4–3 Relation of Stress Components to
Strain Energy Density Function for an Adiabatic Deformation Process, 104. 4–4 Generalized Hooke's Law, 106.
4–5 Isotropic Media. Homogeneous Media, 109. 4–6
Strain Energy Density for Elastically Isotropic Medium
under Adiabatic Conditions, 110. 4–7 Special States of
Stress, 112. 4–8 Equations of Thermoelasticity for Isotropic Media, 114. 4–9 Thermoelastic Compatibility
Equations in Terms of Components of Stress and Temperature, 115. 4–10 Boundary Conditions, 118. 4–11 Uniqueness Theorem for Equilibrium Problem of Elasticity, 119.
4–12 Elementary Three-dimensional Problems of Elasticity.
Semi-inverse Method, 121. 4–13 Torsion of Shaft with
Constant Circular Cross Section, 123. Appendix: Stress-
strain Relations of Elasticity, 128. A4–1 Stress-strain Energy Density Function Relation, 128. A4–2 Generalized
Hooke's Law, 129.

5 *BASIC EQUATIONS OF THE PLANE THEORY OF ELASTICITY* **131**

5–1 Plane Strain, 131. 5–2 Generalized Plane Stress, 133.
5–3 Compatibility Equation in Terms of Stress Components,
136. 5–4 Airy Stress Function, 138. 5–5 Polynomial
Solutions of Two-dimensional Problems in Rectangular Cartesian Coordinates, 145. 5–6 Displacement Components
for Plane Elasticity, 148.

6 *PLANE ELASTICITY IN POLAR COORDINATES* **152**

6–1 Equilibrium Equations in Polar Coordinates, 152. 6–2
Stress Components in Terms of Airy Stress Function
$F = F (r, \theta)$, 153. 6–3 Compatibility Equation for Plane
Elasticity in Terms of Polar Coordinates, 154. 6–4 Axially
Symmetric Problems, 155. 6–5 Strain Components in
Polar Coordinates, 158.

7 *PRISMATIC BAR SUBJECTED TO END LOAD* **162**

7–1 General Problem of Three-dimensional Elastic Bars
Subjected to Transverse End Loads, 162. 7–2 Torsion of
Prismatic Bars. Saint-Venant's Solution. Warping Function,
164. 7–3 Prandtl Torsion Function, 168. 7–4 A Method
of Solution of the Torsion Problem: Elliptic Cross Section,
172. 7–5 Remarks on Solutions of Laplace Equation,
$\nabla^2 F = 0$, 175. 7–6 Torsion of Bars with Tubular Cavities,
178. 7–7 Transfer of Axis of Twist, 181. 7–8 Shearing-
stress Component in Any Direction, 182. 7–9 Solution of
Torsion Problem by the Prandtl Membrane Analogy, 185.
7–10 Solution by Method of Series. Rectangular Section,
190. 7–11 Bending of a Bar Subjected to Transverse End
Force, 195. 7–12 Displacement of a Cantilever Beam Subjected to Transverse End Force, 203. 7–13 Center of
Shear, 206. 7–14 Bending of a Bar with Elliptic Cross
Section, 209. 7–15 Bending of a Bar with Rectangular
Cross Section, 211.

8 *THERMAL STRESS* **216**

8–1 Introduction, 216. 8–2 The Differential Equation of Heat Conduction, 218. 8–3 Elementary Approach to Thermal-stress Problem in One and Two Variables, 220. 8–4 Transformation of the Equations of Thermal Stress to Equivalent Displacement Problem, 224. 8–5 Spherically Symmetrical Stress Distribution (The Sphere), 227. 8–6 Plane Theory of Thermoelasticity, 229. 8–7 Concept of Displacement Potential. Plane Theory of Thermoelasticity, 232. 8–8 Thermoelastic Equations for Axially Symmetrical Stress Distribution, 236.

APPENDIX

A *EQUATIONS OF EQUILIBRIUM AND STRAIN DISPLACEMENT RELATIONS IN ORTHOGONAL CURVILINEAR COORDINATES* **241**

A–1 Geometrical Preliminaries, 241. A–2 Equations of Equilibrium, 243. A–3 Strain-Displacement Relations, 246.

APPENDIX

B *NUMERICAL APPROXIMATION OF TORSION PROBLEM* **250**

B–1 Introduction, 250. B–2 Finite Difference Approximations, 250. B–3 Application of Difference Equations to the Torsion Problem, 252. B–4 Higher-order Difference Approximations, 253. B–5 Stress Components of Torsion Problem, 254. B–6 Relaxation Technique, 255.

INDEX **257**

*ELASTICITY IN
ENGINEERING MECHANICS*

1
PRELIMINARY MATHEMATICS

This chapter sets down some prerequisite mathematics that will be useful in subsequent developments in the text proper and in appendices.

1-1 Brief Summary of Vector Algebra

A boldface letter will denote a vector quantity, unless an explicit statement to the contrary is given. Thus, **A** denotes a vector. Frequently, we denote a vector by the set of its projections (A_x, A_y, A_z) on rectangular cartesian axes (x, y, z). Thus,

$$\mathbf{A} = (A_x, A_y, A_z) \qquad (1\text{--}1.1)$$

The magnitude of a vector **A** is denoted by

$$|\mathbf{A}| = A = (A_x^2 + A_y^2 + A_z^2)^{1/2} \qquad (1\text{--}1.2)$$

We may also express a vector in terms of its components with respect to (x, y, z) axes. For example,

$$\mathbf{A} = \mathbf{i}A_x + \mathbf{j}A_y + \mathbf{k}A_z \qquad (1\ 1.3)$$

where $\mathbf{i}A_x, \mathbf{j}A_y, \mathbf{k}A_z$ are components of **A** with respect to axes (x, y, z) and **i**, **j**, **k**, are unit vectors directed along positive (x, y, z) axes, respectively. In general, the symbols **i**, **j**, **k** will denote *unit* vectors.

Vector quantities obey the *associative law of vector addition*

$$\mathbf{A} + (\mathbf{B} + \mathbf{C}) = (\mathbf{A} + \mathbf{B}) + \mathbf{C} = \mathbf{A} + \mathbf{B} + \mathbf{C} \qquad (1\text{--}1.4)$$

and the *commutative law of vector addition*

$$\mathbf{A} + \mathbf{B} + \mathbf{C} = \mathbf{B} + \mathbf{A} + \mathbf{C} = \mathbf{B} + \mathbf{C} + \mathbf{A} \qquad (1\text{--}1.5)$$

Symbolically, we may represent a vector quantity by an arrow (Fig. 1–1.1), with the understanding that the addition of any two arrows (vectors) must obey the commutative law [Eq. (1–1.5)].

The *scalar product* of two vectors **A**, **B** is defined to be

$$\mathbf{A} \cdot \mathbf{B} = A_x B_x + A_y B_y + A_z B_z \qquad (1\text{--}1.6)$$

where the symbol • is a conventional notation for the scalar product. By the above definition, it follows that the scalar product of vectors is commutative; that is,

$$\mathbf{A} \cdot \mathbf{B} = \mathbf{B} \cdot \mathbf{A} \qquad (1\text{--}1.7)$$

A useful property of the scalar product of two vectors is

$$\mathbf{A} \cdot \mathbf{B} = AB \cos \theta \qquad (1\text{--}1.8)$$

where A and B denote the magnitudes of vectors **A** and **B**, respectively, and the angle θ denotes the angle formed by vectors **A** and **B** (Fig. 1–1.2).

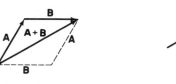

Figure 1-1.1   **Figure 1-1.2**

If **B** is a unit vector in the x direction, Eqs. (1–1.3) and (1–1.8) yield $A_x = A \cos \alpha$, where α is the direction angle between the vector **A** and the positive x axis. Similarly, $A_y = A \cos \beta$, $A_z = A \cos \gamma$, where β, γ denote direction angles between the vector **A** and the y axis and the z axis, respectively. Substitution of these expressions into Eq. (1–1.2) yields the relation

$$\cos^2 \alpha + \cos^2 \beta + \cos^2 \gamma = 1 \qquad (1\text{--}1.9)$$

Thus, the direction cosines of vector **A** *are not independent*. They must satisfy Eq. (1–1.9).

The scalar-product law of vectors has other properties in common with the product of numbers. For example,

$$\mathbf{A} \cdot (\mathbf{B} + \mathbf{C}) = \mathbf{A} \cdot \mathbf{B} + \mathbf{A} \cdot \mathbf{C} \qquad (1\text{--}1.10)$$

$$(\mathbf{A} + \mathbf{B}) \cdot (\mathbf{C} + \mathbf{D}) = (\mathbf{A} + \mathbf{B}) \cdot \mathbf{C} + (\mathbf{A} + \mathbf{B}) \cdot \mathbf{D}$$

$$= \mathbf{A} \cdot \mathbf{C} + \mathbf{B} \cdot \mathbf{C} + \mathbf{A} \cdot \mathbf{D} + \mathbf{B} \cdot \mathbf{D} \qquad (1\text{--}1.11)$$

The *vector product* of two vectors **A** and **B** is defined to be a third vector **C** whose magnitude C is given by the relation

$$C = AB \sin \theta \qquad (1\text{--}1.12)$$

The direction of vector **C** is perpendicular to the plane formed by vectors **A** and **B**. The sense of **C** is such that the three vectors, **A**, **B**, **C** form a right-handed or left-handed system according as the coordinate system (x, y, z) is right-handed or left-handed (see Fig. 1–1.3).

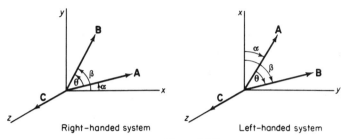

Right–handed system   Left–handed system

Figure 1-1.3

Symbolically, we denote the vector product of **A** and **B** in the form

$$\mathbf{C} = \mathbf{A} \times \mathbf{B} \tag{1–1.13}$$

where $\times$ denotes vector product (or cross product). In determinant notation, Eq. (1–1.13) may be written

$$\mathbf{C} = \begin{vmatrix} \mathbf{i} & \mathbf{j} & \mathbf{k} \\ A_1 & A_2 & A_3 \\ B_1 & B_2 & B_3 \end{vmatrix} \tag{1–1.13a}$$

where (A_1, A_2, A_3), (B_1, B_2, B_3) denote $(\mathbf{i}, \mathbf{j}, \mathbf{k})$ components of vectors $(\mathbf{A}, \mathbf{B})$ respectively.

The vector product of vectors has the following property:

$$\mathbf{A} \times \mathbf{B} = -\mathbf{B} \times \mathbf{A} \tag{1–1.14}$$

Accordingly, the vector product of vectors is not commutative.

The vector product also has the following properties:

$$\mathbf{R} \times (\mathbf{A} + \mathbf{B}) = \mathbf{R} \times \mathbf{A} + \mathbf{R} \times \mathbf{B}$$
$$(\mathbf{A} + \mathbf{B}) \times \mathbf{R} = \mathbf{A} \times \mathbf{R} + \mathbf{B} \times \mathbf{R} \tag{1–1.15}$$

$$(\mathbf{A} + \mathbf{B}) \times (\mathbf{C} + \mathbf{D}) = (\mathbf{A} + \mathbf{B}) \times \mathbf{C} + (\mathbf{A} + \mathbf{B}) \times \mathbf{D}$$
$$= \mathbf{A} \times \mathbf{C} + \mathbf{B} \times \mathbf{C} + \mathbf{A} \times \mathbf{D} + \mathbf{B} \times \mathbf{D} \tag{1–1.16}$$

The scalar triple product of three vectors **A**, **B**, **C** is defined by the relation

$$\mathbf{A} \cdot (\mathbf{B} \times \mathbf{C}) = A_x(B_yC_z - B_zC_y) + A_y(B_zC_x - B_xC_z) + A_z(B_xC_y - B_yC_x) \tag{1–1.17}$$

In determinant notation, the scalar triple product is

$$\mathbf{A} \cdot (\mathbf{B} \times \mathbf{C}) = \begin{vmatrix} A_x & A_y & A_z \\ B_x & B_y & B_z \\ C_x & C_y & C_z \end{vmatrix} \qquad (1\text{-}1.18)$$

Since only the sign of a determinant changes when two rows are interchanged, two consecutive transpositions of rows leave a determinant unchanged. Consequently,

$$\mathbf{A} \cdot (\mathbf{B} \times \mathbf{C}) = \mathbf{C} \cdot (\mathbf{A} \times \mathbf{B}) = \mathbf{B} \cdot (\mathbf{C} \times \mathbf{A}) \qquad (1\text{-}1.19)$$

Another useful property is the relation

$$(\mathbf{A} \times \mathbf{B}) \cdot \mathbf{C} = \mathbf{A} \cdot (\mathbf{B} \times \mathbf{C}) \qquad (1\text{-}1.20)$$

The vector triple product of three vectors $\mathbf{A}, \mathbf{B}, \mathbf{C}$ is defined as follows:

$$\mathbf{A} \times (\mathbf{B} \times \mathbf{C}) = \mathbf{B}(\mathbf{A} \cdot \mathbf{C}) - \mathbf{C}(\mathbf{A} \cdot \mathbf{B}) \qquad (1\text{-}1.21)$$

Furthermore,

$$(\mathbf{A} \times \mathbf{B}) \cdot (\mathbf{C} \times \mathbf{D}) = \mathbf{A} \cdot \mathbf{B} \times (\mathbf{C} \times \mathbf{D}) = \mathbf{A} \cdot [\mathbf{C}(\mathbf{B} \cdot \mathbf{D}) - (\mathbf{B} \cdot \mathbf{C})\mathbf{D}]$$

$$= (\mathbf{A} \cdot \mathbf{C})(\mathbf{B} \cdot \mathbf{D}) - (\mathbf{A} \cdot \mathbf{D})(\mathbf{B} \cdot \mathbf{C}) \qquad (1\text{-}1.22)$$

Equation (1–1.22) follows from Eqs. (1–1.20) and (1–1.21).

1-2 Scalar Point Functions

Any scalar function $f(x, y, z)$ that is defined at all points in a region of space is called a *scalar point function*. Conceivably, the function f may depend on time, but, if it does, attention can be confined to conditions at a particular instant. The region of space in which f is defined is called a *scalar field*. It is assumed that f is differentiable in this scalar field. Physical examples of scalar point functions are the mass density of a compressible medium, the temperature in a body, the flux density in a nuclear reactor, and the potential in an electrostatic field.

Consider the rate of change of the function f in various directions at some point $P: (x, y, z)$ in the scalar field for which f is defined. Let (x, y, z) take increments (dx, dy, dz). Then, the function f takes an increment

$$df = \frac{\partial f}{\partial x} dx + \frac{\partial f}{\partial y} dy + \frac{\partial f}{\partial z} dz \qquad (1\text{-}2.1)$$

Consider the infinitesimal vector $\mathbf{i}\, dx + \mathbf{j}\, dy + \mathbf{k}\, dz$, where $(\mathbf{i}, \mathbf{j}, \mathbf{k})$ are unit vectors in the (x, y, z) directions, respectively. Its magnitude is $ds = (dx^2 + dy^2 + dz^2)^{1/2}$, and its direction cosines are

$$\cos \alpha = \frac{dx}{ds}, \qquad \cos \beta = \frac{dy}{ds}, \qquad \cos \gamma = \frac{dz}{ds}$$

The vector $\mathbf{i}(dx/ds) + \mathbf{j}(dy/ds) + \mathbf{k}(dz/ds)$ is a unit vector in the direction of $\mathbf{i}\, dx + \mathbf{j}\, dy + \mathbf{k}\, dz$ since division of a vector by a scalar alters only the magnitude of the vector. Dividing Eq. (1–2.1) by ds, we obtain

$$\frac{df}{ds} = \frac{\partial f}{\partial x}\frac{dx}{ds} + \frac{\partial f}{\partial y}\frac{dy}{ds} + \frac{\partial f}{\partial z}\frac{dz}{ds}$$

or

$$\frac{df}{ds} = \frac{\partial f}{\partial x}\cos\alpha + \frac{\partial f}{\partial y}\cos\beta + \frac{\partial f}{\partial z}\cos\gamma \qquad (1\text{–}2.2)$$

From Eq. (1–2.2) it is apparent that df/ds depends on the direction of s; that is, it depends on the direction (α, β, γ). For this reason, df/ds is known as the *directional derivative* of f in the direction (α, β, γ). It represents the rate of change of f in the direction (α, β, γ). For example, if $\alpha = 0$

$$\frac{df}{ds} = \frac{\partial f}{\partial x} \qquad (a)$$

This is the rate of change of f in the direction of the x axis.

Maximum value of the directional derivative. Gradient. By definition of the scalar product of two vectors, Eq. (1–2.2) may be written in the form

$$\frac{df}{ds} = \mathbf{n} \cdot \operatorname{grad} f \qquad (1\text{–}2.3)$$

where $\mathbf{n} = \mathbf{i}\cos\alpha + \mathbf{j}\cos\beta + \mathbf{k}\cos\gamma$ is a unit vector in the direction (α, β, γ), and

$$\operatorname{grad} f = \mathbf{i}\frac{\partial f}{\partial x} + \mathbf{j}\frac{\partial f}{\partial y} + \mathbf{k}\frac{\partial f}{\partial z} \qquad (1\text{–}2.4)$$

is a *vector* point function (see Art. 1–4) of (x, y, z) called the *gradient* of the scalar function f. Since $\mathbf{n}$ is a unit vector, Eq. (1–2.3) shows that $|\operatorname{grad} f|$ is the maximum value of df/ds at the point $P: (x, y, z)$, and that the direction of $\operatorname{grad} f$ is the direction in which $f(x, y, z)$ *increases* most rapidly. Equation (1–2.3) also shows that the directional derivative of f in any direction is the component of the vector $\operatorname{grad} f$ in that direction.

The equation $f(x, y, z) = C$ defines a family of surfaces, one surface for each value of the constant C. These are called *level surfaces* of the function f. If $\mathbf{n}$ is tangent to a level surface, the directional derivative of f in the direction of $\mathbf{n}$ is zero, since f is constant along a level surface. Consequently, by Eq. (1–2.3) the vector $\mathbf{n}$ must be perpendicular to the vector $\operatorname{grad} f$ when $\mathbf{n}$ is tangent to a level surface. Accordingly, the vector $\operatorname{grad} f$ at the point $P: (x, y, z)$ is normal to the level surface of f through the point $P: (x, y, z)$.

A symbolic vector operator, called *del* or *nabla*, is defined as follows:

$$\nabla = \mathbf{i}\frac{\partial}{\partial x} + \mathbf{j}\frac{\partial}{\partial y} + \mathbf{k}\frac{\partial}{\partial z} \qquad (1\text{–}2.5)$$

By Eqs. (1–2.3), (1–2.4), and (1–2.5),

$$\operatorname{grad} f = \nabla f$$

and

$$\frac{df}{ds} = \mathbf{n} \cdot \nabla f$$

By definition,

$$\nabla \cdot \nabla = \nabla^2 = \frac{\partial^2}{\partial x^2} + \frac{\partial^2}{\partial y^2} + \frac{\partial^2}{\partial z^2} \tag{1-2.6}$$

Consequently, the Laplace equation may be written symbolically as follows:

$$\nabla^2 f = \frac{\partial^2 f}{\partial x^2} + \frac{\partial^2 f}{\partial y^2} + \frac{\partial^2 f}{\partial z^2} = 0 \tag{1-2.7}$$

For this reason the symbolic operator ∇^2 is called the *Laplacian*.

1-3 Vector Fields

Assume that for each point P: (x, y, z) in a region there exists a vector point function $\mathbf{q}(x, y, z)$. This vector point function is called a *vector field*. It may be represented at each point in the region by a vector with length equal to the magnitude of $\mathbf{q}$ and drawn in the direction of $\mathbf{q}$. For example, for each point in a flowing fluid, there corresponds a vector $\mathbf{q}$ that represents the velocity of the particle of fluid at that point. This vector point function is called the velocity field of the fluid. Another example of a vector field is the displacement vector function for the particles of a deformable body. Electric and magnetic field intensities are also vector fields. A vector field is often simply called a "vector."

In any continuous vector field there exists a system of curves, such that the vectors along a curve are everywhere tangent to the curve; that is, the vector field consists exclusively of tangent vectors to the curves. These curves are called the *vector lines* (or *field lines*) of the field. The vector lines of a velocity field are called *stream lines*. The vector lines in an electrostatic or magneto-static field are known as *lines of force*. In general, the vector function $\mathbf{q}$ may depend on x, y, z, and t, where t denotes time. If $\mathbf{q}$ depends on time, the field is said to be *unsteady* or *nonstationary;* that is, the field varies with time. For a *steady field*, $\mathbf{q} = \mathbf{q}(x, y, z)$. For example, if a velocity field changes with time (i.e., if the flow is unsteady), the stream lines may change with time.

A vector field $\mathbf{q} = \mathbf{i}u + \mathbf{j}v + \mathbf{k}w$ is defined by expressing the components, u, v, w, as functions of (x, y, z). If (dx, dy, dz) is an infinitesimal vector in the direction of the vector $\mathbf{q}$, the direction cosines of this vector are $dx/ds = u/q$, $dy/ds = v/q$, $dz/ds = w/q$. Consequently, the differential equations of the system of vector lines of the field are

$$\frac{ds}{q} = \frac{dx}{u} = \frac{dy}{v} = \frac{dz}{w} \tag{1-3.1}$$

In Eq. (1-3.1), the components u, v, w are functions of (x, y, z). The finite equations of the system of vector lines are obtained by integrating Eq. (1–

3.1). The theory of integration of differential equations of this type is explained in most books on differential equations.[1]

If a given vector field **q** is the gradient of a scalar field f (i.e., if $\mathbf{q} = \operatorname{grad} f$), the scalar function f is called a potential function for the vector field, and the vector field is called a potential field. Since $\operatorname{grad} f$ is perpendicular to the level surfaces of f, it follows that the vector lines of a potential field are everywhere normal to the level surfaces of the potential function.

1-4 Differentiation of Vectors

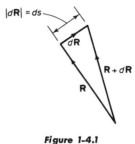

Figure 1-4.1

An infinitesimal increment $d\mathbf{R}$ of a vector **R** need not be collinear with the vector **R**(Fig. 1–4.1). Consequently, in general, the vector $\mathbf{R} + d\mathbf{R}$ differs from the vector **R**, not only in magnitude, but also in direction. It would be misleading to denote the magnitude of the vector $d\mathbf{R}$ by dR, since dR denotes the increment of the magnitude R. Accordingly, the magnitude of $d\mathbf{R}$ is denoted by $|d\mathbf{R}|$, or by another symbol, such as ds. The magnitude of the vector $\mathbf{R} + d\mathbf{R}$ is $R + dR$. Figure 1–4.1 shows that $R + dR \leqq R + |d\mathbf{R}|$. Hence, $dR \leqq |d\mathbf{R}|$.

If the vector **R** is a function of a scalar t (where t may or may not denote time), $d\mathbf{R}/dt$ is defined to be a vector in the direction of $d\mathbf{R}$, with magnitude ds/dt (where $ds = |d\mathbf{R}|$).

Vectors obey the same rules of differentiation as scalars. This fact may be demonstrated by the Δ method that is used for deriving differentiation formulas in scalar calculus. For example, consider the derivative of the vector function $\mathbf{Q} = u\mathbf{R}$, where u is a scalar function of t, and **R** is a vector function of t. If t takes an increment Δt, **R** and u take increments $\Delta\mathbf{R}$ and Δu. Hence

$$\mathbf{Q} + \Delta\mathbf{Q} = (u + \Delta u)(\mathbf{R} + \Delta\mathbf{R}).$$

Subtracting $\mathbf{Q} = u\mathbf{R}$, and dividing by Δt, we obtain

$$\frac{\Delta\mathbf{Q}}{\Delta t} = \mathbf{R}\frac{\Delta u}{\Delta t} + u\frac{\Delta\mathbf{R}}{\Delta t} + \Delta u\frac{\Delta\mathbf{R}}{\Delta t}.$$

As $\Delta t \to 0$, $\Delta u \to 0$, $\Delta\mathbf{Q}/\Delta t \to d\mathbf{Q}/dt$, $\Delta u/\Delta t \to du/dt$, and $\Delta\mathbf{R}/\Delta t \to d\mathbf{R}/dt$. Hence,

$$\frac{d\mathbf{Q}}{dt} = \mathbf{R}\frac{du}{dt} + u\frac{d\mathbf{R}}{dt} \qquad (1\text{–}4.1)$$

---

[1]M. Morris and O. E. Brown, *Differential Equations*, 4th ed. (Englewood Cliffs, N.J.: Prentice-Hall, Inc., 1964). E. L. Ince, *Ordinary Differential Equations* (New York: Dover Publications).

Equation (1–4.1) has the same form as the formula for the derivative of the product of two scalars.

Let $\mathbf{R} = \mathbf{i}u + \mathbf{j}v + \mathbf{k}w$ be a single vector (not a vector field) where $\mathbf{i}, \mathbf{j}, \mathbf{k}$ are unit vectors and (u, v, w) are the $\mathbf{i}, \mathbf{j}, \mathbf{k}$ projections of $\mathbf{R}$, respectively. Let (u, v, w) take increments (du, dv, dw). Then since $(\mathbf{i}, \mathbf{j}, \mathbf{k})$ are constants, $\mathbf{R}$ takes the increment, $d\mathbf{R} = \mathbf{i}\,du + \mathbf{j}\,dv + \mathbf{k}\,dw$, where in general, $d\mathbf{R}$ is not collinear with $\mathbf{R}$. If (u, v, w) are functions of the single variable t,

$$\frac{d\mathbf{R}}{dt} = \mathbf{i}\frac{du}{dt} + \mathbf{j}\frac{dv}{dt} + \mathbf{k}\frac{dw}{dt} \qquad (1\text{–}4.2)$$

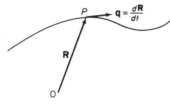

Figure 1-4.2

Hence, $d\mathbf{R}/dt$ is a vector in the direction of $d\mathbf{R}$, with magnitude $[(du/dt)^2 + (dv/dt)^2 + (dw/dt)^2]^{1/2}$.

If $\mathbf{R}$ is the position of a moving particle P measured from a fixed point O (Fig. 1–4.2), $d\mathbf{R}/dt$ is the velocity vector $\mathbf{q}$ of the particle. Likewise, $d\mathbf{q}/dt = d^2\mathbf{R}/dt^2$ is the acceleration vector of the particle. Hence, the vector form of Newton's second law is

$$\mathbf{F} = m\frac{d^2\mathbf{R}}{dt^2} \qquad (1\text{–}4.3)$$

1-5 Differentiation of a Scalar Field

Let $Q(x, y, z, t)$ be a scalar point function in a flowing fluid; e.g., temperature, density, a velocity projection, etc. Then,

$$dQ = \frac{\partial Q}{\partial x}\,dx + \frac{\partial Q}{\partial y}\,dy + \frac{\partial Q}{\partial z}\,dz + \frac{\partial Q}{\partial t}\,dt \qquad (1\text{–}5.1)$$

Here, (dx, dy, dz, dt) are arbitrary increments.

Let (dx, dy, dz) be the displacement that a particle of fluid experiences during a time interval dt. Then, $dx/dt = u$, $dy/dt = v$, $dz/dt = w$, where (u, v, w) is the velocity field. Hence, on dividing Eq. (1–5.1) by dt, we get

$$\frac{dQ}{dt} = u\frac{\partial Q}{\partial x} + v\frac{\partial Q}{\partial y} + w\frac{\partial Q}{\partial z} + \frac{\partial Q}{\partial t} \qquad (1\text{–}5.2)$$

or in vector notation,

$$\frac{dQ}{dt} = \mathbf{q} \cdot \operatorname{grad} Q + \frac{\partial Q}{\partial t} \qquad (1\text{–}5.3)$$

where $\mathbf{q}$ is the velocity field. Although Eq. (1–5.2) is derived for a scalar point function in a flowing fluid, it remains valid for any scalar point function $Q(x, y, z, t)$.

The distinction between $\partial Q/\partial t$ and dQ/dt is very important. The partial derivative, $\partial Q/\partial t$, denotes the rate of change of Q at a fixed point of space, as the fluid flows by. For steady flow, $\partial Q/\partial t = 0$. On the other hand, dQ/dt denotes the rate of change of Q for a certain particle of fluid. For example, if Q is temperature, we determine $\partial Q/\partial t$ by holding the thermometer still. To determine dQ/dt, we must move the thermometer so that it coincides continuously with the same particle of fluid. This, of course, is not feasible, but we do not need to make measurements with moving instruments, since Eq. (1–5.2) gives the relation between dQ/dt and $\partial Q/\partial t$.

1-6 Differentiation of a Vector Field

If $\mathbf{Q}(x, y, z, t)$ is a vector field, Eq. (1–5.2) remains valid; i.e.,

$$\frac{d\mathbf{Q}}{dt} = u\frac{\partial \mathbf{Q}}{\partial x} + v\frac{\partial \mathbf{Q}}{\partial y} + w\frac{\partial \mathbf{Q}}{\partial z} + \frac{\partial \mathbf{Q}}{\partial t} \qquad (1\text{–}6.1)$$

This follows from the fact that Eq. (1–5.2) is valid for each of the components of the vector $\mathbf{Q}$. Equation (1–6.1) may be written in the following form:

$$\frac{d\mathbf{Q}}{dt} = (\mathbf{q} \cdot \nabla)\mathbf{Q} + \frac{\partial \mathbf{Q}}{\partial t} \qquad (1\text{–}6.2)$$

If $\mathbf{Q} = \mathbf{q}$, $d\mathbf{Q}/dt$ is the acceleration vector $\mathbf{a}$. Consequently,

$$a = \frac{d\mathbf{q}}{dt} = u\frac{\partial \mathbf{q}}{\partial x} + v\frac{\partial \mathbf{q}}{\partial y} + w\frac{\partial \mathbf{q}}{\partial z} + \frac{\partial \mathbf{q}}{\partial t} \qquad (1\text{–}6.3)$$

or

$$a = (\mathbf{q} \cdot \nabla)\mathbf{q} + \frac{\partial \mathbf{q}}{\partial t} \qquad (1\text{–}6.4)$$

Thus, the acceleration field is derived from the velocity field.

1-7 Curl of a Vector Field

Let $\mathbf{q} = \mathbf{i}u + \mathbf{j}v + \mathbf{k}w$ be a vector field. Then $\nabla \times \mathbf{q}$ is a vector field that is denoted by curl $\mathbf{q}$. Hence, by Eq. (1–1.13),

$$\operatorname{curl} \mathbf{q} = \nabla \times \mathbf{q} = \begin{vmatrix} \mathbf{i} & \mathbf{j} & \mathbf{k} \\ \dfrac{\partial}{\partial x} & \dfrac{\partial}{\partial y} & \dfrac{\partial}{\partial z} \\ u & v & w \end{vmatrix} \qquad (1\text{–}7.1)$$

or

$$\operatorname{curl} \mathbf{q} = \mathbf{i}\left(\frac{\partial w}{\partial y} - \frac{\partial v}{\partial z}\right) + \mathbf{j}\left(\frac{\partial u}{\partial z} - \frac{\partial w}{\partial x}\right) + \mathbf{k}\left(\frac{\partial v}{\partial x} - \frac{\partial u}{\partial y}\right) \qquad (1\text{–}7.2)$$

It can be shown that the vector field curl $\mathbf{q}$ is independent of the choice of coordinates. A physical significance is later attributed to curl $\mathbf{q}$, if $\mathbf{q}$ denotes the velocity field of a fluid. Curl $\mathbf{q}$ may also be related to the rotation of a volume element of a deformable body.

1-8 Eulerian Continuity Equation for Fluids

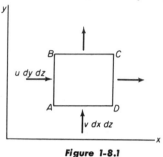

Figure 1-8.1

Let $\mathbf{q} = \mathbf{i}u + \mathbf{j}v + \mathbf{k}w$ be an unsteady velocity field of a compressible fluid. Let us consider the rate of mass flow out of a space cell $dx\,dy\,dz = dV$ fixed with respect to (x, y, z) axes (see Fig. 1–8.1). The mass that flows in through the face AB during a time interval dt is $\rho u\,dy\,dz\,dt$, where ρ is the mass density. The mass that flows out through the face CD during dt is $[\rho u + (\partial(\rho u)/\partial x)dx]\,dy\,dz\,dt$. Consequently, the net mass flow *out* of these two faces during dt is $(\partial(\rho u)/\partial x)\,dx\,dy\,dz\,dt$. Similar expressions are obtained for the mass flows out of the other pairs of faces. Accordingly, the net mass that passes out of the cell dV during dt is

$$\left[\frac{\partial(\rho u)}{\partial x} + \frac{\partial(\rho v)}{\partial y} + \frac{\partial(\rho w)}{\partial z}\right] dV\,dt \tag{a}$$

With the differential operator ∇[see Eq. (1–2.5)], this may be written as follows:

$$\nabla \cdot (\rho\mathbf{q})\,dV\,dt \tag{b}$$

The product $\rho\mathbf{q}$ is called *current density.*

If $\mathbf{a}(x, y, z, t)$ is any vector field, $\nabla \cdot \mathbf{a}$ is called the *divergence* of the field. Accordingly, the notation div $\mathbf{a}$ is sometimes used to denote $\nabla \cdot \mathbf{a}$. Note that div $\mathbf{a}$ is a scalar. Accordingly, by Eq. (b), the mass that flows out of the volume element dV during dt is

$$dV\,dt\ \text{div}\,(\rho\mathbf{q}) \tag{c}$$

The name "divergence" originates in this physical idea.

Since mass is conserved in the velocity field of a fluid, the mass that passes into the fixed cell dV during time dt equals the increase of mass in the cell during dt. Now, the mass in the cell at the time t is $\rho\,dV$. Consequently, the increase of mass during dt is

$$\frac{\partial\rho}{\partial t}\,dV\,dt \tag{d}$$

Since Eq. (d) must be the negative of Eq. (c), we obtain

$$\frac{\partial\rho}{\partial t} + \text{div}\,(\rho\mathbf{q}) = 0 \tag{1–8.1}$$

Equation (1–38) is known as the *Eulerian continuity equation* for fluids. Any real velocity field must conform to this relation. For steady flow, the term $\partial\rho/\partial t$ disappears.

For an incompressible fluid, $\rho = $ constant. Consequently, the Eulerian form of the continuity equation for an incompressible fluid takes the simpler form,

$$\text{div } \mathbf{q} = 0 \qquad \text{or} \qquad \frac{\partial u}{\partial x} + \frac{\partial v}{\partial y} + \frac{\partial w}{\partial z} = 0 \qquad (1\text{-}8.2)$$

This is valid, even for unsteady flow of an incompressible fluid. Liquids may usually be considered to be incompressible, except in the study of compression waves.

The case in which the velocity $\mathbf{q}$ is the gradient of a scalar function has great theoretical importance, that is, the case where

$$\mathbf{q} = -\text{grad } \phi \qquad (1\text{-}8.3)$$

where $\phi(x, y, z, t)$ is a scalar function. The flow is then said to be *irrotational* or "derivable from a potential function ϕ." Then the velocity component in the direction of a unit vector $\mathbf{n}$ is

$$q_n = \mathbf{q} \cdot \mathbf{n} = -\mathbf{n} \cdot \text{grad } \phi \qquad (1\text{-}8.4)$$

Hence, by Eq. (1–2.3),

$$q_n = -\frac{d\phi}{ds} \qquad (1\text{-}8.5)$$

That is, q_n is equal to the negative of the directional derivative of ϕ in the direction $\mathbf{n}$.

Equation (1–39) may be written,

$$u = -\frac{\partial \phi}{\partial x}, \qquad v = -\frac{\partial \phi}{\partial y}, \qquad w = -\frac{\partial \phi}{\partial z}$$

Accordingly, by Eq. (1–8.2), the continuity equation for irrotational flow of an incompressible fluid is

$$\nabla^2 \phi = 0 \qquad (1\text{-}8.6)$$

Thus, the continuity equation for irrotational flow of an incompressible fluid reduces to the Laplace equation (see Art. 1–2). A general expression for the Laplace equation in orthogonal curvilinear coordinates in three-dimensional space is derived in Art. 1–16.

1-9 Divergence Theorem

Let $\mathbf{a}(x, y, z)$ be any continuous and differentiable vector field. We may regard $\mathbf{a}$ as current density in a hypothetical fluid. Then, by Eq. (c), Art. 1–8, div $\mathbf{a}$ $dx\,dy\,dz$ is the net rate at which fluid flows out of the fixed space element $dx\,dy\,dz$. Hence, if R is a given fixed region of space that is bounded by a surface S, the net rate at which fluid passes out of R is

$$\iiint_R \text{div } \mathbf{a} \, dx \, dy \, dz$$

This must also be the rate at which fluid passes through the surface S. If dS is an element of area of this surface with outward-directed unit normal $\mathbf{n}$, the rate of flow through dS is $\mathbf{a} \cdot \mathbf{n} \, dS$. Hence,

$$\iiint_R \text{div } \mathbf{a} \, dx \, dy \, dz = \iint_S \mathbf{a} \cdot \mathbf{n} \, dS \qquad (1\text{--}9.1)$$

Thus, a volume integral is transformed into a surface integral.

Equation (1–9.1) is known as the *divergence theorem*. It is purely mathematical; the reference to flow is simply an artifice to facilitate the derivation. Rigorous mathematical derivations of the theorem are given in books on advanced calculus.[2]

If (U, V, W) are the components of the vector $\mathbf{a}$, Eq. (1–9.1) may be expressed in the following scalar form:

$$\iiint_R \left(\frac{\partial U}{\partial x} + \frac{\partial V}{\partial y} + \frac{\partial W}{\partial z} \right) dx \, dy \, dz = \iint_S (U n_1 + V n_2 + W n_3) \, dS = \iint_S a_n \, dS$$

$$(1\text{--}9.2)$$

where a_n denotes the projection of $\mathbf{a}$ in the direction of $\mathbf{n}$ and (n_1, n_2, n_3) are the direction cosines of the unit vector $\mathbf{n}$; the functions (U, V, W) are unrestricted, aside from requirements of continuity and differentiability. The surface S may consist of a *finite number of smooth* parts that are joined together along edges. If the vector $\mathbf{n}$ is directed inward, the sign of the right side of Eq. (1–9.2) is reversed.

Many useful results can be obtained by giving special forms to the functions (U, V, W). For example, if $U = AB$, $V = W = 0$, we obtain

$$\iiint_R A \frac{\partial B}{\partial x} \, dx \, dy \, dz = -\iiint_R B \frac{\partial A}{\partial x} \, dx \, dy \, dz + \iint_S ABn_1 \, dS \qquad (1\text{--}9.3)$$

Corresponding results for y and z are obtained by setting $V = AB$, $U = W = 0$, etc. These equations are similar, in form, to the formula for integration by parts of a single integral.

Another useful relation may be obtained as follows:

Let $\mathbf{a}$ be the product of a scalar ϕ and a vector $\mathbf{A}$; that is,

$$\mathbf{a} = \phi \mathbf{A}$$

Then $\qquad\qquad \text{div } \mathbf{a} = \phi \, \text{div } \mathbf{A} + \dfrac{\partial \phi}{\partial x} A_x + \dfrac{\partial \phi}{\partial y} A_y + \dfrac{\partial \phi}{\partial z} A_z$

or $\hfill (1\text{--}9.4)$

$$\text{div } \mathbf{a} = \phi \, \text{div } \mathbf{A} + (\text{grad } \phi) \cdot \mathbf{A}$$

---

[2]E. Goursat, *A Course in Mathematical Analysis*, Vol. 1, Art. 149 (Boston: Ginn & Company, 1904).

Accordingly, Eq. (1–9.2) yields

$$\iint_S \phi A_n \, dS = \iiint_R [\phi \operatorname{div} \mathbf{A} + (\operatorname{grad} \phi) \cdot \mathbf{A}] \, dV \qquad (1\text{–}9.5)$$

If furthermore the vector $\mathbf{A}$ is representable as the gradient of a scalar function ψ ($\mathbf{A} = \operatorname{grad} \psi$), then by Eq. (1–8.5), $A_n = (d\psi/dn)$ and

$$\operatorname{div} \mathbf{A} = \frac{\partial^2 \psi}{\partial x^2} + \frac{\partial^2 \psi}{\partial y^2} + \frac{\partial^2 \psi}{\partial z^2} = \nabla^2 \psi$$

Hence, for $\mathbf{A} = \operatorname{grad} \psi$, Eq. (1–9.5) becomes

$$\iint_S \phi \frac{\partial \psi}{\partial n} \, dS = \iiint_R [\phi \, \nabla^2 \psi + (\operatorname{grad} \phi) \cdot (\operatorname{grad} \psi)] \, dV \qquad (1\text{–}9.6)$$

Equation (1–9.6) holds for any two functions ϕ and ψ which are finite, continuous, and twice differentiable within R.

If we subtract from Eq. (1–9.6) the equation obtained by interchanging ϕ and ψ, we obtain

$$\iint_S \left(\phi \frac{\partial \psi}{\partial n} - \psi \frac{\partial \phi}{\partial n} \right) dS = \iiint_R (\phi \, \nabla^2 \psi - \psi \, \nabla^2 \phi) \, dV \qquad (1\text{–}9.7)$$

Both Eqs. (1–9.6) and (1–9.7) are referred to as Green's theorem. They find extensive use in mathematical physics.

1-10 Divergence Theorem in Two Dimensions

The two-dimensional analogue of Eq. (1–9.2) is

$$\iint_R \left(\frac{\partial U}{\partial x} + \frac{\partial V}{\partial y} \right) dx \, dy = \oint_c (U n_1 + V n_2) \, ds \qquad (1\text{–}10.1)$$

where U and V are any continuous and differentiable functions of (x, y). Here, R denotes a region of the $(x \; y)$ plane, and C is the curve that bounds the region R (Fig. 1–10.1). The unit normal vector (n_1, n_2) is directed outward. The element of arc length on the curve C is denoted by ds. The circle on the integral sign shows that the integration extends completely around the curve C.

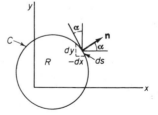

Figure 1-10.1

Referring to the figure, we have $n_1 = \cos \alpha$, $n_2 = \sin \alpha$. Hence, $n_1 \, ds = dy$, $n_2 \, ds = -dx$, where (dx, dy) is the displacement along the curve C, corresponding to the increment ds. Hence, by Eq. (1–10.1),

$$\iint_R \left(\frac{\partial U}{\partial x} + \frac{\partial V}{\partial y} \right) dx \, dy = \oint_c (U \, dy - V \, dx) \qquad (1\text{–}10.2)$$

This relation is sometimes called *Green's theorem of the plane*. Another form of Green's theorem is obtained by the substitution, $U = v$, $V = -u$. Then,

$$\iint_R \left(\frac{\partial v}{\partial x} - \frac{\partial u}{\partial y} \right) dx\, dy = \oint_c (u\, dx + v\, dy) \tag{1–10.3}$$

1-11 Line and Surface Integrals (Application of Scalar Product)

Line integral. Consider a vector $\mathbf{F}$ defined at each point on a curve C (Fig. 1–11.1). The vector $\mathbf{F}$ forms an angle α with the tangent to the curve C at point P. In general, the vector $\mathbf{F}$ may vary in magnitude and direction along the curve. Let s be an arc length measured along the curve. The length of an infinitesimal element of the curve at point P is ds. The vector $d\mathbf{s}$ with magnitude ds is directed along the tangent line to the curve at point P (Fig. 1–11.1). By Eq. (1–1.8), the projection of the vector $\mathbf{F}$ along the tangent to the curve is $\mathbf{F} \cdot d\mathbf{s} = F(\cos \alpha)\, ds$. The integral

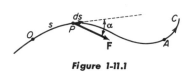

Figure 1-11.1

$$\int_C \mathbf{F} \cdot d\mathbf{s} = \int_C \mathbf{f} (\cos \alpha)\, ds \tag{1–11.1}$$

is called the line integral of the vector $\mathbf{F}$ along the curve C. The C in Eq. (1–11.1) denotes integration along the curve C. By Eq. (1–11.1), it is apparent that the line integral of a vector is the integral of the tangential component of the vector taken along a path.

The line integral Eq. (1–11.1) finds numerous applications in physical problems. For example, if $\mathbf{F}$ denotes a force that acts on a particle P that travels along curve C, the line integral of the tangential component of $\mathbf{F}$ from point O to point A represents the work performed by the force $\mathbf{F}$ as the particle travels from O to A. If $\mathbf{F}$ denotes the electric field intensity, that is, the force that acts on a unit charge in an electric field, the line integral between any two points represents the potential difference between the two points. If $\mathbf{F}$ denotes the velocity at any point in a fluid, the line integral taken around a closed path in the fluid represents the *circulation* of the fluid.

Surface integral. In Art. 1–9 it was shown that the volume of fluid that passes through a surface S in a unit time is

$$\iint_S \mathbf{q} \cdot \mathbf{n}\, dS = \iint_S q_n\, dS \tag{1–11.2}$$

where $\mathbf{q}$ is the velocity field, and $\mathbf{n}$ is the unit normal to the surface. This integral is called the surface integral of the vector $\mathbf{q}$. Accordingly, the expression "surface integral of a vector" denotes the integral of the normal component of the vector over a surface.

1-12 Stokes' Theorem

Equation (1–10.3) may be written as follows:

$$\oint_C \mathbf{q} \cdot d\mathbf{r} = \iint_R \mathbf{n} \cdot \text{curl } \mathbf{q} \, dS \qquad (1\text{–}12.1)$$

where $d\mathbf{r} = (dx, dy)$, $\mathbf{q}$ denotes the vector (u, v, w), and $\mathbf{n}$ now denotes the unit normal to the plane area R [directed in the positive z direction, if the coordinates (x, y, z) are right-handed]. Although Eq. (1–12.1) has been proved only if R is a region in the (x, y) plane, it remains valid if R is any plane area in space with any orientation, for Eq. (1–12.1) is invariant under a coordinate transformation; that is, Eq. (1–12.1) does not depend on the choice of coordinates.

Our result may be generalized still further. The curve C need not be a plane curve; it may be any closed space curve, and R may be any surface S that caps this curve. For any capping surface of the curve C may be divided into infinitesimal cells. Each of these cells is a plane element of area. Consequently, Eq. (1–12.1) applies for any one of the cells. We may then sum Eq. (1–12.1) over all cells. Then the right side of the equation simply becomes the surface integral of curl $\mathbf{q}$ over the entire capping surface S of the curve C. On the left side, we have the sum of the line integrals of $\mathbf{q}$ about the boundaries of the cells. However, the line integrals over the boundaries of contiguous cells cancel, since any inner boundary of a cell is described twice, once in the positive sense, and once in the negative sense. Consequently, only the line integral on the outer boundary C remains.

Accordingly, we have Stokes' theorem: "The line integral of a vector field about any closed curve equals the surface integral of the normal component of the curl of the vector over any capping surface."

If $\mathbf{q}$ is a velocity field, curl $\mathbf{q}$ is called the *vorticity vector*. Consequently, in the terminology of fluid mechanics, Stokes' theorem is expressed as follows: *The circulation on any closed curve equals the flux of vorticity through the loop.*

1-13 Exact Differential

Let $M(x, y)$ and $N(x, y)$ be two functions of x and y, such that M, N, $\partial M/\partial y$, and $\partial N/\partial x$ are continuous and single-valued at every point of a simply-connected[3] region. The differential expression $Mdx + Ndy$ is said to be *exact*, if there exists a function $f(x, y)$ such that $df = Mdx + Ndy$. Now, by definition

$$df = \frac{\partial f}{\partial x} dx + \frac{\partial f}{\partial y} dy \qquad (1\text{-}13.1)$$

Consequently, if $M\,dx + N\,dy$ is exact, $M = \partial f/\partial x$, $N = \partial f/\partial y$. Therefore,

$$\frac{\partial M}{\partial y} = \frac{\partial N}{\partial x} \qquad \text{or} \qquad \frac{\partial N}{\partial x} - \frac{\partial M}{\partial y} = 0 \qquad (1\text{-}13.2)$$

Accordingly, Eq. (1–13.2) is a *necessary* condition for $M\,dx + N\,dy$ to be an exact differential.

Equation (1–13.2) is also a *sufficient* condition. For let us assume that Eq. (1–13.2) is satisfied. Set

$$F(x, y) = \int M\,dx$$

where integration is performed with respect to x. Then $\partial F/\partial x = M$ and

$$\frac{\partial^2 F}{\partial x \, \partial y} = \frac{\partial M}{\partial y} = \frac{\partial N}{\partial x}.$$

Therefore,

$$\frac{\partial}{\partial x}\left(N - \frac{\partial F}{\partial y}\right) = 0 \qquad \text{or} \qquad N = \frac{\partial F}{\partial y} + g(y)$$

Set $f(x, y) = F(x, y) + \int g(y)\,dy$. Then $N = \partial f/\partial y$ and $M = \partial F/\partial x = \partial f/\partial x$. Hence, $M\,dx + N\,dy = df$; that is, $M\,dx + N\,dy$ is an exact differential.

1-14 Orthogonal Curvilinear Coordinates in Three-Dimensional Space

Let three independent scalar functions (u, v, w) be defined in terms of three independent variables (x, y, z) as follows:

$$u = U(x, y, z), \qquad v = V(x, y, z), \qquad w = W(x, y, z) \qquad (1\text{-}14.1)$$

By independent functions, we mean that Eqs. (1–14.1) yield unique solutions for x, y, z; namely;

$$x = X(u, v, w), \qquad y = Y(u, v, w), \qquad z = Z(u, v, w) \qquad (1\text{-}14.2)$$

For example, if (x, y, z) represent rectangular cartesian coordinates, and (u, v, w) represent cylindrical coordinates, Eq. (1–14.2) is of the form

$$x = u \cos v, \qquad y = u \sin v, \qquad z = w \qquad (1\text{-}14.3)$$

---

[3]A simply-connected region has the property that any closed curve drawn in it can, by a continuous deformation, be skrunk to a point without crossing the boundary of the region. For the significance of simple connectivity, see R. Courant, *Differential and Integral Calculus*, Vol. II (New York: Interscience Publishers, Inc., 1950), p. 358.

If (u, v, w) represent spherical coordinates, Eq. (1–14.2) is of the form

$$x = u \sin v \cos w, \qquad y = u \sin v \sin w, \qquad z = u \cos v \qquad (1\text{–}14.4)$$

If (u, v, w) are assigned constant values, Eq. (1–14.1) becomes

$$\begin{aligned} U_0(x, y, z) &= \text{constant} = u_0 \\ V_0(x, y, z) &= \text{constant} = v_0 \qquad\qquad (1\text{–}14.5) \\ W_0(x, y, z) &= \text{constant} = w_0 \end{aligned}$$

Equation (1–14.5) represents three surfaces in space, called *coordinate surfaces*. The intersection of any two of these surfaces (say $U_0 = u_0$ and $V_0 = v_0$) determines a curve in space, the w *curvilinear coordinate line*. The u and v curvilinear coordinate lines are defined similarly. The three surfaces $U_0 = u_0$, $V_0 = v_0$, $W_0 = w_0$ intersect at a point in space. Hence, a point in space is associated with each triplet (u_i, v_i, w_i).

If the three systems of surfaces defined by triplets (u_i, v_i, w_i) are mutually perpendicular (that is, if the curvilinear coordinate lines through any point are mutually perpendicular), the curvilinear coordinate system is said to be *orthogonal*.

A very special case of an orthogonal curvilinear coordinate system is the rectangular cartesian coordinate system. For rectangular coordinates,

$$x = u, \qquad y = v, \qquad z = w$$

Hence, three coordinate surfaces are the mutually perpendicular planes

$$x = u_0, \qquad y = v_0, \qquad z = w_0.$$

The intersection of any two of these planes is a coordinate line; for example, the intersection of planes $x = u_0, y = v_0$ determines a z coordinate line. Cylindrical coordinates [Eq. (1–14.3)] and spherical coordinates [Eq. (1–14.4)] are also examples of orthogonal curvilinear coordinate systems. Another example is elliptic coordinates.

1-15 Expression for Differential Length in Orthogonal Curvilinear Coordinates

Let $(\mathbf{i}, \mathbf{j}, \mathbf{k})$ be unit vectors along (x, y, z) axes, respectively. Let (u, v, w) be a system of orthogonal curvilinear coordinates. Let v and w be constant. Then, at any point the tangent vector to the u coordinate line is

$$\mathbf{U} = x_u \mathbf{i} + y_u \mathbf{j} + z_u \mathbf{k} \qquad (1\text{–}15.1)$$

where the u subscript denotes partial differentiation. Similarly, tangent vectors to the v and w coordinate lines are

$$\mathbf{V} = x_v \mathbf{i} + y_v \mathbf{j} + z_v \mathbf{k}, \qquad \mathbf{W} = x_w \mathbf{i} + y_w \mathbf{j} + z_w \mathbf{k} \qquad (1\text{–}15.2)$$

Vectors $\mathbf{U}, \mathbf{V}, \mathbf{W}$ are mutually perpendicular. Hence, by the scalar-product definition of two vectors

$$\mathbf{U} \cdot \mathbf{V} = \mathbf{V} \cdot \mathbf{W} = \mathbf{W} \cdot \mathbf{U} = 0 \qquad (1\text{--}15.3)$$

Also, if h_1, h_2, h_3 are the magnitudes of the lengths of vectors $\mathbf{U}, \mathbf{V}, \mathbf{W}$, respectively, the scalar-product definition yields

$$h_1^2 = \mathbf{U} \cdot \mathbf{U}, \qquad h_2^2 = \mathbf{V} \cdot \mathbf{V}, \qquad h_3^2 = \mathbf{W} \cdot \mathbf{W} \qquad (1\text{--}15.4)$$

Hence, by Eqs. (1–14.2), (1–15.1), (1–15.2), and (1–15.4), $h_1 = h_1(u, v, w)$, $h_2 = h_2(u, v, w)$, $h_3 = h_3(u, v, w)$.

Consider a line element PQ where $P = P(x, y, z)$ and $Q = Q(x + dx, y + dy, z + dz)$. The differential length ds of the line element PQ is given by the relation

$$ds^2 = dx^2 + dy^2 + dz^2 \qquad (1\text{--}15.5)$$

By Eq. (1–14.2),

$$\begin{aligned}
dx &= x_u\, du + x_v\, dv + x_w\, dw \\
dy &= y_u\, du + y_v\, dv + y_w\, dw \\
dz &= z_u\, du + z_v\, dv + z_w\, dw
\end{aligned} \qquad (1\text{--}15.6)$$

Substituting Eq. (1–15.6) into Eq. (1–15.5) and utilizing Eqs. (1–15.2), (1–15.3), and (1–15.4), we obtain

$$ds^2 = h_1^2\, du^2 + h_2^2\, dv^2 + h_3^2\, dw^2 \qquad (1\text{--}15.7)$$

Equation (1–15.7) expresses the differential length ds in terms of the orthogonal curvilinear coordinates (u, v, w). The coefficients (h_1, h_2, h_3) are called *Lamé coefficients*. The Lamé coefficients are equal in magnitude to the lengths of the vectors $(\mathbf{U}, \mathbf{V}, \mathbf{W})$, tangent to (u, v, w) coordinate lines, respectively. The quantities (h_1^2, h_2^2, h_3^2) are known as the *components of the metric tensor of space*.[4]

1-16 The Gradient and the Laplacian in Orthogonal Curvilinear Coordinates

Consider the infinitesimal parallelepiped whose diagonal is the line element ds. The faces of the parallelepiped coincide with the plane $u = $ constant, $v = $ constant, $w = $ constant (Fig. 1–16.1).

The gradient u, (∇u), has the direction normal to the surface $u = $ constant; that is, the direction of $\mathbf{U}$, namely, the direction of the unit vector $\mathbf{U}/|\mathbf{U}| = \mathbf{U}/h_1$ [see Eq. (1–15.4)]. The magnitude of ∇u is equal to the derivative of u in this direction. Hence, by Eq. (1–15.7), with v and w constant, the magnitude of ∇u is

$$\frac{du}{ds} = \frac{1}{h_1} \qquad (1\text{--}16.1)$$

---

[4] J. L. Synge and A. Schild, *Tensor Calculus* (Toronto: University of Toronto Press, 1956).

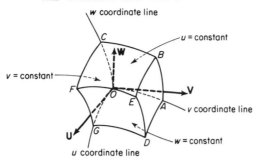

Figure 1-16.1

Hence, the gradient vector is

$$\nabla u = \frac{1}{h_1^2}\mathbf{U} \tag{1-16.2}$$

Similarly, the gradients of v and w are

$$\nabla v = \frac{1}{h_2^2}\mathbf{V}, \qquad \nabla w = \frac{1}{h_3^2}\mathbf{W} \tag{1-16.3}$$

By the definition of ∇ and by the rule for partial differentiation, namely,

$$\frac{\partial f}{\partial x} = \frac{\partial f}{\partial u}\frac{\partial u}{\partial x} + \frac{\partial f}{\partial v}\frac{\partial v}{\partial x} + \frac{\partial f}{\partial w}\frac{\partial w}{\partial x}, \cdots, \cdots$$

if $f(u, v, w)$ is any scalar point function, then the gradient of f is

$$\nabla f = \frac{\partial f}{\partial u}\nabla u + \frac{\partial f}{\partial v}\nabla v + \frac{\partial f}{\partial w}\nabla w \tag{1-16.4}$$

Substituting Eqs. (1–16.2) and (1–16.3) into Eq. (1–16.4), we obtain

$$\nabla f = \frac{1}{h_1}\frac{\partial f}{\partial u}\mathbf{u} + \frac{1}{h_2}\frac{\partial f}{\partial v}\mathbf{v} + \frac{1}{h_3}\frac{\partial f}{\partial w}\mathbf{w} \tag{1-16.5}$$

where $(\mathbf{u}, \mathbf{v}, \mathbf{w})$ are unit vectors in the directions of $(\mathbf{U}, \mathbf{V}, \mathbf{W})$, respectively; that is,

$$\mathbf{u} = \frac{\mathbf{U}}{h_1}, \qquad \mathbf{v} = \frac{\mathbf{V}}{h_2}, \qquad \mathbf{w} = \frac{\mathbf{W}}{h_3} \tag{1-16.6}$$

Equation (1–16.5) represents the gradient of a scalar in orthogonal curvilinear coordinates. Consequently, by Eq. (1–16.5), the expression for the operator ∇ in orthogonal curvilinear coordinates is

$$\nabla = \frac{1}{h_1}\mathbf{u}\frac{\partial}{\partial u} + \frac{1}{h_2}\mathbf{v}\frac{\partial}{\partial v} + \frac{1}{h_3}\mathbf{w}\frac{\partial}{\partial w} \tag{1 16.7}$$

To derive the expression for the Laplacian ∇^2, first, we derive the expression for the divergence of a vector field, $\mathbf{Q} = (Q_1, Q_2, Q_3)$, namely, $\nabla \cdot \mathbf{Q}$, in orthogonal curvilinear coordinates.

Consider again the infinitesimal parallelepiped of Fig. 1–16.1. The lengths of its edges are $h_1\,du$, $h_2\,dv$, $h_3\,dw$, and its volume is $h_1 h_2 h_3\,du\,dv\,dw$. To facilitate the calculation of the divergence of $\mathbf{Q}$, we use Green's theorem for transforming volume integrals into surface integrals:

$$\iiint\limits_{\substack{\text{through}\\\text{volume}}} (\boldsymbol{\nabla} \cdot \mathbf{Q}) \, dV = \iint\limits_{\substack{\text{over}\\\text{bounding}\\\text{surface}}} \mathbf{Q} \cdot \mathbf{n} \, dS \tag{1-16.8}$$

The contribution of the surface $OABC$, Fig. (1–16.1), to the integral over the surface of the parallelepiped taken in the direction of the outward normal is $-Q_1 h_2 \, dv \, h_3 \, dw$. The contribution of the surface $DEFG$ is

$$Q_1 h_2 h_3 \, dv \, dw + \frac{\partial}{\partial u}(Q_1 h_2 h_3) \, du \, dv \, dw$$

Hence, the net contribution of the coordinate surfaces perpendicular to u coordinate lines is

$$\frac{\partial}{\partial u}(Q_1 h_2 h_3) \, du \, dv \, dw \tag{1-16.9}$$

Similarly, the contributions of the coordinate surfaces perpendicular to v and w coordinate lines, respectively, are

$$\frac{\partial}{\partial v}(Q_2 h_1 h_2) \, du \, dv \, dw, \qquad \frac{\partial}{\partial w}(Q_3 h_1 h_2) \, du \, dv \, dw \tag{1-16.10}$$

Since the volume of the infinitesimal parallelepiped, Fig. (1–16.1), is infinitesimal,

$$\operatorname*{Lim}_{V \to 0} \iiint (\boldsymbol{\nabla} \cdot \mathbf{Q}) \, dV \to \boldsymbol{\nabla} \cdot \mathbf{Q} h_1 h_2 h_3 \, du \, dv \, dw \tag{1-16.11}$$

Consequently, by Eqs. (1–16.8) to (1–16.11),

$$\boldsymbol{\nabla} \cdot \mathbf{Q} = \frac{1}{h_1 h_2 h_3}\left[\frac{\partial}{\partial u}(Q_1 h_2 h_3) + \frac{\partial}{\partial v}(Q_2 h_1 h_3) + \frac{\partial}{\partial w}(Q_3 h_1 h_2) \right] = \operatorname{div} \mathbf{Q} \tag{1-16.12}$$

Equation (1–16.12) represents the formula for the divergence of a vector field $\mathbf{Q}$ in terms of general three-dimensional orthogonal curvilinear coordinates.

Setting $\boldsymbol{\nabla} f = \mathbf{Q}$ and noting by Eq. (1–16.5) that $Q_1 = (1/h_1)(\partial f/\partial u)$, $Q_2 = (1/h_2)(\partial f/\partial v)$, $Q_3 = (1/h_3)(\partial f/\partial w)$, we obtain by Eqs. (1–16.6) and (1–16.12)

$$\nabla^2 f = \boldsymbol{\nabla} \cdot \boldsymbol{\nabla} f = \frac{1}{h_1 h_2 h_3}\left[\frac{\partial}{\partial u}\left(\frac{h_2 h_3}{h_1}\frac{\partial f}{\partial u}\right) + \frac{\partial}{\partial v}\left(\frac{h_1 h_3}{h_2}\frac{\partial f}{\partial v}\right) + \frac{\partial}{\partial w}\left(\frac{h_1 h_2}{h_3}\frac{\partial f}{\partial w}\right) \right] \tag{1-16.13}$$

Equation (1–16.13) represents the Laplacian of a scalar function $f(u, v, w)$ in general three-dimensional orthogonal curvilinear coordinates. Hence, the Laplace equation $\nabla^2 f = 0$ in general three-dimensional orthogonal curvilinear coordinates is obtained by setting the right-hand side of Eq. (1–16.13) equal to zero.

For plane (two-dimensional) orthogonal curvilinear coordinates, $h_3 = 1$ and $\partial/\partial w = 0$.

1-17 Index Notation : Summation Convention

Gibbs vector notation may be considered to replace and extend conventional scalar notation. For example, the scalar representation (F_x, F_y, F_z) of a force with respect to rectangular cartesian axes is fully replaced by the vector notation $\mathbf{F}$. Likewise, index notation may be considered to replace and extend Gibbs vector notation. Thus, the vector $\mathbf{F}$ may be represented by the symbol F_i, where the subscript (index) i is understood to take values 1, 2, 3, (or the values x, y, z). Hence the notation F_i is equivalent to (F_1, F_2, F_3) or to (F_x, F_y, F_z), where subscripts (1, 2, 3) or subscripts (x, y, z) denote projects of the force along rectangular cartesian coordinate axes (1, 2, 3) or (x, y, z).

Restricting ourselves to rectangular cartesian coordinates, we indicate coordinates by indexes (1, 2, 3) instead of letters (x, y, z). For example, the coordinates of a general point X in (x, y, z) space are denoted by $x_i = (x_1, x_2, x_3)$ or more briefly by x_i, with the understanding that i takes the values 1, 2, 3. The coordinates of a specific point P are denoted by p_i, the letter p identifying the point and the index i the separate coordinates (see Fig. 1-17.1). Similarly, axes (x, y, z) may be denoted by (x_1, x_2, x_3), or simply by x_i. Axes x_i may also be denoted by the notations (01, 02, 03) or (1, 2, 3).

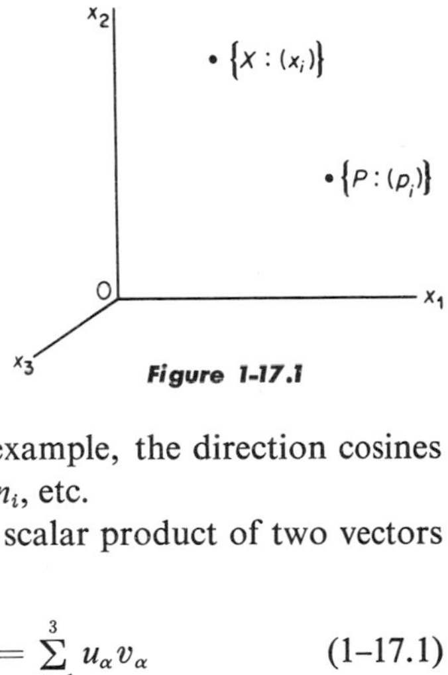

The direction cosines of a line L with respect to axes x_i are denoted by $\alpha_1, \alpha_2, \alpha_3$ or briefly by α_i. Any other letter may replace α. For example, the direction cosines of line L may also be denoted by β_i, by m_i, by n_i, etc.

The sum of two vectors q_i, r_i is $q_i + r_i$. The scalar product of two vectors u_α, v_α is [see Eq. (1-1.6)]

$$\mathbf{u} \cdot \mathbf{v} = u_1 v_1 + u_2 v_2 + u_3 v_3 = \sum_{\alpha=1}^{3} u_\alpha v_\alpha \qquad (1\text{-}17.1)$$

Equation (1-17.1) may be simplified by the use of conventional *summation* notation. For example, we may write Eq. (1-17.1) in the form

$$\mathbf{u} \cdot \mathbf{v} = u_\alpha v_\alpha \qquad (1\text{-}17.2)$$

with the understanding that the *repeated Greek index* α implies summation over the values 1, 2, 3. Accordingly, if m_α and n_α denote the direction cosines of two unit vectors directed along two lines M and N in (x, y, z) space, by the scalar product of vectors, the angle θ between lines M and N is given by the relation [see Eq. (1-1.8) and the discussion following Eq. (1-1.8)]

$$\cos \theta = m_\alpha n_\alpha \qquad (1\text{-}17.3)$$

Figure 1-17.1

If lines M and N coincide, $\theta = 0$. Then Eq. (1–17.3) yields (with $m_\alpha = n_\alpha$)

$$m_1^2 + m_2^2 + m_3^2 = 1 \qquad (1\text{–}17.4)$$

Accordingly, the sum of the squares of the direction cosines of a directed line in (x, y, z) space is equal to one [see Eq. (1–1.9)].

In general, a repeated index which is to be summed will be denoted by a Greek letter. We thus avoid the necessity of using some special notation for a repeated index which is not summed. Since the operation of summing is independent of the Greek index used to denote the summation process, the following representations of $\cos \theta$ are equivalent [see Eq. (1–17.3)]:

$$\cos \theta = m_\alpha n_\alpha = m_\beta n_\beta = m_\gamma n_\gamma = \ldots$$

since each of the representations denotes $m_1 n_1 + m_2 n_2 + m_3 n_3$. Accordingly, a repeated Greek index is called a *summing index* or a *dummy index*. An index which appears only once in a general term is called a *free index*. Thus, in the term $A_{\alpha\beta\beta}$, the index β is a dummy index and the index α is a free index, the value of α being independent of the values of β. For example, if we assign the value 1 to α, the term $A_{\alpha\beta\beta}$ represents the sum $A_{111} + A_{122} + A_{133}$.

If a *repeated* index is *not* to be summed, we will denote it by a *Latin letter*. Thus, $m_i n_i$ denotes any element of the set $(m_1 n_1, m_2 n_2, m_3 n_3)$, depending on the value assigned to i. For example, if $i = 2$, then $m_i n_i$ denotes the element $m_2 n_2$.

If several dummy indexes occur in a general term, summation is implied for each index separately. For example,

$$\begin{aligned}
x_{i\alpha\beta} y_{\alpha\beta} &= x_{i1\beta} y_{1\beta} + x_{i2\beta} y_{2\beta} + x_{i3\beta} y_{3\beta} \\
&= x_{i11} y_{11} + x_{i12} y_{12} + x_{i13} y_{13} \\
&\quad + x_{i21} y_{21} + x_{i22} y_{22} + x_{i23} y_{23} \\
&\quad + x_{i31} y_{31} + x_{i32} y_{32} + x_{i33} y_{33}
\end{aligned}$$

Thus, for every value of the free index i, there are nine terms in the sum $x_{i\alpha\beta} y_{\alpha\beta}$.

In modern algebra, the range of the index is often extended from $(1, 2, 3)$ to $(1, 2, 3, \ldots, n)$. Thus, we may write

$$A_{i\alpha} x_\alpha = A_{i1} x_1 + A_{i2} x_2 + \cdots + A_{in} x_n$$

where the summing index α takes values $(1, 2, 3, \ldots, n)$.

To avoid confusion, an index already appearing in a general term as a free index should not be used as a dummy index, since no meaning is given indexes that appear more than twice. Thus, notations such as $A_{\beta\beta} x_\beta$ should be avoided. For example, if $x = A_\alpha y_\alpha$ and $y_i = B_{i\alpha} z_\alpha$, the expression for x in terms of (z_1, z_2, z_3) is written

$$x = A_\alpha B_{\alpha\beta} z_\beta$$

not in the meaningless form

$$x = A_\alpha B_{\alpha\alpha} z_\alpha$$

Rectangular arrays. A set of numbers arranged in the following form is called a *rectangular array:*

$$
\begin{array}{ccccc}
a_{11} & a_{12} & a_{13} & \ldots & a_{1n} \\
a_{21} & a_{22} & a_{23} & \ldots & a_{2n} \\
\cdots & \cdots & \cdots & \cdots & \cdots \\
a_{m1} & a_{m2} & a_{m3} & \ldots & a_{mn}
\end{array}
\tag{1–17.5}
$$

where, in general, $m \neq n$.

More generally such an array of numbers is called a *matrix.* In the study of matrix theory extensive rules are laid down for the multiplication of matrices. However, we shall have no need to consider multiplication of such arrays (matrices), the role of products in matrix theory being, to a large extent, replaced by summation convention. Accordingly, we refer to these sets of numbers (elements) simply as arrays. A typical element of an array is denoted by a_{ij}, the index i referring to the ith row of the array and the index j to the jth column. For brevity, the entire array [Eq. (1–17.5)] is denoted by

$$(a_{ij}) \tag{1–17.6}$$

If $m = n$, the array is called a *square array.* In the theory of continuous media, we shall be concerned primarily with square arrays.

If the arrays (a_{ij}), (b_{ij}), (c_{ij}), $\ldots$ all have the same number of rows and the same number of columns, a linear combination (h_{ij}) of (a_{ij}), (b_{ij}), (c_{ij}), $\ldots$ is defined by

$$h_{ij} = Aa_{ij} + Bb_{ij} + Cc_{ij} + \cdots \tag{1–17.7}$$

where A, B, C, $\ldots$ are arbitrary constants independent of i and j. In particular, the *sum* $(a_{ij} + b_{ij} + c_{ij})$ of the three arrays (a_{ij}), (b_{ij}), (c_{ij}) has the typical element $a_{ij} + b_{ij} + c_{ij}$.

A square array (a_{ij}) is said to be symmetric if

$$a_{ij} = a_{ji} \tag{1–17.8}$$

for all pairs of values of i, j; a square array is said to be *skew-symmetric* or *antisymmetric* if

$$a_{ij} = -a_{ji} \tag{1–17.9}$$

for all pairs of i, j. For an antisymmetric array, it follows by Eq. (1–17.9) that $a_{ii} = a_{jj} = 0$.

An arbitrary square array (neither symmetric nor antisymmetric) may be represented as the sum of a symmetric array and an antisymmetric array. For example, any two numbers r and s can always be written in the form

$$r = \tfrac{1}{2}(x + y), \qquad s = \tfrac{1}{2}(x - y)$$

by letting

$$x = r + s, \qquad y = r - s$$

Hence, we may express a typical element of the arbitrary square array (a_{ij}) in the form

$$a_{ij} = \tfrac{1}{2}(a_{ij} + a_{ij}) + \tfrac{1}{2}(a_{ji} - a_{ji})$$
$$= \tfrac{1}{2}(a_{ij} + a_{ji}) + \tfrac{1}{2}(a_{ij} - a_{ji})$$

or

$$a_{ij} = c_{ij} + d_{ij} \qquad (1\text{--}17.10)$$

where

$$c_{ij} = \tfrac{1}{2}(a_{ij} + a_{ji}) = c_{ji}$$

denotes a symmetric square array and

$$d_{ij} = \tfrac{1}{2}(a_{ij} - a_{ji}) = -d_{ji}$$

denotes an antisymmetric square array.

1-18 Transformation of Tensors under Change of Rectangular Cartesian Coordinate System

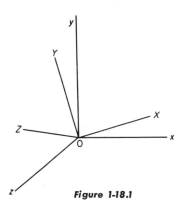

In this article we consider briefly some tensor transformations and properties which are important in the theory of deformable media. For simplicity, we restrict our discussion to rectangular cartesian coordinates. Accordingly, the results presented here are special cases of more general tensor transformations.[5]

Let (x, y, z) and (X, Y, Z) denote two right-handed rectangular cartesian coordinate systems with common origin (Fig. 1–18.1). The cosines of the angles between the six coordinate axes may be represented in tabular

Figure 1-18.1

form (Table 1–18.1). Each entry in Table 1–18.1 is the cosine of the angle between

Table 1-18.1

	x	y	z
X	a_{11}	a_{12}	a_{13}
Y	a_{21}	a_{22}	a_{23}
Z	a_{31}	a_{32}	a_{33}

the two coordinate axes designated at the top of its column and the left of its row. For example, a_{23} denotes the cosine of the angle between the z axis

---

[5]Synge and Schild, *Tensor Calculus*.

and the Y axis; that is, $a_{\alpha\beta}$ represents the direction cosines of the angle between the axes designated by the row α and the column β of Table 1–18.1. Since the elements of Table 1–18.1 are direction cosines, they satisfy the following relations:[6]

$$a_{1\beta}^2 + a_{2\beta}^2 + a_{3\beta}^2 = 1, \qquad \beta = 1, 2, 3$$
$$a_{\alpha1}^2 + a_{\alpha2}^2 + a_{\alpha3}^2 = 1, \qquad \alpha = 1, 2, 3 \tag{1–18.1}$$

Equation (1–18.1) signifies that the sum of the squares of the elements of any row or column of Table 1–18.1 is one. Furthermore, since the axes (X, Y, Z) are mutually perpendicular, we have

$$a_{\alpha1}a_{\beta1} + a_{\alpha2}a_{\beta2} + a_{\alpha3}a_{\beta3} = 0, \qquad \alpha, \beta = 1, 2, 3, \quad \alpha \neq \beta \tag{1–18.2}$$

Similarly, since (x, y, z) are mutually perpendicular, we have further

$$a_{1\beta}a_{1\alpha} + a_{2\beta}a_{2\alpha} + a_{3\beta}a_{3\alpha} = 0, \qquad \alpha, \beta = 1, 2, 3, \quad \alpha \neq \beta \tag{1–18.3}$$

Equations (1–18.2) and (1–18.3) signify that the sum of the products of corresponding elements in any two rows or any two columns in Table 1–18.1 is zero. In other words, they express the orthogonality of axes (X, Y, Z) and the orthogonality of axes (x, y, z). For this reason, they are called *orthogonality relations*.

Another important relationship between the coefficients of Table 1–18.1 may be obtained as follows: Noting that the direction cosines of a unit vector with respect to (x, y, z) axes are identical to the projections of the unit vector on the coordinate axes, we regard the direction cosines (a_{11}, a_{12}, a_{13}) as the components on (x, y, z) axes of a unit vector in the X direction. Similarly, (a_{21}, a_{22}, a_{23}) and (a_{31}, a_{32}, a_{33}) represent unit vectors in the Y direction and the Z direction, respectively. Hence, by the vector product of vectors [see Eq. (1–1.13)], if the two coordinate systems (x, y, z) and (X, Y, Z) are both right-handed (or both left-handed), we obtain the vector relation

$$(a_{11}, a_{12}, a_{13}) = (a_{21}, a_{22}, a_{23}) \times (a_{31}, a_{32}, a_{33})$$

or in scalar notation,

$$a_{11} = a_{22}a_{33} - a_{23}a_{32}$$
$$a_{12} = a_{31}a_{23} - a_{21}a_{33} \tag{1–18.4}$$
$$a_{13} = a_{21}a_{32} - a_{22}a_{31}$$

Similar relations hold for $(a_{21}, a_{22}, a_{23}), \ldots, (a_{13}, a_{23}, a_{33})$. In index notation the entire set of relations may be written

$$a_{kr} = a_{ip}a_{jq} - a_{iq}a_{jp} \tag{1–18.5}$$

where (i, j, k), the first indexes of each direction cosine, may take any cyclic order of 1, 2, 3, 1, 2, . . . and where (p, q, r), the second indexes of each direc-

---

[6] L. P. Eisenhart, *Coordinate Geometry* (Boston: Ginn & Company, 1939), Art 30.

tion cosine, take independently any cyclic order of $1, 2, 3, 1, 2, \ldots$ For example, let (i, j, k) be $(2, 3, 1)$ and let (p, q, r) be $(2, 3, 1)$. Then, Eq. $(1-18.5)$ yields

$$a_{11} = a_{22}a_{33} - a_{23}a_{32}$$

Similarly, $(i, j, k) = (1, 2, 3), (p, q, r) = (3, 1, 2)$ yields

$$a_{32} = a_{13}a_{21} - a_{11}a_{23}$$

Equations $(1-18.5)$ are also referred to as orthogonality relations, since they express the orthogonality of axes (x, y, z) and of axes (X, Y, Z).

In view of Eqs. $(1-18.4)$, the second equation of Eqs. $(1-18.1)$, with $\alpha = 1$, may be written

$$a_{11}(a_{22}a_{33} - a_{23}a_{32}) + a_{12}(a_{31}a_{23} - a_{21}a_{33}) + a_{13}(a_{21}a_{32} - a_{22}a_{31}) = 1$$

Similar expressions hold for $\alpha = 2, 3, \beta = 1, 2, 3$.

In determinant notation, the above equation may be written in the form

$$\det(a_{\alpha\beta}) = \begin{vmatrix} a_{11} & a_{12} & a_{13} \\ a_{21} & a_{22} & a_{23} \\ a_{31} & a_{32} & a_{33} \end{vmatrix} = 1 \qquad (1-18.6)$$

where "det" denotes determinant. If the coordinate system is left-handed, it may be shown that $\det(a_{\alpha\beta}) = -1$. Consequently, we have the following theorem:

Theorem 1–18.1. *Any one of the direction cosines of a set of right-handed (left-handed) rectangular cartesian axes measured with respect to a second set of right-handed (left-handed) rectangular cartesian axes is equal to its cofactor (the negative of its cofactor) in the determinant formed from the square array of direction cosines [see Eqs. $(1-18.4)$ and $(1-18.6)$]. Furthermore, the numerical value of the determinant is $1 (-1)$.*

In the following, we consider right-handed coordinate systems only.

Let the coordinates of a point P be (x, y, z) with respect to axes (x, y, z). Then, with respect to (X, Y, Z) axes, the coordinates of P may be expressed in terms of coordinates (x, y, z) by the equations

$$\begin{aligned} X &= a_{11}x + a_{12}y + a_{13}z \\ Y &= a_{21}x + a_{22}y + a_{23}z \\ Z &= a_{31}x + a_{32}y + a_{33}z \end{aligned} \qquad (1-18.7)$$

For (X, Y, Z) axes with origin at (a_{10}, a_{20}, a_{30}), Eqs. $(1-18.7)$ may be generalized by the substitution $X = X - a_{10}, Y = Y - a_{20}, Z = Z - a_{30}$.

Conversely, with respect to (x, y, z) axes, the coordinates of P expressed in terms of X, Y, Z are given by the relations (since $\det a_{\alpha\beta} = 1$)

$$\begin{aligned} x &= a_{11}X + a_{21}Y + a_{31}Z \\ y &= a_{12}X + a_{22}Y + a_{32}Z \\ z &= a_{13}X + a_{23}Y + a_{33}Z \end{aligned} \qquad (1-18.8)$$

With the summation notation introduced in Art. 1–17, Eq. (1–18.7) becomes

$$X_\alpha = a_{\alpha 1}x_1 + a_{\alpha 2}x_2 + a_{\alpha 3}x_3; \qquad \alpha = 1, 2, 3 \qquad (1\text{–}18.9)$$

or

$$X_\alpha = a_{\alpha\beta}x_\beta; \qquad \alpha, \beta = 1, 2, 3$$

Similarly, Eq. (1–18.8) may be written

$$x_\beta = a_{1\beta}X_1 + a_{2\beta}X_2 + a_{3\beta}X_3; \qquad \beta = 1, 2, 3$$
$$x_\beta = a_{\alpha\beta}X_\alpha; \qquad \alpha, \beta = 1, 2, 3 \qquad (1\text{–}18.10)$$

For given values of α and β, the value of $a_{\alpha\beta}$ in Eq. (1–18.9) is identical to the value of $a_{\alpha\beta}$ in Eq. (1–18.10). This follows from the definition of the entries in Table 1–18.1.

With the understanding that α, β take values 1, 2, 3, Eqs. (1–18.9) and (1–18.10) are written

$$X_\alpha = a_{\alpha\beta}x_\beta \qquad (1\text{–}18.11)$$

and

$$x_\beta = a_{\alpha\beta}X_\alpha \qquad (1\text{–}18.12)$$

Since a repeated Greek index is always summed, it may be replaced by any convenient letter, as noted in Art. 1–17. Accordingly, the following forms for Eq. (1–18.11) are all equivalent:

$$X_\alpha = a_{\alpha\beta}x_\beta = a_{\alpha\gamma}x_\gamma = a_{\alpha\xi}x_\xi$$

Scalars. Quantities such as temperature and density which may be represented by a single number, for example, $10°F$ or 30 grams/cm³, are called scalars. Under a transformation of coordinate axes, scalars remain unchanged; that is, scalars are invariant under coordinate transformations. For this reason, scalars are often called invariants. In tensor theory, scalars are called *tensors of zero order*.

Vectors. In summation notation, a vector is represented by the symbol u_i (Art. 1–17). Suppose the arrow OP representing the vector u_i is attached to a rectangular cartesian coordinate system (x, y, z), Fig. 1–18.2. Then the coordinates of P correspond to the components (u_1, u_2, u_3) of vector u_i. Consequently, under a transformation from one rectangular cartesian coordinate system to another, the components of a three-dimensional vector transform according to the relationship [see Eq. (1–18.11)]

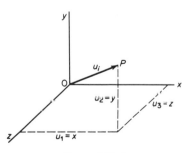

Figure 1-18.2

$$U_\alpha = a_{\alpha\beta}u_\beta \qquad (1\text{–}18.13)$$

the vector u_i remaining fixed in space. Such sets of three components, that is, vectors, are called *tensors of the first order*. Tensors of first order require only one index for their representation. Multiplication of a first-order tensor by a zero-order tensor (that is, multiplication of a vector by a scalar) yields another first-order tensor. For example, multiplications of u_i by a constant c yields cu_i. Hence, by Eq. (1–18.13), $a_{\alpha\beta}(cu_\alpha) = c(a_{\alpha\beta}u_\alpha) = cU_\beta$. Thus, cu_i is a tensor of first order, since it obeys the rules of transformation of a tensor of first order. Furthermore, the addition of two tensors of first order (two vectors) yields a tensor of first order (a vector). For example, if u_p, v_p are two tensors of first order, by Eq. (1–18.13), we have

$$U_\alpha = a_{\alpha\beta}u_\beta, \qquad V_\alpha = a_{\alpha\beta}v_\beta$$

Addition of these equations yields

$$U_\alpha + V_\alpha = a_{\alpha\beta}u_\beta + a_{\alpha\beta}b_\beta = a_{\alpha\beta}(u_\beta + v_\beta)$$

Hence, $u_p + v_p$ is a tensor of first order, since it transforms according to Eq. (1–18.13).

Tensors of higher order. Multiplication of tensors of the first order leads to quantities which are not tensors of zero or first order. For example, let u_ζ and v_η be two first-order tensors in the rectangular cartesian coordinate system (x, y, z). Let U_α, V_β denote the corresponding tensors in the rectangular cartesian coordinate system (X, Y, Z). Then, by Eq. (1–18.13),

$$U_\alpha V_\beta = (a_{\alpha\zeta}u_\zeta)(a_{\beta\eta}v_\eta) = a_{\alpha\zeta}a_{\beta\eta}u_\zeta v_\eta$$

or

$$W_{\alpha\beta} = a_{\alpha\zeta}a_{\beta\eta}w_{\zeta\eta} \tag{1–18.14}$$

where $W_{\alpha\beta} = U_\alpha V_\beta$ and $w_{\zeta\eta} = u_\zeta v_\eta$ represent the products of the vectors u_ζ, v_η in the (X, Y, Z) system and in the (x, y, z) system, respectively.

Since both ζ, η are dummy indexes, for given values of α, β the right-hand side of Eq. (1–18.14) contain nine terms. Accordingly, Eq. (1–18.14) represents nine equations, each with nine terms. Quantities which transform according to Eq. (1–18.14) are called *tensors of second order*. In the symbolical representation of tensors of second order, two indexes are required. Many quantities, other than the product of two vectors, transform according to Eq. (1–18.14). For example, components of stress and components of strain transform according to Eq. (1–18.14) under a change of rectangular coordinate systems (see Chapters 2 and 3). Accordingly, the components of stress and the components of strain form second-order tensors.

In a similar fashion, a *tensor of third order* is formed by multiplying together three first-order tensors, and so on. Thus, an nth-order tensor may be formed by multiplying together n first-order tensors. Essentially, this means that we have available means of specifying components of nth-order tensors with respect to any set of rectangular cartesian axes and rules for transforming these components to any other set of rectangular cartesian axes. Hence, the statement that a quantity is a tensor quantity may be proved by comparison with these known tensor transformations. For example, this technique was employed in the proof that the sum of two first-order tensors yields a first-order tensor.

In summary, a tensor of zero order (scalar) is a single quantity which depends on position in space, but not on the coordinate system. A tensor of first order (vector) is a quantity whose components transform according to Eq. (1–18.13). Hence, with respect to a rectangular cartesian coordinate system in three-dimensional space, a tensor of first order contains $3^1 = 3$ elements or components. A tensor of second order is a quantity that transforms according to Eq. (1–18.14). With respect to rectangular cartesian coordinate systems in three-dimensional space, a second-order tensor has $3^2 = 9$ elements.

A tensor of nth order is a quantity whose components transform according to the rule[7]

$$T_{p_1 p_2 \cdots p_n} = a_{p_1 q_1} a_{p_2 q_2} \cdots a_{p_n q_n} t_{q_1 q_2 \cdots q_n} \tag{1–18.15}$$

With respect to rectangular cartesian coordinate axes in three-dimensional space, an nth-order tensor has 3^n elements. Thus, a fourth-order tensor has 81 elements, a fifth-order tensor has 243 elements; and a tenth-order tensor has 59,049 elements.

In general developments of continuous-media mechanics, fourth-order tensors play a prominent role.[8]

1-19 Symmetric and Antisymmetric Parts of a Tensor

If we interchange α and β in Eq. (1–18.14), we obtain

$$W_{\beta\alpha} = a_{\beta\zeta} a_{\alpha\eta} w_{\zeta\eta} \tag{1–19.1}$$

Since ζ and η are dummy indices, we may interchange them. Thus, Eq. (1–19.1) may be written

$$W_{\beta\alpha} = a_{\beta\eta} a_{\alpha\zeta} w_{\eta\zeta} = a_{\alpha\zeta} a_{\beta\eta} w_{\eta\zeta} \tag{1–19.2}$$

Hence, comparing Eqs. (1–18.14) and (1–19.2), we see that $w_{\eta\zeta}$ transforms according to the same rule as $w_{\zeta\eta}$. The tensor $w_{\zeta\eta}$ is said to be *conjugate* to $w_{\eta\zeta}$. Thus, if $w_{\zeta\eta}$ is a tensor of second order, another tensor of second order is obtained by interchanging η and ζ. Consequently, $w_{\zeta\eta} + w_{\eta\zeta}$ and $w_{\zeta\eta} - w_{\eta\zeta}$ are tensors of second order. Symbolically, we may represent the tensors $w_{\zeta\eta}$ and $w_{\eta\zeta}$ as follows:

[7]Synge and Schild, *Tensor Calculus*. Here, we let dummy indexes be denoted by $q_1, q_2, \ldots, q_n$.

[8]A. E. Green and W. Zerna, *Theoretical Elasticity* (London: Oxford University Press, 1960).

$$w_{\zeta\eta} = \begin{pmatrix} w_{11} & w_{12} & w_{13} \\ w_{21} & w_{22} & w_{23} \\ w_{31} & w_{32} & w_{33} \end{pmatrix}$$

and

$$w_{\eta\zeta} = \begin{pmatrix} w_{11} & w_{21} & w_{31} \\ w_{12} & w_{22} & w_{32} \\ w_{13} & w_{23} & w_{33} \end{pmatrix}$$

Then,

$$w_{\zeta\eta} + w_{\eta\zeta} = \begin{pmatrix} 2w_{11} & w_{12} + w_{21} & w_{13} + w_{31} \\ w_{21} + w_{12} & 2w_{22} & w_{23} + w_{32} \\ w_{31} + w_{13} & w_{32} + w_{23} & 2w_{33} \end{pmatrix} \tag{1-19.3}$$

$$= w_{\eta\zeta} + w_{\zeta\eta}$$

and

$$w_{\zeta\eta} - w_{\eta\zeta} = \begin{pmatrix} 0 & w_{12} - w_{21} & w_{13} - w_{31} \\ w_{21} - w_{12} & 0 & w_{23} - w_{32} \\ w_{31} - w_{13} & w_{32} - w_{23} & 0 \end{pmatrix} \tag{1-19.4}$$

$$= -(w_{\eta\zeta} - w_{\zeta\eta})$$

Since $w_{\zeta\eta} + w_{\eta\zeta}$ is unaltered by interchanging ζ and η, it is called a symmetrical tensor of second order. However, when ζ and η are interchanged in $w_{\zeta\eta} - w_{\eta\zeta}$, each element changes in sign. Hence, $w_{\zeta\eta} - w_{\eta\zeta}$ is called an antisymmetrical tensor of second order. Also, by Eqs. (1-19.3) and (1-19.4),

$$w_{\zeta\eta} = \tfrac{1}{2}(w_{\zeta\eta} + w_{\eta\zeta}) + \tfrac{1}{2}(w_{\zeta\eta} - w_{\eta\zeta}) \tag{1-19.5}$$

Consequently, a second-order tensor may be resolved into symmetric and antisymmetric parts. Furthermore, since the antisymmetric part contains only three components, $w_{12} - w_{21}$, $w_{13} - w_{31}$, $w_{23} - w_{32}$, it may be associated with a vector u_i. Equation (1-19.5) is analogous to Eq. (1-17.10).

1-20 The Symbols δ_{ij} and ϵ_{ijk}

The use of the following notation often simplifies the writing of equations:

$$\delta_{ij} = \begin{cases} 1 & \text{for } i = j \\ 0 & \text{for } i \neq j \end{cases} \tag{1-20.1}$$

The symbol δ_{ij} is called the Kronecker delta.

Using the notation δ_{ij}, with respect to axes (x, y, z) we may write the second of Eqs. (1-18.1) and Eqs. (1-18.2) collectively as

$$a_{\alpha\gamma} a_{\beta\gamma} = \delta_{\alpha\beta} \tag{1-20.2}$$

Similarly, with respect to axes (X, Y, Z) we may express the first of Eqs. (1-18.1) and Eqs. (1-18.3) in the form

$$a_{\gamma\beta}a_{\gamma\alpha} = \delta_{\beta\alpha} \qquad (1\text{--}20.3)$$

The Kronecker delta has the following important properties:

(i) $\quad \delta_{\lambda\lambda} = \delta_{11} + \delta_{22} + \delta_{33} = 3$

(ii) $\quad \delta_{i\lambda}\delta_{j\lambda} = \delta_{ij} \qquad (1\text{--}20.4)$

(iii) $\quad p_{i\lambda}\delta_{j\lambda} = p_{ij}$

The property (iii) is a generalization of (ii). It is called the *rule of substitution* of *indexes*, since the multiplication by $\delta_{j\lambda}$ substitutes the index j for the index λ.

The set of quantities δ_{ij}, $i,j = 1, 2, 3$ constitute a *tensor of the second order*. To prove this, we must show that δ_{ij} transforms according to Eq. (1–18.14) under a transformation of rectangular cartesian axes. The array δ_{ij} consists of the elements $\delta_{11} = 1$, $\delta_{22} = 1$, $\delta_{33} = ,1$, $\delta_{12} = 0$, $\delta_{23} = 0$, $\delta_{13} = 0$. Accordingly, if we set $\delta_{\sigma\gamma} = w_{\sigma\gamma}$ and substitute in Eq. (1–18.14), we get

$$W_{\alpha\beta} = \delta'_{\alpha\beta} = a_{\alpha\sigma}a_{\beta\gamma}\delta_{\sigma\gamma} = a_{\alpha1}a_{\beta1} + a_{\alpha2}a_{\beta2} + a_{\alpha3}a_{\beta3}$$

Hence, by Eqs. (1–20.1) and (1–20.2),

$$\delta'_{\alpha\beta} = \begin{cases} 1 & \text{for } \alpha = \beta \\ 0 & \text{for } \alpha \neq \beta \end{cases}$$

Thus, it follows that the array ($\delta_{11} = \delta_{22} = \delta_{33} = 1$, $\delta_{12} = \delta_{13} = \delta_{23} = 0$) is transformed into itself by the tensor transformation Eq. (1–18.14). This transformation is in accord with the definition of Eq. (1–20.1). Hence, $\delta_{\alpha\beta}$ is a second-order tensor. A tensor whose respective components (elements) are the same with respect to all sets of coordinate systems is called an *isotropic tensor*. In view of the fact that δ_{ij} is a tensor and in view of the substitution property (iii), δ_{ij} is sometimes referred to as the *substitution tensor*.

Symbol ϵ_{ijk}. The symbol ϵ_{ijk} is defined as follows:

$$\epsilon_{ijk} = \begin{cases} 1 & \text{if } i, j, k \text{ are in cycle order } 1, 2, 3, 1, 2, \ldots \\ 0 & \text{if any two of } i, j, k \text{ are equal} \\ -1 & \text{if } i, j, k \text{ are in anticyclic order } 3, 2, 1, 3, 2 \end{cases} \qquad (1\text{--}20.4)$$

For example,

$$\epsilon_{123} = \epsilon_{312} = \epsilon_{231} = 1$$
$$\epsilon_{112} = \epsilon_{121} = \epsilon_{322} - \cdots = 0 \qquad (1\text{--}20.5)$$
$$\epsilon_{321} = \epsilon_{213} = \epsilon_{132} = -1$$

By definition of δ_{ij} and ϵ_{ijk} it follows that (no summation)

$$\epsilon_{ijk}\delta_{ij} = \epsilon_{iik} = 0 \qquad (1\text{--}20.6)$$

Furthermore, it follows by Eq. (1–20.5) and (1–20.6) that

$$\epsilon_{\alpha\beta k}\delta_{\alpha\beta} = 0 \qquad \text{(summed)} \qquad (1\text{--}20.7)$$

In terms of ϵ_{ijk}, the orthogonality relations [Eq. (1–18.5)] may be written

$$\epsilon_{ij\alpha} a_{\alpha n} = \epsilon_{\alpha\beta n} a_{i\alpha} a_{j\beta} \tag{1–20.8}$$

where i, j, n take independently any value 1, 2, 3. The proof of Eq. (1–20.8) is left for the problems.

The array ϵ_{ijk} transforms according to the rules of transformation of a third-order isotropic tensor. To show this, we note that a third-order tensor transforms according to the rule [see Eq. (1–18.15)]

$$T_{ijk} = a_{i\alpha} a_{j\beta} a_{k\gamma} t_{\alpha\beta\gamma} \tag{1–20.9}$$

Hence, we must show that $\epsilon_{\alpha\beta\gamma}$ transforms according to the rule

$$\epsilon_{ijk} = a_{i\alpha} a_{j\beta} a_{k\gamma} \epsilon_{\alpha\beta\gamma} \tag{1–20.10}$$

Substituting Eq. (1–20.8) into the right-hand side of Eq. (1–20.10), we obtain

$$a_{k\gamma} a_{\alpha\gamma} \epsilon_{ij\alpha}$$

But $a_{k\gamma} a_{\alpha\gamma} = \delta_{k\alpha}$, by Eq. (1–20.2). Hence,

$$a_{k\gamma} a_{\alpha\gamma} \epsilon_{ij\alpha} = \delta_{k\alpha} \epsilon_{ij\alpha} = \epsilon_{ijk}$$

Accordingly, Eq. (1–20.10) is verified.

1-21 Homogeneous Quadratic Forms

The most general homogeneous quadratic form in the variables X_i, $i = 1, 2, 3$ may be written in index notation as

$$Q = a_{\alpha\beta} X_\alpha X_\beta, \qquad \alpha, \beta = 1, 2, 3 \tag{1–21.1}$$

where a_{ij} denotes the following square array of real elements:

$$\begin{pmatrix} a_{11} & a_{12} & a_{13} \\ a_{21} & a_{22} & a_{23} \\ a_{31} & a_{32} & a_{33} \end{pmatrix} \tag{1–21.2}$$

The quadratic form Q written in expanded form is

$$Q = a_{11} X_1^2 + a_{22} X_2^2 + a_{33} X_3^2 + (a_{12} + a_{21}) X_1 X_2$$
$$+ (a_{13} + a_{31}) X_1 X_3 + (a_{23} + a_{32}) X_2 X_3 \tag{1–21.3}$$

The determinant $\det (a_{ij})$ is called the *determinant* of the array [Eq. (1–21.2)]. The expression Eq. (1–21.1) [or Eq. (1–21.3)] is called the *quadratic form* associated with the array (a_{ij}). Without loss of generality, the array may be assumed symmetrical; that is, we may set $a_{ij} = a_{ji}$. Then, Eq. (1–21.3) becomes

$$Q = a_{11} X_1^2 + a_{22} X_2^2 + a_{33} X_3^2 + 2a_{12} X_1 X_2 + 2a_{13} X_1 X_3 + 2a_{23} X_2 X_3 \tag{1–21.4}$$

where we have simply replaced the notation $(a_{12} + a_{21})$, etc., in Eq. (1–21.3) by $2a_{12}$, etc. in Eq. (1–21.4).

The equation

$$\begin{vmatrix} a_{11} - r & a_{12} & a_{13} \\ a_{21} & a_{22} - r & a_{23} \\ a_{31} & a_{32} & a_{33} - r \end{vmatrix} = 0$$

or in index notation

$$|a_{ij} - r\delta_{ij}| = 0 \tag{1–21.5}$$

is called the *characteristic* equation of the array (a_{ij}). The three roots (r_1, r_2, r_3) of Eq. (1–21.5) are called the characteristic roots, or latent roots, or eigenvalues of the array (a_{ij}).[9] In general, the r_i are distinct. However, special cases may occur in which two or all of the r_i are equal.

A necessary and sufficient condition that a set of linear algebraic equations

$$c_{i\alpha} X_\alpha = 0, \qquad i = 1, 2, 3 \tag{1–21.6}$$

possesses a solution other than the trivial solution $X_1 = X_2 = X_3 = 0$ is that the determinant of the coefficients $c_{i\alpha}$ of Eq. (1–21.6) vanishes.[10] Accordingly,

$$|c_{i\alpha}| = 0 \tag{1–21.7}$$

represents a necessary and sufficient condition that Eq. (1–21.6) possesses a solution X_i ($X_i \neq 0$). Accordingly, by Eqs. (1–21.5), (1–21.6), and (1–21.7) it follows that for every r such that $|a_{ij} - r\delta_{ij}| = 0$, an array (X_i) exists such that

$$(a_{i\alpha} - r\delta_{i\alpha}) X_\alpha = 0$$

Rewriting, we have

$$a_{i\alpha} X_\alpha = r\delta_{i\alpha} X_\alpha = r X_i \tag{1–21.8}$$

In other words, Eq. (1–21.5) expresses the necessary and sufficient condition that Eq. (1–21.8) possesses nontrivial solutions X_i. The nontrivial solutions of Eq. (1–21.8) are called the *eigenvectors* of the array (a_{ij}).

Let y_i denote any arbitrary array (y_1, y_2, y_3). Then, by Eq. (1–21.8),

$$a_{\alpha\beta} X_\alpha y_\beta = r X_\alpha y_\alpha \tag{1–21.9}$$

If $y_i = X_i$,

$$a_{\alpha\beta} X_\alpha X_\beta = r X_\alpha X_\alpha \tag{1–21.10}$$

Orthogonality of eigenvectors. Consider the case where the array X_i corresponds to the array m_i of direction cosines [Eq. (1–17.4)]. Let us assume that there exists two nonequal characteristic roots $r^{(1)}, r^{(2)}$ of Eq. (1–21.5).

---

[9]Eisenhart, *Coordinate Geometry*.

[10]L. Pipes, *Applied Mathematics for Engineers and Physicists*, 2nd ed. (New York: McGraw-Hill Book Company, 1959).

Then the corresponding solutions (eigenvectors) of Eq. (1–21.8) may be denoted by $m_i^{(1)}$, $m_i^{(2)}$. Accordingly, Eq. (1–21.8) becomes

$$a_{i\alpha} m_\alpha^{(1)} = r^{(1)} m_i^{(1)} \qquad \text{for } r = r^{(1)}$$

$$a_{i\alpha} m_\alpha^{(2)} = r^{(2)} m_i^{(2)} \qquad \text{for } r = r^{(2)} \tag{1–21.11}$$

Multiplying the first of Eqs. (1–21.11) by $m_i^{(2)}$ and the second of Eqs. (1–21.11) by $m_i^{(1)}$ and subtracting, we obtain (since $a_{ij} = a_{ji}$)

$$[r^{(2)} - r^{(1)}] m_\beta^{(1)} m_\beta^{(2)} = 0$$

However, since by hypothesis, $r^{(2)} \neq r^{(1)}$, it follows that

$$m_\beta^{(1)} m_\beta^{(2)} = 0 \tag{1–21.12}$$

Accordingly, the directions (eigenvectors) $m_\beta^{(1)}$, $m_\beta^{(2)}$ which correspond to the characteristic roots $r^{(1)}$ and $r^{(2)}$ are orthogonal. Furthermore, if $r^{(1)}$ and $r^{(2)}$ are two distinct characteristic roots and $m_\beta^{(1)}$ and $m_\beta^{(2)}$ are the corresponding direction cosines, by Eq. (1–21.9), we have

$$a_{\alpha\beta} m_\alpha^{(1)} m_\beta^{(2)} = r^{(2)} m_\beta^{(1)} m_\beta^{(2)} = r^{(1)} m_\beta^{(1)} m_\beta^{(2)} = 0$$

Hence,

$$a_{\alpha\beta} m_\alpha^{(1)} m_\beta^{(2)} = 0 \tag{1–21.13}$$

Finally, we note that the characteristic roots $r^{(1)}, r^{(2)}$ are real. We prove this by contradiction as follows: assume that $r^{(1)}$ is complex. Denote its complex conjugate by $\bar{r}^{(1)}$. Then, taking the complex conjugate of the first of Eq. (1–21.11), we obtain

$$a_{\alpha\beta} \bar{m}_\beta^{(1)} = \bar{r}^{(1)} \bar{m}_\alpha^{(1)} \tag{1–21.14}$$

Multiplying (1–21.14) by $m_\alpha^{(1)}$, we get

$$a_{\alpha\beta} m_\alpha^{(1)} \bar{m}_\beta^{(1)} = \bar{r}^{(1)} m_\alpha^{(1)} \bar{m}_\alpha^{(1)} \tag{1–21.15}$$

Multiplying the first of Eq. (1–21.11) by $\bar{m}_\alpha^{(1)}$, we get

$$a_{\alpha\beta} \bar{m}_\alpha^{(1)} m_\beta^{(1)} = r^{(1)} m_\alpha^{(1)} \bar{m}_\alpha^{(1)} \tag{1–21.16}$$

Comparison of Eqs. (1–21.15) and (1–21.16) yields

$$[\bar{r}^{(1)} - r^{(1)}] m_\alpha^{(1)} \bar{m}_\alpha^{(1)} = 0$$

Since $m_\alpha^{(1)} \bar{m}_\alpha^{(1)}$ is the sum of squares of real numbers, it cannot be zero unless $m_1 = m_2 = m_3 = 0$. However, this is not possible since by Eq. (1–17.4)

$$m_1^2 + m_2^2 + m_3^2 = 1.$$

Hence,

$$r^{(1)} = \bar{r}^{(1)}.$$

That is, $r^{(1)}$ is equal to its conjugate $\bar{r}^1$. Accordingly, $r^{(1)}$ must be real.

2
THEORY OF STRESS
FOR CONTINUOUS MEDIA

This chapter presents the general three-dimensional theory of stress for a continuous medium. By a continuous medium we mean a material in which each small volume of substance is sufficiently dense so that concepts such as stress at a point, density at a point, temperature at a point, etc., have physical meaning. Alternatively, we may define a continuous medium as one which admits macroscopic average values of physical properties such as stress, density, and temperature. We refer to the physical model which we treat as that of a continuous medium. Within the restrictions indicated, the theory of stress is applicable to all materials regardless of their mechanical behavior, that is, whether they behave elastically, plastically, viscoelastically, or in any other manner. A fundamental assumption of the present stress theory is that stress couples are assumed to vanish.[1]

2-1 Definition of Stress

It is noted in elementary mechanics that point forces never really occur in nature; forces are always distributed throughout regions. Nevertheless, the point force is an indispensable concept in mechanics. For example, distributed forces that act on a rigid body are dynamically equivalent to a single point force and a couple.

---

[1]For a lucid discussion of the concept of stress couples see R. D. Mindlin and H. F. Tiersten "Effect of Couple-stresses in Linear Elasticity," *Archive for Rational Mechanics and Analysis*, **11**, 5 (1962), pp. 415–48. See also R. D. Mindlin, "Influence of Couple-stresses on Stress Concentration," The William M. Murray Lecture, 1962, *Experimental Mechanics* (January 1963).

To gain insight into the nature of distributed forces, we consider the forces that act inside a solid or a fluid. The theories of deformable bodies (fluid mechanics, elasticity, and plasticity) are based on the concept of action by direct contact. If we imagine a body to be partitioned into cells by fictitious surfaces, one cell does not exert a direct effect on another cell, unless it is in contact with it. If two cells are in contact with each other along one of the fictitious surfaces of separation, a force may be transmitted from the first cell to the second cell, and vice versa. To elaborate on this idea, let us pass a fictitious plane Q through a body, and let us mark an area A on the plane. One side of the plane Q will be designated as positive, and the other side as negative (Fig. 2–1.1). The material on the positive side of the plane Q exerts a force upon the material on the negative side. This force is transmitted through the plane Q by direct contact of material on the two sides of the plane. The force that is transmitted through the area A is denoted by $\mathbf{F}$. In accordance with Newton's law of reaction, the material on the negative side of plane Q transmits, through the area A, a force equal to $-\mathbf{F}$. The force $\mathbf{F}$ is an internal force, since its reaction is exerted within the body.

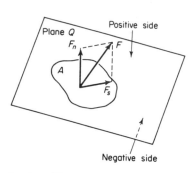

Fig. 2-1.1 Normal force and shearing force on a plane area.

The force $\mathbf{F}$ may be resolved into components $\mathbf{F}_n$ and $\mathbf{F}_s$, such that the component $\mathbf{F}_n$ is perpendicular to plane Q, and the component $\mathbf{F}_s$ is tangent to plane Q (Fig. 2–1.1). The component $\mathbf{F}_n$ is called the *normal force* on the area A, and the component $\mathbf{F}_s$ is called the *shearing force* on the area A. The word "normal" has the same meaning as the word "perpendicular."

The foregoing concepts are equally applicable to stationary bodies and to deforming bodies (e.g., to flowing fluids). During a deformation process, $\mathbf{F}_n$ and $\mathbf{F}_s$ ordinarily vary with time. The forces $\mathbf{F}_n$ and $\mathbf{F}_s$ naturally depend on the area A. The magnitudes of the average forces per unit area are F_n/A and F_s/A. These ratios are called the average normal stress and the average shearing stress on the area A. The *concept of stress at a point* is obtained by letting area A be infinitesimal. Then, the forces $\mathbf{F}_n$ and $\mathbf{F}_s$ approach zero, but the ratios F_n/A and F_s/A usually approach limits different from zero. The limiting values of the ratios F_n/A and F_s/A are called the *normal stress* and the *shearing stress* on plane Q at the point where the infinitesimal area A is located. In general, these stresses depend not only on the coordinates of the infinitesimal area A, but also on the plane in which the area A lies. The normal stress and the shearing stress may be regarded as normal and tangential projections of a *stress vector* that is associated with the infinitesimal area A.

Accordingly, we may speak of the *direction of the stress* that acts at a given point on a given plane; it is the direction of the infinitesimal force that acts on the elemental area. Mathematically, the foregoing remarks may be summarized as follows:

$$\operatorname{Lim}_{A \to 0} \frac{F_n}{A} = \sigma, \qquad \operatorname{Lim}_{A \to 0} \frac{F_s}{A} = \tau$$

where σ is the normal stress at a point in area A in plane Q and τ is the shearing stress at the same point in area A in plane Q.

There are significant differences between the internal forces in fluids and in solids. Solids frequently sustain large internal tensile forces. On the other hand, normal forces in fluids are usually compressive. In other words, the normal force that is transmitted from the fluid on one side of a fictitious plane to the fluid on the other side is usually a push, rather than a pull.

The materials that are known as fluids have another property that distinguishes them from solids. Fluid materials flow (that is, they deform continuously) whenever shearing stresses exist. It is customary to designate this property as the definition of a fluid. Accordingly, *shearing stresses cannot exist in a fluid that is at rest.* This definition may be applied to ascertain whether a given material is a fluid. For example, clay does not flow unless the absolute value of the shearing stress exceeds a certain positive value. Consequently, clay is classified as a plastic solid, rather than a fluid.

Intuitively, we should expect that the shearing stress in free-flowing fluids, such as air and water, must be small, even though the fluids are in motion. This observation has led to the concept of a *frictionless fluid*, that is, an *ideal fluid. A frictionless fluid is defined to be a material in which shearing stresses cannot be developed.* Much of classical hydrodynamics is concerned with frictionless fluids. However, the theory of frictionless fluids has not been so useful as it was originally expected to be, since significant shearing stresses always exist in a flowing fluid in the regions near solid boundaries.

A fluid in which shearing stresses are developed when flow occurs is said to be *viscous*. To some extent, all real fluids are viscous.

2-2 Stress Notation

In the theory of stress of continuous bodies a distinction is made between the following two types of forces: (a) *body forces*, acting on the elements of volume (or mass) of the body, and (b) *stresses*, acting on surface elements inside or on the boundary of the body. Examples of body forces are gravitational forces, magnetic forces, and inertia forces. Examples of stresses (or surface forces) are contact forces between solid bodies, or hydrostatic pressure between a solid body and a fluid.

The notation σ_x denotes the stress component normal to a plane that is

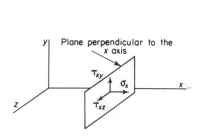

Fig. 2-2.1 Normal and shear components of stress.

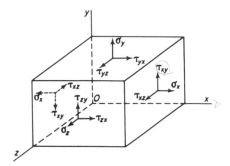

Fig. 2-2.2 Sign convention for stress components.

perpendicular to the x axis (Fig. 2–2.1). The notations τ_{xy}, τ_{xz} denote the components of the shearing-stress vector that lies in a plane perpendicular to the x axis (Fig. 2–2.1), the components being directed in the y and z directions, respectively.

For example, consider an infinitesimal cubic element at a point O in body, with sides parallel to the (x, y, z) axes (Fig. 2–2.2). The normal stress components $\sigma_x, \sigma_y, \sigma_z$ are taken to be *positive* when they produce tension. They are shown as positive in Fig. 2–2.2. The shearing-stress components that act on a plane perpendicular to the x axis are taken to be in the positive sense; that is, the components τ_{xy}, τ_{xz} are directed in the positive y and z directions when they act on a plane for which σ_x is directed in the positive x direction. On the left face of the cube σ_x is directed in the negative x direction. Then, the positive senses of τ_{xy}, τ_{xz} are in the negative y direction and the negative z direction, respectively. Equivalent sign conventions hold for the planes perpendicular to the y and z axes.

The stress notation illustrated in Fig. 2–2.2 is somewhat conventional in engineering. However, other stress notations are common. The more frequent notations for components of the stress tensor are listed in Table 2–2.1.

Table 2-2.1   SUMMARY OF STRESS NOTATIONS

Engineering (this text)	σ_x	σ_y	σ_z	$\tau_{xy} = \tau_{yx}{}^*$	$\tau_{xz} = \tau_{zx}{}^*$	$\tau_{yz} = \tau_{zy}{}^*$
Some American writers	τ_{xx}	τ_{yy}	τ_{zz}	$\tau_{xy} = \tau_{yx}$	$\tau_{xz} = \tau_{zx}$	$\tau_{yz} = \tau_{zy}$
Love (also some Russian and English writers)	X_x	Y_y	Z_z	$X_y = Y_x$	$X_z = Z_x$	$Y_z = Z_y$
Planck	$-X_x$	$-Y_y$	$-Z_z$	$-X_y = -Y_x$	$-X_z = -Z_x$	$-Y_z = -Z_y$
Some English writers	P	Q	R	S	T	U

*See Eq. (2–3.3).

2-3 Equilibrium of Moments. Stress on an Oblique Plane

By the foregoing sign convention, the stress components with reference to rectangular coordinates (x, y, z) may be tabulated in the following array:

$$\begin{pmatrix} \sigma_x & \tau_{xy} & \tau_{xz} \\ \tau_{yx} & \sigma_y & \tau_{yz} \\ \tau_{zx} & \tau_{zy} & \sigma_z \end{pmatrix} \qquad (2\text{-}3.1)$$

In this array, the stress components in the first row act on a plane perpendicular to the x axis, the stress components in the second row act on a plane perpendicular to the y axis, and the stress components in the third row act on a plane perpendicular to the z axis. Apparently, nine stress components are required to define stress at a point in a body. However, by simple consideration of equilibrium of moments of a differential element, the number of stress components can be reduced by three.

Returning to Fig. 2–2.2, we note that if the element is in equilibrium, summation of moments with respect to (x, y, z) axes yields the following equations[2] (in the absence of body moments due to other sources such as magnetic effects):

$$M_x = (\tau_{yz}\, dx\, dz)\, dy - (\tau_{zy}\, dx\, dy)\, dz = 0$$
$$M_y = (\tau_{zx}\, dx\, dy)\, dz - (\tau_{xz}\, dy\, dz)\, dx = 0 \qquad (2\text{-}3.2)$$
$$M_z = (\tau_{xy}\, dy\, dz)\, dx - (\tau_{yx}\, dx\, dz)\, dy = 0$$

where M_x, M_y, M_z denote moments with respect to the (x, y, z) axes, respectively. Hence, by Eq. (2–3.2),

$$\tau_{yz} = \tau_{zy}, \qquad \tau_{zx} = \tau_{xz}, \qquad \tau_{xy} = \tau_{yx} \qquad (2\text{-}3.3)$$

With Eq. (2–3.3), Eq. (2–3.1) may be written in the form

$$\begin{pmatrix} \sigma_x & \tau_{xy} & \tau_{xz} \\ \tau_{xy} & \sigma_y & \tau_{yz} \\ \tau_{xz} & \tau_{yz} & \sigma_z \end{pmatrix} \qquad (2\text{-}3.4)$$

This array of stress components is symmetrical with respect to the diagonal (running from the upper left-hand corner to the lower right-hand corner); that is, the shearing-stress components (the off-diagonal components) are equal in pairs. Hence, in the absence of body moments, only six stress

---

[2] If we let $\sigma_x, \tau_{xy}, \tau_{xz}$ be the stress components on the left face of the element, then in general, the stress components on the right face will be $\sigma_x + (\partial\sigma/\partial x)\, dx$, $\tau_{xy} + (\partial\tau_{xy}/\partial x)\, dx$, $\tau_{xz} + (\partial\tau_{xz}/\partial x)\, dx$. Similar relations hold for the other pairs of faces. However, the terms $(\partial\sigma_x/\partial x)\, dx$, etc., contribute only higher-order terms to Eq. (2–3.2).

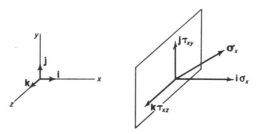

Fig. 2-3.1 Stress vector on plane perpendicular
to the x axis.

components are required to define stress at a point in a body. That is, Eq.
(2–3.4) is a square symmetric array (see Art. 1–21).

The stress vectors on planes that are perpendicular respectively to the
x, y, and z axes are

$$\boldsymbol{\sigma}_x = \mathbf{i}\sigma_x + \mathbf{j}\tau_{xy} + \mathbf{k}\tau_{xz}$$
$$\boldsymbol{\sigma}_y = \mathbf{i}\tau_{yx} + \mathbf{j}\sigma_y + \mathbf{k}\tau_{yz} \qquad (2\text{–}3.5)$$
$$\boldsymbol{\sigma}_z = \mathbf{i}\tau_{zx} + \mathbf{j}\tau_{zy} + \mathbf{k}\sigma_z$$

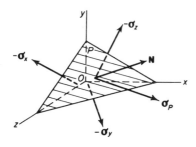

where $\mathbf{i}$, $\mathbf{j}$, $\mathbf{k}$ are unit vectors in the x, y,
and z directions, respectively (see Fig.
2–3.1).

Consider the stress vector $\boldsymbol{\sigma}_P$ on an
oblique plane P through point O of a
body (Fig. 2–3.2). The unit normal vector
to the plane is

$$\mathbf{N} = \mathbf{i}l + \mathbf{j}m + \mathbf{k}n \qquad (2\text{–}3.6)$$

where l, m, n are the direction cosines of
the unit vector $\mathbf{N}$. By Fig. 2–3.2, for

Fig. 2-3.2 Equilibrium of infinitesimal
tetrahedron.

equilibrium of the infinitesimal tetrahedron

$$\boldsymbol{\sigma}_P = l\boldsymbol{\sigma}_x + m\boldsymbol{\sigma}_y + n\boldsymbol{\sigma}_z \qquad (2\text{–}3.7)$$

Substitution of Eq. (2–3.5) into Eq. (2–3.7) yields

$$\boldsymbol{\sigma}_P = \mathbf{i}(l\sigma_x + m\tau_{yx} + n\tau_{zx})$$
$$+ \mathbf{j}(l\tau_{xy} + m\sigma_y + n\tau_{zy}) + \mathbf{k}(l\tau_{xz} + m\tau_{yz} + n\sigma_z) \qquad (2\text{–}3.8)$$

By definition,

$$\boldsymbol{\sigma}_P = \mathbf{i}\sigma_{Px} + \mathbf{j}\sigma_{Py} + \mathbf{k}\sigma_{Pz} \qquad (2\text{–}3.9)$$

where σ_{Px}, σ_{Py}, σ_{Pz} are the (x, y, z) projections of the vector $\boldsymbol{\sigma}_P$. Equating
Eqs. (2–3.8) and (2–3.9), we obtain the scalar equations

$$\sigma_{Px} = l\sigma_x + m\tau_{yx} + n\tau_{zx}$$
$$\sigma_{Py} = l\tau_{xy} + m\sigma_y + n\tau_{zy} \qquad (2\text{-}3.10)$$
$$\sigma_{Pz} = l\tau_{xz} + m\tau_{yz} + n\sigma_z$$

Thus the components of stress on any oblique plane, defined by the direction cosines (l, m, n), can easily be calculated from Eq. (2–3.10), provided the six components of stress $\sigma_x, \sigma_y, \sigma_z, \tau_{xy} = \tau_{yx}, \tau_{xz} = \tau_{zx}, \tau_{yz} = \tau_{zy}$ at point O are known. If the plane P is tangent at point O to the surface bounding the body, Eqs. (2–3.10) are the *stress boundary conditions at point O in terms of the stresses' components*.

Normal stress and shearing stress on an oblique plane. The normal stress σ_{PN} on the plane P is the projection of the vector $\boldsymbol{\sigma}_P$ in the direction N; that is, $\sigma_{PN} = \mathbf{N} \cdot \boldsymbol{\sigma}_P$. Hence, by Eqs. (2–3.6) and (2–3.8)

$$\sigma_{PN} = l^2\sigma_x + m^2\sigma_y + n^2\sigma_z + 2mn\tau_{yz} + 2nl\tau_{zx} + 2lm\tau_{xy} \qquad (2\text{-}3.11)$$

By Eq. (2–3.11), the normal stress σ_{PN} on an oblique plane P with normal N whose direction cosines are l, m, n is expressed in terms of the six stress components σ_x, $\sigma_y, \sigma_z, \tau_{yz}, \tau_{zx}, \tau_{xy}$. Often the maximum value of σ_{PN} is of importance in design. We shall return later to the problem of computing the maximum value of σ_{PN}.

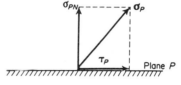

By geometry (see Fig. 2–3.3), the magnitude of the shearing stress on plane P is

Figure 2-3.3

$$\tau_P = \sqrt{\sigma_{Px}^2 + \sigma_{Py}^2 + \sigma_{Pz}^2 - \sigma_{PN}^2} \qquad (2\text{-}3.12)$$

Substituting Eqs. (2–3.10) and (2–3.11) into Eq. (2–3.12), we obtain the formula for τ_P in terms of $\sigma_x, \ldots, \tau_{yz}$ and (l, m, n).

PROBLEM SET 2-3

1 Determine how Eqs. (2–3.2) are modified in the presence of a magnetic field which exerts body moments about x, y, and z axes.

2 Derive Eq. (2–3.7).

3 Derive Eq. (2–3.11)

4 The stress tensor is

$$\begin{pmatrix} 3 & 1 & 4 \\ 1 & 2 & -5 \\ 4 & -5 & 0 \end{pmatrix}$$

Determine $\sigma_{Px}, \sigma_{Py}, \sigma_{Pz}, \sigma_{PN}, \tau_P$ for the plane whose normal has direction cosines $(1/\sqrt{3}, 1/\sqrt{3}, -1/\sqrt{3})$.

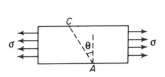

Figure P2-3(5)

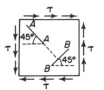

Figure P2-3(6)

5 The flat strip shown in Fig. P2–3(5) is subjected to tensile stress σ. Express the tensile stress σ' and the shearing stress τ on the oblique section AC in terms of θ and σ. [*Ans.* $\sigma' = \sigma \cos^2 \theta, \tau = \sigma \sin \theta \cos \theta$.]

6 The square plate is subjected to shearing stress τ on its edges [see Fig. P2–3(6)]. Determine the shearing stresses and the tensile stresses on sections A-A and B-B. [*Ans.* Section A-A: $\sigma' = \tau, \tau' = 0$; Section B-B: $\sigma' = -\tau, \tau' = 0$.]

7 A rectangular plate is subjected to axial compression stress σ along two parallel edges and axial tension stress σ along the other two parallel edges, in the perpendicular direction. (a) Determine the shearing stress and the tensile stress on a section A-A that forms an angle θ with the direction of the axial tension. Express the results in terms of σ and θ. Evaluate for $\theta = 45°$. (b) Repeat for a rectangular plate loaded by axial tension σ along its four edges. [*Ans.* (a) $\sigma' = \sigma \cos 2\theta, \tau' = -\sigma \sin 2\theta$, (b) $\sigma' = \sigma, \tau' = 0$.]

8 Compute τ for equilibrium.

9 Compute τ for equilibrium.

10 The square plate is loaded as shown. Compute the shearing stresses and the

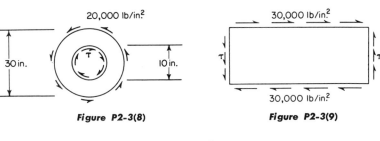

Figure P2-3(8)   Figure P2-3(9)

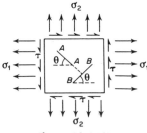

Figure P2-3(10)

tensile stresses on sections A-A and B-B in terms of σ_1, σ_2, τ, and θ. Specialize the result (a) for $\sigma_1 = \sigma_2$ and $\theta = 45°$, (b) for $\sigma_1 = \sigma_2 = 0$.

2-4 Tensor Character of Stress. Transformation of Stress Components under Change of Coordinate System

Let (x, y, z) and (X, Y, Z) be two rectangular coordinate systems with a common origin (Fig. 2–4.1). The cosines of the angles between the six coordinate axes may be neatly represented in the following tabular form:

TABLE OF DIRECTION COSINES

	x	y	z
X	l_1	m_1	n_1
Y	l_2	m_2	n_2
Z	l_3	m_3	n_3

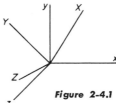

Figure 2-4.1

Each entry in this table is the cosine of the angle between the two coordinate axes designated at the top of its column and the left of its row. The stress components σ_X, τ_{XY}, etc., are defined with reference to the coordinates (X, Y, Z) in the same manner as the stress components σ_x, τ_{xy}, etc., are defined with reference to the coordinates (x, y, z). The normal stresses on planes that are perpendicular to the X, Y, Z axes are $(\sigma_X, \sigma_Y, \sigma_Z)$, respectively. Hence, by Eq. (2–3.10), noting that the unit normals to the planes perpendicular to X, Y, Z axes are (l_1, m_1, n_1), (l_2, m_2, n_2), and (l_3, m_3, n_3), respectively, relative to axes (x, y, z), we obtain

$$\sigma_X = l_1^2\sigma_x + m_1^2\sigma_y + n_1^2\sigma_z + 2m_1 n_1\tau_{yz} + 2n_1 l_1\tau_{zx} + 2l_1 m_1\tau_{xy}$$
$$\sigma_Y = l_2^2\sigma_x + m_2^2\sigma_y + n_2^2\sigma_z + 2m_2 n_2\tau_{yz} + 2n_2 l_2\tau_{zx} + 2l_2 m_2\tau_{xy} \quad (2\text{-}4.1)$$
$$\sigma_Z = l_3^2\sigma_x + m_3^2\sigma_y + n_3^2\sigma_z + 2m_3 n_3\tau_{yz} + 2n_3 l_3\tau_{zx} + 2l_3 m_3\tau_{xy}$$

The shearing stress component τ_{XY} is the component in the Y direction of the stress vector on a plane perpendicular to the X axis; that is, it is the Y component of the vector $\boldsymbol{\sigma}_X$. This may be calculated by evaluating the scalar product of the vector $\boldsymbol{\sigma}_X$ [determined by Eq. (2–3.8)] with the unit normal vector parallel to the Y axis; that is, with the unit vector $\mathbf{N}_2 = l l_2 + \mathbf{j}m_2 + \mathbf{k}n_2$. By Eq. (2–3.8),

$$\boldsymbol{\sigma}_X = (l_1\sigma_x + m_1\tau_{yx} + n_1\tau_{zx})\mathbf{i} + (l_1\tau_{xy} + m_1\sigma_y + n_1\tau_{zy})\mathbf{j}$$
$$+ (l_1\tau_{xz} + m_1\tau_{yz} + n_1\sigma_z)\mathbf{k}.$$

Hence,

$$\tau_{XY} = \mathbf{N}_2 \cdot \boldsymbol{\sigma}_X$$
$$= l_1 l_2\sigma_x + m_1 m_2\sigma_y + n_1 n_2\sigma_z + (m_1 n_2 + m_2 n_1)\tau_{yz} \quad (2\text{-}4.2)$$
$$+ (l_1 n_2 + l_2 n_1)\tau_{zx} + (l_1 m_2 + l_2 m_1)\tau_{xy}$$

The components τ_{YZ}, τ_{ZX} may be calculated similarly. Hence, the formulas for τ_{YZ} and τ_{ZX} are obtained by replacing the subscripts $(1, 2)$ by $(2, 3)$ and $(3, 1)$, respectively.

Equations (2–4.1) and (2–4.2) determine the stress components in any system of orthogonal axes, if they are known for one system. There are many things that transform in the manner defined by Eqs. (2–4.1) and (2–4.2) besides stresses, e.g., strain components and the moments and products of inertia of a body with respect to orthogonal axes. Any symmetrical set of nine quantities that transforms in accordance with Eqs. (2–4.1) and (2–4.2) is called a *second-order tensor;* hence, the nine components of stress, taken collectively, are called the *stress tensor.* [See Eqs. (2–3.1) and (2–3.4).] Tensor quantities of second and higher order are discussed in Art. 1–18.

PROBLEM SET 2-4

1 Let (x, y, z) and (X, Y, Z) be two systems of rectangular coordinates with the same origin. The cosine of the angle between any two of the axes is designated in the table of Art. 2–4. For example, the cosine of the angle between the Y axis and the z axis is n_2. Show that the sum of the squares of the numbers in any row or any column of this table is one. Show that the sum of the products of the numbers in any row (or column) with the corresponding numbers in any other row (or column) is zero.

2 Show by means of Eq. (2–4.1) that $\sigma_X + \sigma_Y + \sigma_Z = \sigma_x + \sigma_y + \sigma_z$; that is, that the sum of the normal stress components is a constant in all rectangular coordinate systems (or in other words is invariant).

3 Show that for a body subjected to hydrostatic pressure p

$$\sigma_X + \sigma_Y + \sigma_Z = \sigma_x + \sigma_y + \sigma_z = -3p$$

2-5 Principal Stresses. Stress Invariants. Extremum Values

It will be shown that for any general state of stress, through any point P in a body, there exist three mutually perpendicular planes on which the shearing stresses vanish identically. The resulting stresses on these planes are normal stresses, and they are called *principal stresses* (that is, extremum or stationary values of stress). Axes through the point coincident with the principal stress directions are called principal axes.[3] Planes on which shearing stresses vanish are called *principal planes.* Thus, by definition, principal stresses are perpen-

---

[3]The concept of "principal axes" may be developed without reference to physical things. The algebraic theory of principal axes is closely related to the idea of normal coordinates in vibration theory. See L. P. Eisenhart, *Coordinate Geometry*, (Boston: Ginn & Company, 1939). The concept of principal axes (principal stresses) is also closely related to the concept of eigenvectors (eigenvalues); see Art. 1–21.

dicular to the planes on which they act; that is, principal stresses are normal to principal planes. A body subjected to principal stresses is easily visualized, since the forces on the surface are normal to the faces.

To show that for the general system of surface stresses the principal planes are orthogonal, we assume that at least two principal planes exist, and we let θ be the dihedral angle between them. We consider a prismatic element of length c, perpendicular to the paper (Fig. 2–5.1). For equilibrium, the moment about the axis O of the element must vanish. Consequently,

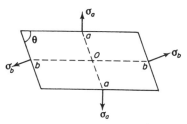

$$M_0 = -(ac\sigma_a)b \cos \theta$$
$$+ (bc\sigma_b)a \cos \theta = 0$$

or

$$(\sigma_b - \sigma_a) \cos \theta = 0$$

Figure 2-5.1

In general, σ_a is not equal to σ_b. Hence, the general solution of this equation is $\theta = 90°$. Consequently, the two principal planes are perpendicular. The plane perpendicular to these two principal planes is also a principal plane since by Eqs. (2–3.3) the shearing stresses on it are zero. Then all principal planes (and principal axes) are perpendicular at a point. Hence, there are three mutually perpendicular principal axes. However, cases arise in which $\sigma_a = \sigma_b$ (e.g., frictionless fluids). Then all planes through the axis O are principal planes, and all stresses at point O are principal stresses.

Let us seek the plane P on which the shearing stress vanishes. On such a plane $\boldsymbol{\sigma}_P = \sigma \mathbf{N}$, where $\mathbf{N}$ is the unit normal to the plane, and σ is the magnitude of the vector $\boldsymbol{\sigma}_P$. Therefore, since $\mathbf{N} = \mathbf{i}l + \mathbf{j}m + \mathbf{k}n$, $\sigma_{Px} = \sigma l$, $\sigma_{Py} = \sigma m$, $\sigma_{Pz} = \sigma n$. Consequently, by Eq. (2–3.10),

$$\sigma l = l\sigma_x + m\tau_{yx} + n\tau_{zx}$$
$$\sigma m = l\tau_{xy} + m\sigma_y + n\tau_{zy}$$
$$\sigma n = l\tau_{xz} + m\tau_{yz} + n\sigma_z$$

Rearranging, we obtain

$$l(\sigma_x - \sigma) + m\tau_{yx} + n\tau_{zx} = 0$$
$$l\tau_{xy} + m(\sigma_y - \sigma) + n\tau_{zy} = 0 \qquad (2\text{-}5.1)$$
$$l\tau_{xz} + m\tau_{yz} + n(\sigma_z - \sigma) = 0$$

Equations (2-5.1) are linear homogeneous equations in l, m, and n. The trivial solution $l = m = n = 0$ is impossible since $l^2 + m^2 + n^2 = 1$. Consequently, by the theory of linear algebraic equations, the preceding equations are consistent if, and only if,

$$F(\sigma) = \begin{vmatrix} \sigma_x - \sigma & \tau_{yx} & \tau_{zx} \\ \tau_{xy} & \sigma_y - \sigma & \tau_{zy} \\ \tau_{xz} & \tau_{yz} & \sigma_z - \sigma \end{vmatrix} = 0 \qquad (2\text{-}5.2)$$

(See the discussion in Art. 1–21. Note particularly the analogy between eigenvalues r_i and principal stresses σ_i and the analogy between eigenvectors X_i and direction cosines l, m, n.)

We now show that Eq. (2–5.2) has three distinct roots $\sigma_1, \sigma_2, \sigma_3$. Hence, there exists three sets of direction cosines corresponding to the three distinct roots (i.e., corresponding to the three principal stresses). Inspection of Eq. (2–5.2) shows that the highest-degree term in its expansion is $-\sigma^3$. Hence, if $\sigma \to +\infty$, $F(\sigma)$ is negative, and if $\sigma \to -\infty$, $F(\sigma)$ is positive. Consequently, at least one real root exists (Fig. 2–5.2). The remaining two roots may be real and distinct, real and equal, or complex conjugates. Since there is at least one real root of the cubic $F(\sigma) = 0$, let it be σ_3. Choose a coordinate system so that the z axis coincides in direction with the principal axis of stress corresponding to σ_3. Then, $\sigma_z = \sigma_3$, $\tau_{xz} = \tau_{yz} = 0$. Then by Eq. (2–5.2),

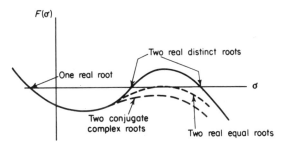

Figure 2-5.2

$$F(\sigma) = \begin{vmatrix} \sigma_x - \sigma & \tau_{yx} & 0 \\ \tau_{xy} & \sigma_y - \sigma & 0 \\ 0 & 0 & \sigma_3 - \sigma \end{vmatrix} = 0$$

It should be noted that the principal stresses are independent of the choice of (x, y, z) axes, but the stress components $(\sigma_x, \sigma_y , \ldots, \tau_{xy})$ are changed by the rotation of the axes. In the absence of moments due to magnetic effects, etc., $\tau_{yx} = \tau_{xy}$. Hence, expansion of the determinantal equation yields

$$(\sigma_x - \sigma)(\sigma_y - \sigma) - \tau_{xy}^2 = 0$$

$$\sigma^2 - \sigma(\sigma_x + \sigma_y) + \sigma_x \sigma_y - \tau_{xy}^2 = 0$$

Therefore, by the theory of quadratic equations,

$$\sigma = \frac{\sigma_x + \sigma_y}{2} \pm \frac{1}{2} \sqrt{(\sigma_x + \sigma_y)^2 - 4(\sigma_x \sigma_y - \tau_{xy}^2)}$$

$$= \frac{\sigma_x + \sigma_y}{2} \pm \frac{1}{2} \sqrt{(\sigma_x - \sigma_y)^2 + 4\tau_{xy}^2}$$

The two roots of these equations are evidently real. Thus, it has been proved that Eq. (2–5.2) always possesses three real roots $(\sigma_1, \sigma_2, \sigma_3)$. This result has been obtained in essence in a different manner in Art. 1–21.

Expansion of the determinant in Eq. (2–5.2) yields

$$\sigma^3 - I_1\sigma^2 + I_2\sigma - I_3 = 0 \qquad (2\text{–}5.3)$$

in which

$$I_1 = \sigma_x + \sigma_y + \sigma_z$$

$$I_2 = \sigma_y\sigma_z + \sigma_z\sigma_x + \sigma_x\sigma_y - \tau_{yz}^2 - \tau_{zx}^2 - \tau_{xy}^2$$

$$I_3 = \begin{vmatrix} \sigma_x & \tau_{yx} & \tau_{zx} \\ \tau_{xy} & \sigma_y & \tau_{zy} \\ \tau_{xz} & \tau_{yz} & \sigma_z \end{vmatrix} \qquad (2\text{–}5.4)$$

Equation (2–5.3) determines the roots $(\sigma_1, \sigma_2, \sigma_3)$. Since these roots are independent of the choice of axes (x, y, z), it follows by Eq. (2–5.3) that the coefficients (I_1, I_2, I_3) are independent of the orientation of the coordinate axes, since otherwise the roots would change. Also, if $(\sigma_1, \sigma_2, \sigma_3)$ are the three roots of Eq. (2–5.3), by the theory of equations,

$$I_1 = \sigma_1 + \sigma_2 + \sigma_3$$

$$I_2 = \sigma_2\sigma_3 + \sigma_3\sigma_1 + \sigma_1\sigma_2 \qquad (2\text{–}5.5)$$

$$I_3 = \sigma_1\sigma_2\sigma_3$$

Equation (2–5.5) also shows that I_1, I_2, I_3 are invariants; that is, they are independent of coordinate axes (x, y, z). Since I_1, I_2, I_3 are determined by the stress components (Eq. 2–5.4), they are called *stress invariants*. By definition, pressure is $p = -I_1/3$.

When $(\sigma_1, \sigma_2, \sigma_3)$ have been determined, the directions of the axes of principal stresses are given by Eq. (2–5.1) and the condition $l^2 + m^2 + n^2 = 1$. If two principal stresses are equal, these directions are not unique. Then, all planes through the principal axis for which the stress has a different value from the other two principal stresses are principal planes. If $\sigma_1 = \sigma_2 = \sigma_3$, all planes are principal planes. This is true for the ideal fluid for which the only stresses are equal principal stresses.

In summary the *principal stresses* $\sigma_1, \sigma_2, \sigma_3$ are *extremum values of* stress. They act on planes (*principal planes*) for which the shearing-stress components vanish identically

Extremum values of shearing stress. In terms of principal axes (1, 2, 3) the shearing stress τ_P on an oblique plane is, by Eqs. (2–3.10), (2–3.11), and (2–3.12),

$$\tau_P^2 = \sigma_{Px}^2 + \sigma_{Py}^2 + \sigma_{Pz}^2 - \sigma_{PN}^2$$

$$= (l\sigma_1)^2 + (m\sigma_2)^2 + (n\sigma_3)^2 - (l^2\sigma_1 + m^2\sigma_2 + n^2\sigma_3)^2 \qquad (2\text{–}5.6)$$

To determine maximum and minimum values of τ_P, we may use the

Lagrange multiplier technique[4] to simplify the calculations. Accordingly, we consider the function

$$f = \tau_P^2 + \lambda^2(l^2 + m^2 + n^2) \tag{2-5.7}$$

where λ^2 is the Lagrange multiplier. The conditions for extremum values of f are

$$\frac{\partial f}{\partial l} = \frac{\partial f}{\partial m} = \frac{\partial f}{\partial n} = 0 \tag{2-5.8}$$

Equations (2–5.6), (2–5.7), and (2–5.8) yield

$$l\sigma_1^2 - (l^2\sigma_1 + m^2\sigma_2 + n^2\sigma_3)(2l\sigma_1) + \lambda^2 l = 0$$
$$m\sigma_2^2 - (l^2\sigma_1 + m^2\sigma_2 + n^2\sigma_3)(2m\sigma_2) + \lambda^2 m = 0 \tag{2-5.9}$$
$$n\sigma_3^2 - (l^2\sigma_1 + m^2\sigma_2 + n^2\sigma_3)(2n\sigma_3) + \lambda^2 n = 0$$

Equations (2–5.9) are necessary and sufficient conditions for f to be an extremum. To seek extrema of τ_P, we require further that $l^2 + m^2 + n^2 = 1$. Obvious solutions of Eqs. (2–5.9) are

$$l = m = 0, \qquad n = \pm 1 \tag{a}$$

Accordingly, by Eqs. (2–5.9), $\lambda = \sigma_3$, and now by Eq. (2–5.6), $\tau_P = 0$. However, since $l = m = 0$, $n = \pm 1$ defines the principal axis 3, this result is known a priori.

Similarly,

$$l = n = 0, \qquad m = \pm 1 \tag{b}$$

yields $\lambda = \sigma_2$ and $\tau_P = 0$; and

$$m = n = 0, \qquad l = \pm 1 \tag{c}$$

yields $\lambda = \sigma_1$ and $\tau_P = 0$.

For (l, m, n) all having nonzero values, that is, for $l \neq 0$, $m \neq 0$, $n \neq 0$, Eqs. (2–5.9) have the single solution $\sigma_1 = \sigma_2 = \sigma_3$. Hence, again Eq. (2–5.6) yields $\tau_P = 0$.

The remaining possibility is that only one of the direction cosines be zero. For example, consider $l = 0$, $m \neq 0$, $n \neq 0$. Then, the first of Eqs. (2–5.9) is satisfied identically. By the last two of Eqs. (2–5.9) we get, after some simplification,

$$(n^2 - m^2)(\sigma_2 - \sigma_3)^2 = 0 \tag{d}$$

For $\sigma_2 \neq \sigma_3$, Eq. (d) yields $n^2 = m^2$. Since $m^2 + n^2 = 1$, we have $m = \pm\sqrt{\frac{1}{2}}$, $n = \pm\sqrt{\frac{1}{2}}$. With $l = 0$, $m = \pm\sqrt{\frac{1}{2}}$, $n = \pm\sqrt{\frac{1}{2}}$, Eq. (2–5.6) yields

$$\tau_P = \pm\tfrac{1}{2}(\sigma_2 - \sigma_3) \tag{2-5.10}$$

Similarly, for $m = 0$, $l = \pm\sqrt{\frac{1}{2}}$, $n = \pm\sqrt{\frac{1}{2}}$, we get

$$\tau_P = \pm\tfrac{1}{2}(\sigma_1 - \sigma_3) \tag{2-5.11}$$

---

[4]R. Courant, *Differential and Integral Calculus*, Vol. II (New York: Interscience Publishers, Inc., 1950).

and for $n = 0$, $l = \pm\sqrt{\frac{1}{2}}$, $m = \pm\sqrt{\frac{1}{2}}$,

$$\tau_P = \pm\tfrac{1}{2}(\sigma_1 - \sigma_2) \tag{2-5.12}$$

The results derived above are tabulated in Table 2-5.1.

Table 2-5.1 EXTREMUM VALUES OF SHEAR STRESS

l	± 1	0	0	$\pm\sqrt{\frac{1}{2}}$	$\pm\sqrt{\frac{1}{2}}$	0
m	0	± 1	0	$\pm\sqrt{\frac{1}{2}}$	0	$\pm\sqrt{\frac{1}{2}}$
n	0	0	± 1	0	$\pm\sqrt{\frac{1}{2}}$	$\pm\sqrt{\frac{1}{2}}$
τ_P	0	0	0	$\pm\tfrac{1}{2}(\sigma_1 - \sigma_2)$	$\pm\tfrac{1}{2}(\sigma_1 - \sigma_3)$	$\pm\tfrac{1}{2}(\sigma_2 - \sigma_3)$

Example 2–5.1. Transformation of stress tensor. Let the stress tensor relative to axes (x, y, z) be given by the following array.

$$\begin{pmatrix} 4 & 1 & 2 \\ 1 & 6 & 0 \\ 2 & 0 & 8 \end{pmatrix} \tag{a}$$

Hence, by Eqs. (a) and (2–5.4), the stress invariants are

$$I_1 = 18, \qquad I_2 = 99, \qquad I_3 = 160 \tag{b}$$

Consider a rotation of the (x, y) axes $45°$ counterclockwise in the (x, y) plane to form axes (X, Y). Let axes Z and z coincide. Then the transformation between axes (x, y, z) and (X, Y, Z) is given by Table A.

TABLE A

	x	y	z
X	$\dfrac{1}{\sqrt{2}}$	$\dfrac{1}{\sqrt{2}}$	0
Y	$-\dfrac{1}{\sqrt{2}}$	$\dfrac{1}{\sqrt{2}}$	0
Z	0	0	1

By Eqs. (2–4.1) and (2–4.2) and Table A, we find the following stress components relative to axes (X, Y, Z):

$$\sigma_X = 6, \quad \sigma_Y = 4, \quad \sigma_Z = 8, \quad \tau_{XY} = 1, \quad \tau_{XZ} = \sqrt{2}, \quad \tau_{YZ} = -\sqrt{2} \tag{c}$$

Thus, relative to axes (X, Y, Z), the stress tensor is defined by the following array:

$$\begin{pmatrix} 6 & 1 & \sqrt{2} \\ 1 & 4 & -\sqrt{2} \\ \sqrt{2} & -\sqrt{2} & 8 \end{pmatrix} \tag{d}$$

By Eqs. (d) and (2–5.4), we find

$$I_1 = 18, \qquad I_2 = 99, \qquad I_3 = 160 \tag{e}$$

Equations (b) and (e) verify that I_1, I_2, I_3 are invariants under the transformation of Table A.

PROBLEM SET 2-5

1 The stress tensor is defined by the following array:

$$\begin{pmatrix} 3 & 5 & 8 \\ 5 & 1 & 0 \\ 8 & 0 & 2 \end{pmatrix}$$

Determine the principal stresses and the principal directions. Write down the numerical values of the stress invariants.

2 Consider axes (x, y, z) and (X, Y, Z). Let the stress tensor of Prob. 1 be taken relative to axes (x, y, z). Let axes (X, Y, Z) be defined relative to (x, y, z) by direction cosines

$$l_1 = \frac{\sqrt{3}}{2}, \quad m_1 = \frac{1}{2}, \quad n_1 = 0, \quad l_2 = -\frac{1}{2}, \quad m_2 = \frac{\sqrt{3}}{2},$$

$$n_2 = 0, \quad l_3 = m_3 = 0, \quad n_3 = 1$$

Compute the components of the stress relative to axes (X, Y, Z).

2-6 Mean and Deviator Stress Tensor. Octahedral Stress

Experiments indicate that yielding and plastic deformation of many metals are essentially independent of the applied mean stress σ_m, where by definition

$$\sigma_m = \frac{\sigma_x + \sigma_y + \sigma_z}{3} = \frac{\sigma_1 + \sigma_2 + \sigma_3}{3} = \frac{1}{3} I_1 \tag{2–6.1}$$

Hence, most plasticity theories postulate that plastic behavior of materials is related primarily to that part of the stress tensor which is independent of σ_m. Accordingly, the stress tensor [Eq. (2–3.4)] is rewritten in the following form:

$$T = T_m + T_d \tag{2–6.2}$$

where T symbolically represents the stress tensor and where

$$T_m = \begin{pmatrix} \sigma_m & 0 & 0 \\ 0 & \sigma_m & 0 \\ 0 & 0 & \sigma_m \end{pmatrix} \tag{2–6.3}$$

and

$$T_d = \begin{pmatrix} \dfrac{2\sigma_x - \sigma_y - \sigma_z}{3} & \tau_{xy} & \tau_{xz} \\[2ex] \tau_{xy} & \dfrac{2\sigma_y - \sigma_x - \sigma_z}{3} & \tau_{yz} \\[2ex] \tau_{xz} & \tau_{yz} & \dfrac{2\sigma_z - \sigma_y - \sigma_x}{3} \end{pmatrix} \qquad (2\text{-}6.4)$$

The validity of Eq. (2–6.2) follows from the definition of a tensor.[5]

The tensor T_m is called the *mean stress tensor*. The tensor T_d is called the *deviator stress tensor*, since it is, in a certain sense, a measure of the deviation of the state of stress from a spherically symmetric state, that is, from the state of stress which exists in an ideal (frictionless) fluid.

If (x, y, z) are principal axes, then

$$\sigma_x = \sigma_1, \quad \sigma_y = \sigma_2, \quad \sigma_z = \sigma_3; \quad \tau_{xy} = \tau_{xz} = \tau_{yz} = 0$$

and Eq. (2–6.2) is simplified accordingly. Application of Eqs. (2–5.5) to Eqs. (2–6.3) and (2–6.4) yields the following stress invariants for T_m and T_d:

For T_m: $I_{1m} = I_1 = 3\sigma_m$

$$I_{2m} = \tfrac{1}{3}I_1^2 = 3\sigma_m^2 \qquad (2\text{-}6.5)$$

$$I_{3m} = \tfrac{1}{27}I_1^3 = \sigma_m^3$$

For T_d: $I_{1d} = 0$

$$I_{2d} = I_2 - \tfrac{1}{3}I_1^2 = -\tfrac{1}{6}[(\sigma_1 - \sigma_2)^2 + (\sigma_2 - \sigma_3)^2 + (\sigma_3 - \sigma_1)^2]$$

$$I_{3d} = I_3 - \tfrac{1}{3} I_1 I_2 + \tfrac{2}{27}I_1^3 \qquad (2\text{-}6.6)$$

$$= \tfrac{1}{27}(2\sigma_1 - \sigma_2 - \sigma_3)(2\sigma_2 - \sigma_3 - \sigma_1)(2\sigma_3 - \sigma_1 - \sigma_2)$$

Many of the formulas of the mathematical theory of plasticity are often written in terms of the stress invariants of the deviator stress tensor[6] T_d.

Octahedral shearing stress. Another concept frequently employed in plasticity theory is that of octahedral shearing stress.[7] Octahedral shearing stress is defined as follows:

Consider the directions defined by the conditions

$$l^2 = m^2 = n^2 = \tfrac{1}{3} \qquad (2\text{-}6.7)$$

where l, m, n are direction cosines *relative to principal axes*. There are eight planes through any point O in space whose direction cosines satisfy Eqs. (2–6.7). Consequently, the eight planes whose direction cosines satisfy Eqs.

---

[5] J. L. Synge and A. Schild, *Tensor Calculus* (Toronto: University of Toronto Press, 1956).

[6] V. V. Sokolovski, *Theory of Plasticity* (in Russian) (Moscow: 1950). See also the German translation (Berlin: VEB Verlag Technik, 1955).

[7] W. Prager and P. Hodge, Jr., *Theory of Perfectly Plastic Solids* (New York: John Wiley & Sons, 1951).

(2–6.7) are called the octahedral planes. These planes form equal angles with the principal directions. The shearing stress τ_0 that acts on the octahedral planes is called the octahedral shearing stress. By Eqs. (2–3.10), (2–3.11), (2–3.12), and (2–6.7), we find that

$$9\tau_0^2 = (\sigma_1 - \sigma_2)^2 + (\sigma_1 - \sigma_3)^2 + (\sigma_2 - \sigma_3)^2 \qquad (2\text{–}6.8)$$

where $(\sigma_1, \sigma_2, \sigma_3)$ denote principal stresses. Since $(\sigma_1, \sigma_2, \sigma_3)$ are invariant under a transformation of coordinate axes, it follows that the octahedral shearing stress τ_0 is invariant.

Equation (2–6.8) may be written in the form

$$9\tau_0^2 = 2I_1^2 - 6I_2 = -6I_{2d} \qquad (2\text{–}6.9)$$

where I_1, I_2 are the stress invariants defined by Eq. (2–5.5) and I_{2d} is defined by Eq. (2–6.6). Expressing I_1 and I_2 in terms of stress components taken relative to arbitrary (x, y, z) axes, by means of Eqs. (2–5.4) and (2–6.9), we obtain

$$9\tau_0^2 = (\sigma_x - \sigma_y)^2 + (\sigma_y - \sigma_z)^2 + (\sigma_z - \sigma_x)^2 + 6\tau_{xy}^2 + 6\tau_{xz}^2 + 6\tau_{yz}^2 \quad (2\text{–}6.10)$$

PROBLEM SET 2-6

1 Derive Eq. (2–6.2).

2 Derive Eqs. (2–6.5) and (2–6.6).

3 Derive Eqs. (2–6.8).

4 Derive Eqs. (2–6.9) and (2–6.10).

5 Show that T_d (Eq. 2–6.4) may be written

$$T_d = \begin{pmatrix} S_x & \tau_{xy} & \tau_{xz} \\ \tau_{xy} & S_y & \tau_{yz} \\ \tau_{xz} & \tau_{yz} & S_z \end{pmatrix}$$

where $S_x = \sigma_x - \sigma_m$, $S_y = \sigma_y - \sigma_m$, and $S_z = \sigma_z - \sigma_m$.

6 Show that I_{2d} and I_{3d} [Eq. (2–6.6)] may be written $I_{2d} = -\frac{1}{6}[(S_1 - S_2)^2 + (S_2 - S_3)^2 + (S_3 - S_1)^2]$ and $I_{3d} = S_1 S_2 S_3$, where $S_1 = \sigma_1 - \sigma_m$, $S_2 = \sigma_2 - \sigma_m$, and $S_3 = \sigma_3 - \sigma_m$.

7 Show that the normal stress component σ_{oct} on the octahedral planes $(l^2 = m^2 = n^2 = \frac{1}{3}$ relative to principal axes) is given by the relation

$$\sigma_{\text{oct}} = \frac{\sigma_x + \sigma_y + \sigma_z}{3} = \frac{\sigma_1 + \sigma_2 + \sigma_3}{3} = \sigma_m$$

2-7 Plane Stress

The state of plane stress is defined by the conditions $\sigma_z = \tau_{xz} = \tau_{yz} = 0$. (See Art. 5–2). Thus for a state of plane stress, the table of direction cosines of the axes becomes

	x	y	z
X	$\cos\theta$	$\sin\theta$	0
Y	$-\sin\theta$	$\cos\theta$	0
Z	0	0	1

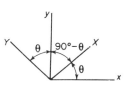

Figure 2-7.1

(See Fig. 2–7.1) Hence, Eqs. (2–4.1) and (2–4.2) yield

$$\sigma_X = \sigma_x \cos^2\theta + \sigma_y \sin^2\theta + 2\tau_{xy}\sin\theta\cos\theta$$
$$\sigma_Y = \sigma_x \sin^2\theta + \sigma_y \cos^2\theta - 2\tau_{xy}\sin\theta\cos\theta \qquad (2\text{–}7.1)$$
$$\tau_{XY} = (\sigma_y - \sigma_x)\sin\theta\cos\theta + (\cos^2\theta - \sin^2\theta)\tau_{xy}$$

By means of trigonometric double angle formulas, these equations may be rewritten in the form

$$\sigma_X = \tfrac{1}{2}(\sigma_x + \sigma_y) + \tfrac{1}{2}(\sigma_x - \sigma_y)\cos 2\theta + \tau_{xy}\sin 2\theta$$
$$\sigma_Y = \tfrac{1}{2}(\sigma_x + \sigma_y) - \tfrac{1}{2}(\sigma_x - \sigma_y)\cos 2\theta - \tau_{xy}\sin 2\theta \qquad (2\text{–}7.2)$$
$$\tau_{XY} = \tfrac{1}{2}(\sigma_y - \sigma_x)\sin 2\theta + \tau_{xy}\cos 2\theta$$

Graphical interpretation of plane stress. Circle of stress (Mohr's circle). In the form of Eq. (2–7.2), the plane transformation of stress components is particularly suited for graphical interpretation. Furthermore, if we choose (x, y) axes to coincide with principal axes, Eqs. (2–7.2) are simplified further. Consequently, we let axes (x, y) be principal axes. Then $\tau_{xy} = 0$. Accordingly, Eqs. (2–7.2) become

$$\sigma_X = \tfrac{1}{2}(\sigma_1 + \sigma_2) + \tfrac{1}{2}(\sigma_1 - \sigma_2)\cos 2\theta$$
$$\sigma_Y = \tfrac{1}{2}(\sigma_1 + \sigma_2) - \tfrac{1}{2}(\sigma_1 - \sigma_2)\cos 2\theta \qquad (2\text{–}7.3)$$
$$\tau_{XY} = -\tfrac{1}{2}(\sigma_1 - \sigma_2)\sin 2\theta$$

where (σ_1, σ_2) denote principal stresses with $\sigma_1 > \sigma_2$ (see Art. 2–5 and Fig. 2–7.2).

Recalling the physical significance of σ_X, τ_{XY}, we note that the stress

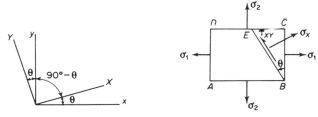

Fig. 2-7.2 Element in state of plane stress; principal axes coincident with axes (x, y).

components on plane BE perpendicular to the X axis are σ_x, τ_{XY}. The plane BE forms an angle θ, in the positive direction of rotation (counterclockwise in Fig. 2–7.2), with the plane on which σ_1 acts. Similarly, the stress components σ_Y, τ_{YX} ($\tau_{YX} = \tau_{XY}$) act on a plane forming an angle of $90°$, in the positive direction of rotation, with plane BE. Accordingly, Eqs. (2–7.3) represent stress components on planes forming angles of θ and $(\pi/2) + \theta$ with the plane on which σ_1 acts. Hence, the variation of the stress components may be depicted graphically by constructing a diagram in which σ_x and τ_{XY} (or σ_Y and τ_{YX}) are coordinates. For each plane BE, there will be a point on the diagram whose coordinates correspond to values of σ_x and τ_{XY}.

Squaring the first and third of Eq. (2–7.3) and adding, we obtain

$$[\sigma_x - \tfrac{1}{2}(\sigma_1 + \sigma_2)]^2 + (\tau_{XY})^2 = \tfrac{1}{4}(\sigma_1 - \sigma_2)^2 \qquad (2\text{–}7.4)$$

Equation (2–7.4) is the equation of a circle in the σ_x, τ_{XY} plane with center at

$$\tfrac{1}{2}(\sigma_1 + \sigma_2), \qquad 0 \qquad (2\text{–}7.5)$$

and with radius

$$\tfrac{1}{2}(\sigma_1 - \sigma_2) \qquad (2\text{–}7.6)$$

Consequently, the geometrical representation of Eqs. (2–7.3) is a circle (see Fig. 2–7.3). This stress circle is frequently called *Mohr's circle* in honor of O. Mohr who first employed it to study plane stress problems.[8]

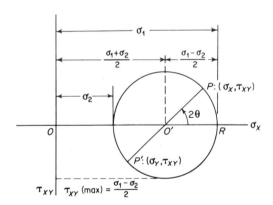

Fig. 2-7.3 Mohr's circle.

In the stress circle, we have taken the τ_{XY} axis positive downward. Hence, the point P, whose coordinates are the stress components on plane BE (Fig. 2–7.2), is obtained by rotating the radius $O'R$ of the circle counterclockwise (Fig. 2–7.3), through an angle of 2θ [see Eqs. (2–7.3)]; that is, to determine the stress components (coordinates of point P) on a plane which forms an

---

[8]See O. Mohr, *Zivilingenieur*, 1882, p. 113. See Also, his *Technische Mechanik*, 2nd ed. (1914).

angle θ (counterclockwise) with plane BC, we rotate the radius $O'R$ of the stress circle counterclockwise through an angle of 2θ. Accordingly, the normal stress component on a plane perpendicular to the Y axis is given by the coordinates of a point P' obtained by rotating $O'P$ through $180°$ counterclockwise, since the plane perpendicular to the Y axis forms an angle of $90°$ with plane BE (Fig. 2–7.2). The sense of the shearing stress on this plane is given by the sign convention established in Arts. 2–2 and 2–3.

With the construction outlined above, the signs of the stress components agree with those given by Eq. (2–7.3). Thus, the complete state of plane stress at a point in a medium is characterized by Mohr's circle, provided the principal stresses σ_1 and σ_2 are known. Alternatively, if the states of plane stress on two planes through a point are known, Mohr's circle may be constructed, and principal stresses may be determined. The stress circle construction may also be extended to three-dimensional problems.[9] More generally the Mohr circle construction is applicable to any second-order tensor[10] in rectangular cartesian coordinates (x, y, z).

Extreme values of normal stress and shear stress. Referring to Eqs. (2–7.3) and Fig. (2–7.3), we see that the maximum value σ_{max} of the normal stress occurs for $\theta = 0°$. Thus, by Eq. (2–7.3),

$$\sigma_{max} = \sigma_1 \tag{a}$$

Similarly, the minimum value σ_{min} of the normal stress is

$$\sigma_{min} = \sigma_2 \tag{b}$$

For the shearing stress, we have by Fig. (2–7.3)

$$\tau_{max} = \tfrac{1}{2}(\sigma_1 - \sigma_2)$$
$$\tau_{min} = -\tfrac{1}{2}(\sigma_1 - \sigma_2) \tag{c}$$

Equations (a), (b), and (c) agree with the results obtained in Art. 2–5 (see also Table 2–5.1).

PROBLEM SET 2-7

1 $\sigma_x = 4$, $\sigma_y = 2$, $\sigma_z = -2$, $\tau_{yz} = 8$, $\tau_{zx} = -2$, $\tau_{xy} = 3$. Compute the stress vectors on planes with unit normals $(\tfrac{2}{3}, \tfrac{2}{3}, \tfrac{1}{3})$ and $(1/\sqrt{14}, 2/\sqrt{14}, 3/\sqrt{14})$. Compute the normal stresses on these planes. The shearing stresses.

2 Determine the magnitude and the direction of the principal stresses, and the maximum shearing stresses, for the following cases (stresses are in $lb/in.^2$):

---

[9]*Loc. cit.*
[10]Synge and Schild, *Tensor Calculus.*

	σ_x	σ_y	σ_z	τ_{xy}	τ_{xz}	τ_{yz}
(a)	15,000	−4,000	10,000	−3,000	0	1,000
(b)	10,000	−5,000	0	−5,000	0	0
(c)	−10,000	−5,000	10,000	2,000	3,000	4,000
(d)	10,000	−5,000	−5,000	2,000	2,000	0
(e)	10,000	0	0	0	0	0
(f)	0	0	−10,000	5,000	−5,000	5,000

3 Show that for plane stress $\sigma_x + \sigma_y$ and $\begin{vmatrix} \sigma_x & \tau_{xy} \\ \tau_{xy} & \sigma_y \end{vmatrix}$ are invariants.

2-8 Differential Equations of Motion of a Deformable Body

It is known from elementary mechanics that the resultant force that acts on any body is equal to the time rate of change of momentum of the body, and the resultant moment is equal to the time rate of change of moment of momentum. In the case of rigid bodies (i.e., bodies which do not deform), these conditions lead to a system of six equations (three force equations and three moment equations) which completely specify the motion of the body. However, the motion of deformable bodies is not, by any means, completely defined by these conditions.

Nevertheless, the momentum principles may be used to derive equations which (together with stress-strain relationships derived later) describe the motion of a deformable body. It is necessary to apply the momentum principles not only to the body as a whole, but to each element of which the body is composed.

Let S be an arbitrary closed surface within the body. Let V be the element of volume enclosed by S. The external force on the volume V consists of two parts: (a) body force, (b) tractive or surface force. Let (x, y, z) denote rectangular cartesian coordinate axes in the deformed body.

The projection of the resultant body force vector (Fig. 2–8.1) on the x-axis is

$$\iiint_{\substack{\text{through} \\ \text{the volume}}} X \, dV \tag{a}$$

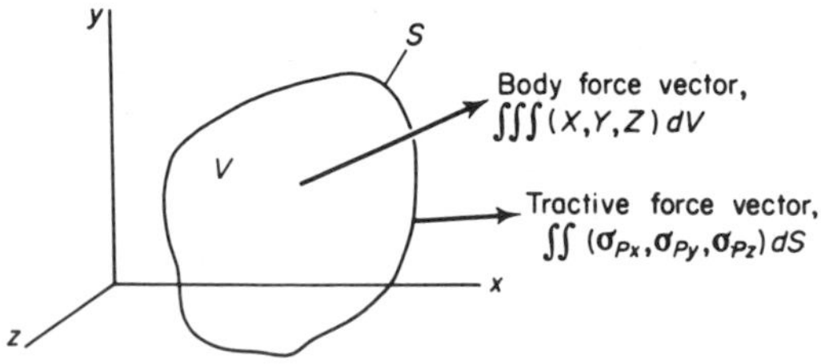

Figure 2-8.1

If the body force is entirely due to gravity, as is common, $X = \rho g_x$, where ρ is the mass density and g_x is the x projection of the vector acceleration of gravity (directed toward the center of the earth).

The projection of the resultant traction vector (Fig. 2–8.1) exerted on the surface S is

$$\int\int \sigma_{Px}\, dS \qquad\qquad (b)$$

over S

By Eq. (2–3.10), Eq. (b) may be written in the form

$$\int\int (l\sigma_x + m\tau_{yx} + n\tau_{zx})\, dS \qquad\qquad (c)$$

over S

The x projection of the momentum vector of the material in region V is $\int\int\int \dot{u}\, dm = \int\int\int \rho\dot{u}\, dV$, where m denotes mass, ρ denotes mass density, u is the x projection of the displacement vector, and the dot denotes differentiation with respect to time. Hence, the time rate of change of the x projection of momentum is (since we consider mass to be conserved, $\rho\, dV = dm =$ constant)

$$\frac{d}{dt}\int\int\int \rho\dot{u}\, dV = \int\int\int \rho\ddot{u}\, dV \qquad\qquad (d)$$

over V \qquad over V

Equating the x projection of the resultant force that acts on the volume to its time rate of change of momentum, by Eqs. (a), (c), and (d) we obtain

$$\int\int\int X\, dV + \int\int (l\sigma_x + m\tau_{yx} + n\tau_{zx})\, dS = \int\int\int \rho\ddot{u}\, dV \qquad (2\text{–}8.1)$$

over V \qquad over S \qquad over V

Applying the divergence theorem (see Art. 1–9) to the surface integral in Eq. (2–8.1) and regrouping, we obtain

$$\int\int\int \left(\frac{\partial\sigma_x}{\partial x} + \frac{\partial\tau_{yx}}{\partial y} + \frac{\partial\tau_{zx}}{\partial z} + X - \rho\ddot{u}\right) dV = 0 \qquad (2\text{–}8.2)$$

over V

Since Eq. (2–8.2) applies for any volume V in the body, the integrand must vanish identically; that is,

$$\frac{\partial\sigma_x}{\partial x} + \frac{\partial\tau_{yx}}{\partial y} + \frac{\partial\tau_{zx}}{\partial z} + X = \rho\ddot{u} \qquad (2\text{–}8.3)$$

In a similar manner, summations of forces in the y and z directions yield two more equations. The set of three equations thus obtained is the following.

$$\frac{\partial\sigma_x}{\partial x} + \frac{\partial\tau_{yx}}{\partial y} + \frac{\partial\tau_{zx}}{\partial z} + X = \rho\ddot{u}$$

$$\frac{\partial\tau_{xy}}{\partial x} + \frac{\partial\sigma_y}{\partial y} + \frac{\partial\tau_{zy}}{\partial z} + Y = \rho\ddot{v} \qquad (2\text{–}8.4)$$

$$\frac{\partial\tau_{xz}}{\partial x} + \frac{\partial\tau_{yz}}{\partial y} + \frac{\partial\sigma_z}{\partial z} + Z = \rho\ddot{w}$$

where (u, v, w) is the displacement vector of a point in the infinitesimal volume element dV, and where (x, y, z) denote rectangular cartesian coordinate axes in the deformed body.

Equations (2–8.4) are the *differential equations of motion* of a deformable continuous body. Alternatively, they may be derived by summation of forces that act on the faces of a cubic element, considering the variation of stress through the cube. For an incompressible body, $\rho = $ constant. If the body is in equilibrium, the right-hand terms in Eqs. (2–8.4) are zero. Equations (2–8.4) are then called the *differential equations of equilibrium*.

In vector notation, Eq. (2–8.4) may be written in the form

$$\nabla \cdot \boldsymbol{\sigma}_x + X = \rho \ddot{u}, \qquad \nabla \cdot \boldsymbol{\sigma}_y + Y = \rho \ddot{v}, \qquad \nabla \cdot \boldsymbol{\sigma}_z + Z = \rho \ddot{w} \qquad (2\text{–}8.5)$$

where $\boldsymbol{\sigma}_x, \boldsymbol{\sigma}_y, \boldsymbol{\sigma}_z$ are defined by Eq. (2–3.5), and where

$$\nabla = \mathbf{i}\frac{\partial}{\partial x} + \mathbf{j}\frac{\partial}{\partial y} + \mathbf{k}\frac{\partial}{\partial z} \qquad (2\text{–}8.6)$$

The equations of this chapter summarize the general theory of stress. For plane stress $\sigma_z = \tau_{xz} = \tau_{yz} = 0$, and the equations are modified accordingly. If body forces are negligible, $X = Y = Z = 0$.

Finally, it may be remarked that the equilibrium equations (Eqs. 2–8.4) may be represented with respect to rectangular cartesian axes relative to the *undeformed* body. However, then the results become much more complicated.[11]

PROBLEM SET 2-8

1 Using the principle that the resultant moment with respect to any fixed axis of all forces acting on volume V is equal to the time rate of change of moment of momentum of the volume with respect to the axis, derive the equations that result from consideration of moments with respect to the x axis. Simplify the equations for equilibrium. How would these equations be altered in the presence of a body moment due to an electric or magnetic field, that is, in the presence of a moment proportional to a mass element?

2 Derive Eq. (2–8.4) by applying the principle $\mathbf{F} = m\mathbf{a}$ to a cubic element in the body. [*Hint:* If the normal stress on the plane perpendicular to the x axis at point x is σ_x, then the normal stress that acts on the plane perpendicular to the x axis at the point $x + dx$ is $\sigma_x + (\partial\sigma_x/\partial_x)\, dx$, etc.]

Review Problems

R-1 Determine the stress component normal to the plane with unit normal vector $(1/\sqrt{3}, 1/\sqrt{3}, 1/\sqrt{3})$ with respect to principal axes of stress. Express the result

---

[11]V. V. Novozhilov, *Foundations of the Nonlinear Theory of Elasticity* (Rochester, N.Y.: Graylock Press, 1953), p. 79.

in terms of principal stresses $\sigma_1, \sigma_2, \sigma_3$. Hence, express the result in terms of stress components with respect to any rectangular cartesian axes (x, y, z).

R-2 The components of the stress tensor are (with respect to rectangular cartesian axes x, y, z)

$$\sigma_x = \sigma_y = 0, \quad \sigma_z = -10; \quad \tau_{yz} = -5, \quad \tau_{zx} = 5, \quad \tau_{xy} = 5$$

Determine the principal stresses. Determine the direction cosines of the principal axes. Use the cross-product relation to get the last principal axis after the other two are determined.

R-3 The following state of stress exists at a point in a body: $\sigma_x = 4, \sigma_y = 8$, $\sigma_z = -12, \tau_{xz} = 2, \tau_{xy} = \tau_{yz} = 0$. Compute the magnitude of the maximum shearing stress.

Appendix: Theory of Stress in Index Notation

In this appendix we present the theory of stress in index notation. For brevity, we do not discuss in detail the physical significance of the results (see Chapter 2). With some reference to the discussion of Chapter 2, and to Arts. 1–17 through 1–21, the reader may wish to develop the theory of stress directly in index notation, thus by-passing the algebraic development in Chapter 2.

A2-1 Stress Notation. Stress Formulas

The nine components of stress taken collectively [see Eq. (2–3.1)] are called the *stress tensor* or the *stress array*. Consider the following change in notation:

$$\sigma_x = \sigma_{11}, \quad \sigma_y = \sigma_{22}, \quad \sigma_z = \sigma_{33}$$
$$\tau_{xy} = \sigma_{12}, \quad \tau_{xz} = \sigma_{13}, \quad \tau_{yz} = \sigma_{23}$$
$$(A2\text{–}1.1)$$

With this change in notation, the stress array may be denoted in index notation (Art. 1–17) by $\sigma_{\alpha\beta}$, where $\alpha, \beta = 1, 2, 3$, and where $\sigma_{\alpha\beta} = \sigma_{\beta\alpha}$. That is, the stress array is symmetric [Eq. (2–3.4)].

The stress vector p_α on a plane P with unit normal vector n_α ($n_\alpha n_\alpha = 1$) is

$$p_\alpha = \sigma_{\alpha\beta} n_\beta \qquad (A2\text{–}1.2)$$

where $n_\alpha = (n_1, n_2, n_3)$ is taken relative to axes x_i.

The scalar product of p_α and n_α defines the normal stress p on plane P. Thus, by Eq. (A2–1.2),

$$p = p_\alpha n_\alpha = \sigma_{\alpha\beta} n_\alpha n_\beta \qquad (A2\text{–}1.3)$$

The magnitude τ of the shearing stress (the tangential stress) on plane P is obtained by the Pythagorean formula:

$$\tau = \sqrt{p_\alpha p_\alpha - p^2} \qquad (A2\text{–}1.4)$$

A2-2 Transformation of Stress Components under Change of Coordinate System

Let x_α and X_α denote two rectangular cartesian coordinate systems with common origin. Let $a_{\alpha\beta}$ denote the direction cosines between axes X_α and x_β. Then by Eq. (A2–1.2) the stress vector σ_β on a plane perpendicular to the axis X_n is

$$\sigma_\beta = \sigma_{\alpha\beta} a_{n\alpha} \tag{a}$$

The component of σ_β in the direction of the axis X_m is $\sigma'_{mn} = \sigma_\beta a_{m\beta}$, or by Eq. (a) (with $\sigma_{\alpha\beta} = \sigma_{\beta\alpha}$),

$$\sigma'_{mn} = \sigma_{\alpha\beta} a_{m\alpha} a_{n\beta} \tag{A2–2.1}$$

where primes denote components with respect to the X_i reference axes. Conversely,

$$\sigma_{mn} = \sigma'_{\alpha\beta} a_{\alpha m} a_{\beta n} \tag{A2–2.2}$$

Equations (A2–2.1) and (A2–2.2) represent the law of transformation of stress components from one system of rectangular cartesian coordinates to another.

A2-3 Principal Stress. Principal Directions

Principal stresses are defined as the resulting stress that acts on planes (called principal planes) on which the shearing-stress components vanish (see Art. 2–5). Hence, principal stresses are normal stresses. Denoting the principal stress magnitude by σ, we may write the stress vector on the principal plane as σn_i, where n_i denotes the direction cosines of the principal axis (that is, the axis perpendicular to the principal plane) relative to x_i axes. Accordingly, by Eq. (a) of Art. A2–2, we may write (with $\sigma_{\alpha\beta} = \sigma_{\beta\alpha}$)

$$\sigma n_i = \sigma_{i\alpha} n_\alpha$$

or

$$(\sigma_{i\alpha} - \sigma\delta_{i\alpha})n_\alpha = 0 \tag{A2–3.1}$$

where n_α are the direction cosines of an axis of principal stress and δ_{ij} is Kronecker's delta function (see Art. 1–20). Equations (A2–3.1) may be solved for the direction cosines n_α (subject to the condition $n_\alpha n_\alpha = 1$) if, and only if, the determinant of the coefficients of n_α satisfies the determinantal equation (see Arts. 2–5 and 1–21).

$$|\sigma_{\alpha\beta} - \sigma\delta_{\alpha\beta}| = 0 \tag{A2–3.2}$$

Equation (A2.3.2) is a cubic algebraic equation in σ. The principal stresses (say $\sigma_1, \sigma_2, \sigma_3$) are the three roots of Eq. (A2–3.2). When the three principal roots (stresses) have been determined, the direction cosines n_α for each of the principal stresses, that is, the direction cosines of the principal axes, are determined by Eqs. (A2–3.1). The principal stresses (eigenvalues, see Art. 1–21) are all real. Hence, the direction cosines (eigenvectors) of the principal axes exist. Furthermore, the principal axes are orthogonal (Art. 1–21).

A2-4 Equations of Motion

Let S be a closed surface within a body, and let V denote the volume enclosed by S (Fig. 2–8.1). The external force that acts on the body consists of two parts (Art. 2–8): the body force and the tractive or surface force. The body force is ρB_i per unit volume, where ρ denotes mass density and B_i is the body-force function. (In Art. 2–8, $X = \rho B_x$, etc.) if the body force is due entirely to a planet's gravity, then B_i is the vector acceleration of gravity (directed toward the center of the planet). The tractive force (or surface force) per unit area of surface S is p_i, the stress vector on surface S. This stress is exerted on the surface S by material outside of and contiguous to the volume V. Accordingly, the net external force acting on V is

$$F_i = \int_S p_i \, dS + \int_V \rho B_i \, dV \qquad (a)$$

where the S denotes surface integral and the V volume integral.

The momentum of material in V is $\int_V \rho \dot{u}_i \, dV$, where u_i denotes the displacement vector, and the dot denotes the time derivative. Equating the external force F_i acting on the volume region V to the rate of change of momentum, and noting that $\rho \, dV$ is a constant (relative to Lagrangian coordinate axes; see Art. 3–2), we find

$$\int_S p_i \, dS + \int_V \rho(B_i - \ddot{u}_i) \, dV = 0 \qquad (b)$$

By Eq. (A2–1.2), we may rewrite Eq. (b) in the form

$$\int_S \sigma_{\alpha\beta} n_\beta \, dS + \int_V \rho(B_\alpha - \ddot{u}_\alpha) \, dV = 0 \qquad (c)$$

where n_β is the outward-directed unit normal vector to surface S (Fig. 2–8.1).

By means of the divergence theorem [Eq. (1–9.2)] we may transform the surface integral in Eq. (c) into a volume integral. Thus, we obtain

$$\int_V \left[\frac{\partial \sigma_{\alpha\beta}}{\partial x_\beta} + \rho(B_\alpha - \ddot{u}_\alpha) \right] dV = 0 \qquad (d)$$

Equation (d) holds for every volume V. Hence, the integrand of Eq. (d) must vanish identically. Accordingly, we have

$$\frac{\partial \sigma_{\alpha\beta}}{\partial x_\beta} + \rho B_\alpha = \rho \ddot{u}_\alpha \qquad (A2–4.1)$$

Equations (A2–4.1) are the *equations of motion*. If the body is in static equilibrium, $\ddot{u}_\alpha = 0$, and then Eqs. (A2–4.1) are called the *equations of equilibrium*. Equations (A2–4.1) are equivalent to Eqs. (2–8.4), with $\rho B_1 = X$, $\rho B_2 = Y$, $\rho B_3 = Z$.

More briefly still, Eqs. (A2–4.1) may be written

$$\sigma_{\alpha\beta,\beta} + \rho B_\alpha = \rho \ddot{u}_\alpha \tag{A2–4.2}$$

where, β denotes differentiation with respect to the variable x_β. In the absence of body force and acceleration, we have simply the three equilibrium equations

$$\sigma_{\alpha\beta,\beta} = 0 \tag{A2–4.3}$$

3
THEORY OF DEFORMATION
FOR CONTINUOUS MEDIA

A body is said to be *continuous* if it is composed of space-filling material. Indirectly, this viewpoint leads to average values of phenomena that occur at the atomic level. A change in distance between material points of a body is called a *deformation*. If a change in distance between material points of a body is possible, the body is said to be *deformable*. In nature, all bodies are deformable to some extent. For certain purposes the deformation of a body may be neglected; then the body is said to act as a *rigid body*.

In this chapter we deal with the geometry of deformation of continuous bodies. First, we review a few basic concepts of rigid-body displacements, that is, displacements of the particles (material points) of the body for which distances between particles after the displacements are the same as the distances between the particles initially.

3-1 Rigid-body Displacements

Displacement of a particle. By definition, the displacement of a particle is determined by its initial and final locations; the path of the particle between these points is irrelevant. A displacement of a particle is a vector quantity, since displacements of particles may be represented by arrows that combine by vector addition. For example, in Fig. 3–1.1, q_1 denotes a displacement of a particle from point O to point

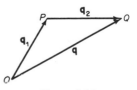

Figure 3-1.1

P, and $\mathbf{q}_2$ denotes a displacement of the particle from point P to Q. The resultant displacement from point O to point Q is represented by the vector sum $\mathbf{q} = \mathbf{q}_1 + \mathbf{q}_2$.

Translation of a mechanical system. A mechanical system is said to undergo a translation if the displacement vectors of all its particles are equal. A translation is said to be a type of "rigid-body displacement," since the final distances between the particles of the systems are the same as the initial distances. A translation of a system may be represented by a single vector which represents the displacement of any particle of the system.

A rigid-body displacement is a translation if, after the displacement, all lines connecting particles of the body retain their original directions and senses.[1]

Rotation. A mechanical system is said to undergo a rotation through an angle θ about an axis x if all particles of the system describe circular arcs of angle θ with their centers on the axis and with their planes perpendicular to the x axis. A rotation is a rigid-body displacement.

Plane displacements. A rigid body is said to experience a plane displacement if the displacement vectors of all its particles are parallel to a plane. Translations and rotations are plane displacements. To study plane displacements of a rigid body, it is necessary to consider only those particles that lie in a cross-sectional plane parallel to the displacement vectors, since the displacement vectors do not vary along a normal to that plane. It may be shown that *any* plane displacement of a rigid body can be performed by a translation or a rotation.[2]

Other theorems on rigid-body displacements. For general rigid-body displacements, we have the following interesting theorems.[3]

Euler's theorem. *Any displacement of a rigid body that has one point fixed can be performed by a rotation about an axis through the fixed point.*

Chasles' theorem. *Any displacement of a rigid body can be performed by a screw motion; that is, by a rotation about an axis, combined with a translation parallel to the axis.* (Chasles' theorem is a generalization of Euler's theorem.)

3-2 Deformation of a Continuous Body

Let R be a closed region that is initially occupied by a body. Let R^* be the closed region occupied by the body after it undergoes a deformation. Stars

---

[1]H. L. Langhaar and A. P. Boresi, *Dynamics for Engineers* (New York: McGraw-Hill Book Company, 1959), Chap. 11.

[2]*Ibid.*

[3]E. Whittaker, *A Treatise on the Analytical Dynamics of Particles and Rigid Bodies*, 4th ed. (New York: Dover Publications, Inc., 1944) Art. 1.

or asterisks are used to designate the deformed
state. Letters without asterisks generally denote
the undeformed state.

Let (x, y, z) be rectangular coordinates (Fig.
3–2.1). The particle (x, y, z) initially in the
undeformed body passes to the point $(x^*, y^*,$
$z^*)$ in the deformed body. Hence, the deformation of the body is defined by the equations

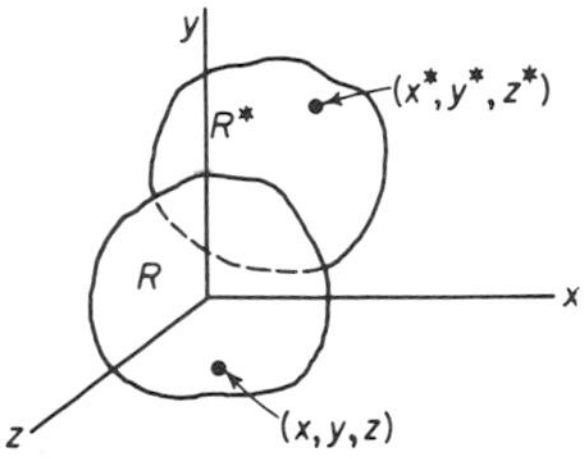

$$x^* = x^*(x, y, z), \qquad y^* = y^*(x, y, z),$$
$$z^* = z^*(x, y, z) \qquad\qquad\qquad (3\text{–}2.1)$$

Figure 3-2.1

where (x, y, z) are restricted to region R and (x^*, y^*, z^*) are restricted to
region R^*. Equation (3–2.1) defines the final location of the particle that
lies at a given point (x, y, z) in the undeformed body. It is assumed that
(x^*, y^*, z^*) are continuous and differentiable in the region R (i.e., in the
variables x, y, z), since a discontinuity of these functions would imply a
rupture of the body. In other words, to each point in region R there corresponds a point in region R^*, and vice versa; that is, Eqs. (3–2.1) denote
a one-to-one correspondence between the points in regions R and R^*. It
follows that in region R^* Eqs. (3–2.1) possess single-valued solutions of the
type

$$x = x(x^*, y^*, z^*), \qquad y = y(x^*, y^*, z^*), \qquad z = z(x^*, y^*, z^*) \qquad (3\text{–}2.2)$$

Equation (3–2.2) defines the initial location of a particle that lies at point
(x^*, y^*, z^*) in the deformed body. Functions (x, y, z) are continuous and
differentiable in region R^*.

Equations (3–2.1) and (3–2.2) allow some freedom of choice of independent variables in describing the deformation of a body. Many modern
writers on large-deformation theory adopt (x^*, y^*, z^*) as independent
variables. Then the basic mathematical problem is to express (x, y, z) as
functions of (x^*, y^*, z^*). This point of view is known as the *Eulerian coordinate method* of describing the deformation of a continuous medium. Although
the Eulerian point of view simplifies the theory of stress, it introduces a
natural difficulty in practical boundary-value problems, since the deformed
shape of a body is not generally known in advance. When problems of
deformable bodies are formulated by means of energy principles, the initial
coordinates (x, y, z) serve most simply and naturally as independent variables.
Then, the basic problem is to define (x^*, y^*, z^*) as functions of (x, y, z). This
point of view is known as the *Lagrangian coordinate method* of describing the
deformation of a continuous medium. The arbitrariness of selection of
Eulerian or Lagrangian coordinates does not arise in the classical (small-
deformation) theories of elasticity and plasticity since there the points $(x,
y, z)$ and (x^*, y^*, z^*) are assumed to lie so close together that it is not neces-
sary to distinguish between them; that is, the displacements are infinitesimally

small. Unless explicitly stated to the contrary, we employ Lagrangian coordinates in what follows.

In the theory of real variables,[4] it is shown that Eqs. (3–2.1) possess a single-valued continuous solution of the type of Eq. (3–2.2) if, and only if, the following determinant does not vanish in the region R:

$$\frac{\partial(x^*, y^*, z^*)}{\partial(x, y, z)} = \begin{vmatrix} \dfrac{\partial x^*}{\partial x} & \dfrac{\partial x^*}{\partial y} & \dfrac{\partial x^*}{\partial z} \\[2mm] \dfrac{\partial y^*}{\partial x} & \dfrac{\partial y^*}{\partial y} & \dfrac{\partial y^*}{\partial z} \\[2mm] \dfrac{\partial z^*}{\partial x} & \dfrac{\partial z^*}{\partial y} & \dfrac{\partial z^*}{\partial z} \end{vmatrix}$$

$$= \begin{vmatrix} x_x^* & x_y^* & x_z^* \\ y_x^* & y_y^* & y_z^* \\ z_x^* & z_y^* & z_z^* \end{vmatrix} \neq 0 \qquad (3\text{–}2.3)$$

where subscripts (x, y, z) denote partial derivatives. The determinant of Eq. (3–2.3) is called the *Jacobian* of the functions (x^*, y^*, z^*). The expression on the left of Eq. (3–2.3) is a conventional notation for the Jacobian.

On the basis of the following physical argument, further restrictions may be placed on the condition of Eq. (3–2.3). If particles of a body are not displaced at all, $x^* = x$, $y^* = y$, $z^* = z$. Then the value of the Jacobian is 1. It follows that since the Jacobian is a continuous function of (x, y, z), it is *positive for small deformations*. Furthermore, it cannot become negative by a continuous deformation of a body without passing through the excluded value zero [Eq. (3–2.3)]. Hence, it can never be negative. In other words, a *necessary* condition for a deformation to be continuously possible is that the following inequality be satisfied throughout region R:[5]

$$D > 0 \qquad (3\text{–}2.4)$$

where D denotes the determinant in Eq. (3–2.3). For example, we cannot subject a piece of putty to the deformation $x^* = -x$, $y^* = y$, $z^* = z$, since then $D = -1$. This type of correspondence is called a "reflection about the yz plane," since the point (x^*, y^*, z^*) may be regarded as the image of the point (x, y, z) in a mirror that lies in the plane $x = 0$.

A deformation of a body is commonly represented by a *displacement vector* (see Art. 1–2),

$$\mathbf{q} = \mathbf{i}u + \mathbf{j}v + \mathbf{k}w \qquad (3\text{–}2.5)$$

---

[4]J. M. H. Olmsted, *Real Variables* (New York: Appleton-Century-Crofts, Inc., 1959).

[5]The condition of Eq. (3–2.4) may also be interpreted as a restriction on strain, the limiting lower value of the strain being -1 if strain is defined by Eq. (3–4.3). If $D < 0$, the resulting strain is less than -1. [See Eqs. (3–2.6) and (3–12.17).]

where

$$u = x^* - x, \qquad v = y^* - y, \qquad w = z^* - z \qquad (3\text{-}2.6)$$

and $\mathbf{i}, \mathbf{j}, \mathbf{k}$ are unit vectors directed along positive (x, y, z) axes, respectively. In view of Eqs. (3–2.1), (u, v, w) are single-valued continuous differentiable functions of (x, y, z) which serve to define the deformation. Physically, (u, v, w) denote the (x, y, z) projections of the displacement vector $\mathbf{q}$. Substitution of Eqs. (3–2.6) into the equation $D > 0$ yields

$$D = \begin{vmatrix} 1 + u_x & u_y & u_z \\ v_x & 1 + v_y & v_z \\ w_x & w_y & 1 + w_z \end{vmatrix} > 0 \qquad (3\text{-}2.7)$$

for a continuously possible deformation.

PROBLEM SET 3-2

1 Determine whether or not $u = k(y - x)$, $v = k(x - y)$, $w = kxz$, where k is a constant, are continuously possible displacement components for a continuous medium. Consider (x, y, z) to be rectangular cartesian coordinates of a point in the body.

2 Show that $u = ayz$, $v = bzx$, $w = cxy$, where (a, b, c) are constants, are the components of a continuously possible displacement vector.

3 A parallelepiped occupies the region $0 \leq x \leq L$, $-h \leq y \leq h$, $-b \leq z \leq b$. It is deformed in such a manner that a material point $P(x, y, z)$ is displaced to $P^*(x^*, y^*, z^*)$, where $x^* = (C - y) \cos (x/C)$, $y^* = (C - y) \sin (x/C)$, $z^* = z$, where C is a constant. Indicate the restrictions that must be imposed upon C in order that the displacement may be continuously possible.

3-3 Strain of Any Line Element

In the classical theory of elasticity, the displacement is assumed to be very small. Hence, the final position (x^*, y^*, z^*) of a point in a body which undergoes a deformation is considered to lie very close to its initial position (x, y, z). Approximations based on the idea of infinitesimal displacement leads to a complete linearization of the theory of deformation. However, in a general treatment of the mechanics of deformable bodies, it is necessary to abandon this restriction. For example, in a general treatment of the theories of plates and shells, some of the quadratic terms in the projections (u, v, w) of the displacement vector $\mathbf{q}$ are essential. Also, in large-displacement theories of elasticity and plasticity, quadratic terms in (u, v, w) are important. Therefore, as far as practical, the theory of strain will be developed without using the linearizing approximations of classical elasticity.

When a body is deformed, the particle at point P: (x, y, z) passes to the point P^*: (x^*, y^*, z^*) (Fig. 3–3.1). Likewise, the particle Q: $(x + dx,$

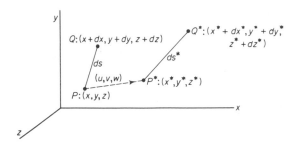

Figure 3-3.1

$y + dy$, $z + dz$) passes to the point Q^*: ($x^* + dx^*$, $y^* + dy^*$, $z^* + dz^*$). The infinitesimal line element PQ is ordinarily elongated or contracted when it passes into the line element P^*Q^*. The length PQ is denoted by ds, and the length P^*Q^* is denoted by ds^*. To express magnification ds^*/ds of this line element in terms of the displacement vector (u, v, w), we denote the infinitesimal vectors **PQ** and **P*Q*** by (dx, dy, dz) and (dx^*, dy^*, dz^*), respectively. The total differentials (dx^*, dy^*, dz^*) of the functions $x^*(x, y, z)$, $y^*(x, y, z)$, $z^*(x, y, z)$ may be expressed in terms of the total differentials (dx, dy, dz) as follows:[6]

$$dx^* = \frac{\partial x^*}{\partial x}\, dx + \frac{\partial x^*}{\partial y}\, dy + \frac{\partial x^*}{\partial z}\, dz$$

$$dy^* = \frac{\partial y^*}{\partial x}\, dx + \frac{\partial y^*}{\partial y}\, dy + \frac{\partial y^*}{\partial z}\, dz \qquad (3\text{--}3.1)$$

$$dz^* = \frac{\partial z^*}{\partial x}\, dx + \frac{\partial z^*}{\partial y}\, dy + \frac{\partial z^*}{\partial z}\, dz$$

With the notation $x_x^* = (\partial x^*/\partial x)$, $x_y^* = (\partial x^*/\partial y)$, $x_z^* = (\partial x^*/\partial z)$, $\ldots$, $\ldots$, the above equations may be written in the form

$$dx^* = x_x^*\, dx + x_y^*\, dy + x_z^*\, dz$$
$$dy^* = y_x^*\, dx + y_y^*\, dy + y_z^*\, dz \qquad (3\text{--}3.2)$$
$$dz^* = z_x^*\, dx + z_y^*\, dy + z_z^*\, dz$$

where the (x, y, z) subscripts denote partial derivatives.

Letting the lengths of the vectors (dx, dy, dz) and (dx^*, dy^*, dz^*) be denoted by ds and ds^*, and noting that $ds^2 = dx^2 + dy^2 + dz^2$, $(ds^*)^2 = (dx^*)^2 + (dy^*)^2 + (dz^*)^2$, with Eqs. (3–2.6) and (3–3.2), we obtain

$$\tfrac{1}{2}[(ds^*)^2 - ds^2] = \epsilon_x\, dx^2 + \epsilon_y\, dy^2 + \epsilon_z\, dz^2 + \gamma_{xy}\, dx\, dy + \gamma_{xz}\, dx\, dz + \gamma_{yz}\, dy\, dz$$
$$(3\text{--}3.3)$$

where the coefficients ϵ_x, ϵ_y, ϵ_z, γ_{xy}, γ_{xz}, γ_{yz} are given by

---

[6]W. Kaplan, *Advanced Calculus* (Reading, Mass.: Addison-Wesley Press, 1955).

$$\epsilon_x = u_x + \tfrac{1}{2}(u_x^2 + v_x^2 + w_x^2)$$
$$\epsilon_y = v_y + \tfrac{1}{2}(u_y^2 + v_y^2 + w_y^2)$$
$$\epsilon_z = w_z + \tfrac{1}{2}(u_z^2 + v_z^2 + w_z^2)$$
$$\gamma_{xy} = v_x + u_y + u_x u_y + v_x v_y + w_x w_y \tag{3-3.4}$$
$$\gamma_{xz} = w_x + u_z + u_x u_z + v_x v_z + w_x w_z$$
$$\gamma_{yz} = w_y + v_z + u_y u_z + v_y v_z + w_y w_z$$

The components of the unit vector $\mathbf{N} = \mathbf{i}l + \mathbf{j}m + \mathbf{k}n$ in the direction of the infinitesimal vector (dx, dy, dz) are

$$l = \frac{dx}{ds}, \qquad m = \frac{dy}{ds}, \qquad n = \frac{dz}{ds} \tag{3-3.5}$$

Consequently, Eq. (3–3.3) yields (after division by ds^2)

$$\mathscr{M} = \frac{1}{2}\left[\left(\frac{ds^*}{ds}\right)^2 - 1\right] = \epsilon_x l^2 + \epsilon_y m^2 + \epsilon_z n^2 + \gamma_{xy} lm + \gamma_{xz} ln + \gamma_{yz} mn \tag{3-3.6}$$

Equation (3–3.6) defines the magnification factor $\mathscr{M}$ of the line element that lies at the point (x, y, z) in the direction (l, m, n), if the functions (u, v, w) are known [see Eq. (3–3.4)].

Alternatively, the deformation of the body may be referred to Eulerian coordinates (x^*, y^*, z^*). For simplicity of writing, let $\xi = x^*$, $\eta = y^*$, $\zeta = z^*$. For example, if (ξ, η, ζ) are considered to be the independent variables [Eq. (3–2.2)], we have

$$dx = x_\xi \, d\xi + x_\eta \, d\eta + x_\zeta \, d\zeta$$
$$dy = y_\xi \, d\xi + y_\eta \, d\eta + y_\zeta \, d\zeta \tag{3-3.7}$$
$$dz = z_\xi \, d\xi + z_\eta \, d\eta + z_\zeta \, d\zeta$$

where (ξ, η, ζ) subscripts denote partial derivatives. Now with Eqs. (3–2.6) and (3–3.7), we obtain

$$\tfrac{1}{2}[(ds^*)^2 - (ds)^2] = E_\xi \, d\xi^2 + E_\eta \, d\eta^2 + E_\zeta \, d\zeta + E_{\xi\eta} \, d\xi \, d\eta + E_{\xi\zeta} \, d\xi \, d\zeta + E_{\eta\zeta} \, d\eta \, d\zeta \tag{3-3.8}$$

where the coefficients $(E_\xi, E_\eta, E_\zeta, E_{\xi\eta}, E_{\xi\zeta}, E_{\eta\zeta})$, relative to Eulerian coordinates (ξ, η, ζ), are given by

$$F_\xi = u_\xi - \tfrac{1}{2}(u_\xi^2 + v_\xi^2 + w_\xi^2)$$
$$E_\eta = v_\eta - \tfrac{1}{2}(u_\eta^2 + v_\eta^2 + w_\eta^2)$$
$$E_\zeta = w_\zeta - \tfrac{1}{2}(u_\zeta^2 + v_\zeta^2 + w_\zeta^2)$$
$$E_{\xi\eta} = v_\xi + u_\eta - (u_\xi u_\eta + v_\xi v_\eta + w_\xi w_\eta) \tag{3-3.9}$$
$$E_{\xi\zeta} = w_\xi + u_\zeta - (u_\xi u_\zeta + v_\xi v_\zeta + w_\xi w_\zeta)$$
$$E_{\eta\zeta} = w_\eta + v_\zeta - (u_\eta u_\zeta + v_\eta v_\zeta + w_\eta w_\zeta)$$

Similar to the derivation of Eq. (3–3.6) the magnification factor $\mathcal{M}^*$, relative to axes (ξ, η, ζ), is found to be

$$\mathcal{M}^* = \frac{1}{2}\left[1 - \left(\frac{ds}{ds^*}\right)^2\right]$$

$$= E_\xi L^2 + E_\eta M^2 + E_\zeta N^2 + E_{\xi\eta}LM + E_{\xi\zeta}LN + E_{\eta\zeta}MN \qquad (3\text{–}3.10)$$

where L, M, N denote direction cosines of line element ds^*, relative to axes (ξ, η, ζ).

We note that $ds^* = ds$ is a necessary and sufficient condition for a rigid-body displacement. Then, $\mathcal{M} = \mathcal{M}^* = 0$. Also, we note that if the displacement (u, v, w) and its derivatives are small, quadratic terms in Eqs. (3–3.4) and (3–3.9) may be discarded. Then, Eqs. (3–3.4) and (3–3.9) are identical in form, since to within higher-degree terms in the displacement, derivatives of the displacement relative to a point (x, y, z) or relative to a point (ξ, η, ζ) are equivalent.

Accordingly, for small displacements, we write simply

$$\begin{aligned}
\epsilon_x &= u_x, & \gamma_{xy} &= u_y + v_x \\
\epsilon_y &= v_y, & \gamma_{xz} &= u_z + w_x \\
\epsilon_z &= w_z, & \gamma_{yz} &= v_z + w_y
\end{aligned} \qquad (3\text{–}3.11)$$

PROBLEM SET 3-3

1 Derive Eqs. (3–3.3) and (3–3.4).

2 Measurements of a strained body yield the following data: $\epsilon_x = 0.002$, $\epsilon_y = 0.002$, $\epsilon_z = -0.002$.

In the direction $\left(\dfrac{2}{\sqrt{5}}, 0, \dfrac{1}{\sqrt{5}}\right)$, $\mathcal{M} = 0.004$

In the direction $\left(\dfrac{3}{\sqrt{10}}, \dfrac{-1}{\sqrt{10}}, 0\right)$, $\mathcal{M} = 0.003$

In the direction $\left(\dfrac{1}{\sqrt{3}}, \dfrac{1}{\sqrt{3}}, \dfrac{1}{\sqrt{3}}\right)$, $\mathcal{M} = 0.001$

Calculate $\gamma_{xy}, \gamma_{xz}, \gamma_{yz}$.

3 A straight bar of length L, with end points 0 and 1, undergoes a displacement such that its length changes to L^*. Under this displacement, the bar remains straight. Derive an expression for $(L^* - L)/L$, expressing the result in terms of the original length L and the displacement components (u_0, v_0), (u_1, v_1) of the end points of the bar. Let u be measured along the axial direction of the initial position of the bar and v be measured perpendicular to the bar in its initial position. Derive an approximate expression for $(L^* - L)/L$ for the case where $(u_1 - u_0) \ll L$, $(v_1 - v_0) \ll L$. Derive an expression for the elongation of the bar in each case.

4 The deformation of a body is defined by the displacement components

$$u = k(3x^2 + y), \qquad v = k(2y^2 + z), \qquad w = k(4z^2 + x),$$

where k is a positive constant. Compute the magnification of a line element ds that passes through the point $(1, 1, 1)$ in the direction $l = m = n = 1/\sqrt{3}$.

3-4 Definition of Strain

Large-deflection definition. In large-deflection theories, it is convenient to *define* the strain ϵ_L of a line element in the body as follows:

$$\epsilon_L = \frac{1}{2}\left[\left(\frac{ds^*}{ds}\right)^2 - 1\right] \tag{3-4.1}$$

Hence, by Eqs. (3–3.6) and (3–4.1),

$$\epsilon_L = \mathscr{M} = \epsilon_x l^2 + \epsilon_y m^2 + \epsilon_z n^2 + \gamma_{xy} lm + \gamma_{xz} ln + \gamma_{yz} mn \tag{3-4.2}$$

If the functions (u, v, w) are known, Eq. (3–4.2) determines the strain ϵ_L of any line element (with direction cosines l, m, n) in the body. It is identical to the magnification factor $\mathscr{M}$. Equation (3–4.2) shows that ϵ_x, ϵ_y, ϵ_z are equal to the strains of the line elements that lie initially in the respective directions of the (x, y, z) axes. For example, if the line element is initially in the direction of the x axis, $l = 1$, $m = n = 0$, and $\epsilon_L = \epsilon_x$, etc.

Engineering definition. In a large class of engineering problems, the displacements of points in bodies acted upon by forces are often small. Then, it is convenient to define the strain of a line element as follows:

$$\epsilon_E = \frac{ds^* - ds}{ds} \tag{3-4.3}$$

Then $ds^*/ds = 1 + \epsilon_E$. Accordingly,

$$\epsilon_E + \frac{1}{2}\epsilon_E^2 = \frac{1}{2}\left[\left(\frac{ds^*}{ds}\right)^2 - 1\right] \tag{3-4.4}$$

Hence, by Eqs. (3–3.6) and (3–4.4),

$$\epsilon_E + \frac{1}{2}\epsilon_E^2 = \mathscr{M}$$
$$= \epsilon_x l^2 + \epsilon_y m^2 + \epsilon_z n^2 + \gamma_{xy} lm + \gamma_{xz} ln + \gamma_{yz} mn \tag{3-4.5}$$

If the strain is small, the term $\frac{1}{2}\epsilon_E^2$ may be neglected with respect to ϵ_E. Hence, for small strains, $\mathscr{M} = \epsilon_L = \epsilon_E + \frac{1}{2}\epsilon_E^2 \approx \epsilon_E$. Accordingly, Eq. (3–4.1) does not differ appreciably from the usual definition of strain, unless the strains are very large.

Logarithmic strain. Inherent in the preceding definitions is the condition that the strain is defined as a relation between the change in length of a line element and its initial length [see Eqs. (3–4.1) and (3–4.3)]. However, in creep and plasticity theories, particularly for large deformations, another definition of strain based on the instantaneous length of a line element is sometimes employed. For example, following Ludwik,[7] we define the increment $\Delta\epsilon_n$ of strain by the relation

$$\Delta\epsilon_n = \frac{\Delta l}{l} \tag{3-4.6}$$

where l denotes the instantaneous length of a finite line element. Accordingly, for an infinitesimal change dl, the infinitesimal increment $d\epsilon_n$ of strain is defined by

$$d\epsilon_n = \frac{dl}{l} \tag{3-4.7}$$

Integration yields

$$\epsilon_n = \log\frac{l}{l_0} = \log\left(1 + \frac{\Delta l}{l_0}\right)$$

or

$$\epsilon_n = \log\left(1 + \epsilon_E\right) \tag{3-4.8}$$

where log denotes natural logarithm, l_0 denotes the initial length of the line element, and by Eq. (3–4.3), $\epsilon_E = \Delta l/l_0$ is the conventional engineering strain. The term ϵ_n is called the *natural* or *true* strain. Because of the relation expressed by Eq. (3–4.8), ϵ_n is sometimes called the *logarithmic* strain.

For $\epsilon_E^2 < 1$, Eq. (3–4.8) may be expanded in the following series form:

$$\epsilon_n = \log\left(1 + \epsilon_E\right) = \epsilon_E - \tfrac{1}{2}\epsilon_E^2 + \tfrac{1}{3}\epsilon_E^3 - \tfrac{1}{4}\epsilon_E^4 + \cdots, \qquad \epsilon_E^2 < 1 \tag{3-4.9}$$

Accordingly, for small strain ϵ_E, Eq. (3–4.9) yields the approximation

$$\epsilon_n = \epsilon_E; \qquad |\epsilon_E| \ll 1 \tag{3-4.10}$$

The definition embodied in Eq. (3–4.8) simplifies some of the equations of the mechanics of a deformable medium (see Art. 3–9). However, in general, the use of natural strain tends to complicate the equations of deformable-body mechanics.

In view of the foregoing observations, the definition of strain has no fundamental importance in the theory of deformation. The essential thing (the mathematical content of the theory) is the geometrical relation expressed by Eq. (3–3.6). The theories of deformable media do not require a definition of strain. Nevertheless, in engineering, it is customary to utilize the definition of strain expressed by Eq. (3–4.3).

3-5 Final Direction of a Deformed Line Element

As a result of a deformation, the line element (dx, dy, dz) deforms into the line element (dx^*, dy^*, dz^*). The lengths of these line elements are denoted by ds and ds^*, respectively. The following relations for the line element ds^* follow from the definition of direction cosines:

---

[7]P. Ludwik, *Elemente der technologischen Mechanik* (Berlin: Springer, 1909).

$$l^* = \frac{dx^*}{ds^*}, \qquad m^* = \frac{dy^*}{ds^*}, \qquad n^* = \frac{dz^*}{ds^*} \qquad (3\text{–}5.1)$$

where (l^*, m^*, n^*) denote the direction cosines of ds^*. Analogous equations for the direction cosines of line element ds are given by Eq. (3–3.5).

Equation (3–5.1) may be written as follows:

$$l^* = \frac{dx^*}{ds}\frac{ds}{ds^*}, \qquad m^* = \frac{dy^*}{ds}\frac{ds}{ds^*}, \qquad n^* = \frac{dz^*}{ds}\frac{ds}{ds^*} \qquad (3\text{–}5.2)$$

Hence, by Eq. (3–3.2),

$$\frac{dx^*}{ds} = x_x^* \frac{dx}{ds} + x_y^* \frac{dy}{ds} + x_z^* \frac{dz}{ds}$$

$$\frac{dy^*}{ds} = y_x^* \frac{dx}{ds} + y_y^* \frac{dy}{ds} + y_z^* \frac{dz}{ds} \qquad (3\text{–}5.3)$$

$$\frac{dz^*}{ds} = z_x^* \frac{dx}{ds} + z_y^* \frac{dy}{ds} + z_z^* \frac{dz}{ds}$$

Also, Eq. (3–2.6) yields

$$x_x^* = 1 + u_x, \qquad x_y^* = u_y, \qquad x_z^* = u_z$$

$$y_x^* = v_x, \qquad y_y^* = 1 + v_y, \qquad y_z^* = v_z \qquad (3\text{–}5.4)$$

$$z_x^* = w_x, \qquad z_y^* = w_y, \qquad z_z^* = 1 + w_z$$

Combining Eqs. (3–5.3), (3–5.4), and (3–3.5), we obtain

$$\frac{dx^*}{ds} = (1 + u_x)l + u_y m + u_z n$$

$$\frac{dy^*}{ds} = v_x l + (1 + v_y)m + v_z n \qquad (3\text{–}5.5)$$

$$\frac{dz^*}{ds} = w_x l + w_y m + (1 + w_z)n$$

By Eq. (3–3.6), we find

$$\frac{ds}{ds^*} = \frac{1}{\sqrt{1 + 2\mathcal{M}}} \qquad (3\text{–}5.6)$$

Consequently, by Eqs. (3–5.2), (3–5.5), and (3–5.6), we obtain

$$l^* = \frac{(1 + u_x)l + u_y m + u_z n}{\sqrt{1 + 2\mathcal{M}}}$$

$$m^* = \frac{v_x l + (1 + v_y)m + v_z n}{\sqrt{1 + 2\mathcal{M}}} \qquad (3\text{–}5.7)$$

$$n^* = \frac{w_x l + w_y + (1 + w_z)n}{\sqrt{1 + 2\mathcal{M}}}$$

Equations (3–5.7) determine the final direction cosines (l^*, m^*, n^*) of a line element with initial direction cosines (l, m, n). The magnification factor

$\mathcal{M}$ that appears in Eq. (3–5.7) is expressed in terms of the displacement (u, v, w) and the direction cosines (l, m, n) by Eqs. (3–3.4) and (3–4.2).

It may be shown that through each point there is at least one line element that does not change direction;[8] that is, there is at least one line element that conforms to the equation

$$l = l^*, \qquad m = m^*, \qquad n = n^*$$

PROBLEM SET 3-5

1 Derive Eq. (3–5.6) in terms of ϵ_E [see Eq. (3–4.3)]. Hence, derive Eq. (3–5.7) in terms of ϵ_E.

2 A rigid-body displacement (that is, a displacement for which $\epsilon_x = \epsilon_y = \cdots$ $= \gamma_{yz} = 0$) is defined by the displacement components

$$u = a_0 + ay - bz$$
$$v = b_0 - ax + cz$$
$$w = c_0 + bx - cy$$

where a_0, b_0, c_0, a, b, c are constants. In terms of the constants $a, b, \ldots$, derive expressions for the direction cosines of the line element that does not change direction under the displacement.

3-6 Shearing Strain

Let (l_1, m_1, n_1) and (l_2, m_2, n_2) be two *mutually perpendicular directions* in a body. When the body is deformed, intersecting line elements in the directions (l_1, m_1, n_1) and (l_2, m_2, n_2) pass into line elements with directions (l_1^*, m_1^*, n_1^*) and (l_2^*, m_2^*, n_2^*). By the scalar product for vectors, the angle θ between the latter line elements is defined by the equation

$$\cos \theta = l_1^* l_2^* + m_1^* m_2^* + n_1^* n_2^* \qquad (a)$$

The directions (l_1^*, m_1^*, n_1^*) and (l_2^*, m_2^*, n_2^*) are expressed in terms of the directions (l_1, m_1, n_1) and (l_2, m_2, n_2) by Eq. (3–5.7). If we substitute Eq. (3–5.7) into Eq. (a), the resulting equations can be simplified by means of the relations $l_1 l_2 + m_1 m_2 + n_1 n_2 = 0$, etc., which follow from the perpendicularity of the two line elements in the undeformed body. Then, denoting the magnification factor of the line elements by $\mathcal{M}_1$ and $\mathcal{M}_2$ and utilizing the notations of Eq. (3–3.4), we obtain

$$\begin{aligned}\Gamma_{12} &= \sqrt{(1 + 2\mathcal{M}_1)(1 + 2\mathcal{M}_2)} \cos \theta \\ &= 2\epsilon_x l_1 l_2 + 2\epsilon_y m_1 m_2 + 2\epsilon_z n_1 n_2 + \gamma_{xy}(l_1 m_2 + l_2 m_1) \qquad (3\text{–}6.1) \\ &\quad + \gamma_{xz}(l_1 n_2 + l_2 n_1) + \gamma_{yz}(m_1 n_2 + m_2 n_1)\end{aligned}$$

[8]V. V. Novozhilov, *Foundations of the Nonlinear Theory of Elasticity* (Rochester, N. Y.: Graylock Press, 1953).

If the quantity $\Gamma_{12} = \sqrt{(1 + 2\mathcal{M}_1)(1 + 2\mathcal{M}_2)} \cos\theta$ is *defined* to be the shearing strain between the given line elements, Eq. (3–6.1) determines the shearing strain between pairs of line elements that are initially parallel to the coordinate axes that are indicated by the subscripts (1, 2).

If $\mathcal{M}_1$ and $\mathcal{M}_2$ are small compared to 1, Eq. (3–6.1) shows that Γ_{12} is approximately equal to $\cos\theta$. Also, since θ is approximately $\pi/2$ for small shearing strains, $\cos\theta$ is approximately $(\pi/2) - \theta$. Accordingly, the preceding definition of shear strain does not differ significantly from the conventional definition $\gamma_{12} = (\pi/2) - \theta$, unless the strains are large compared to 1. The definition of shearing strain is not fundamentally important in the theory of deformation, since the geometrical relation expressed by Eq. (3–6.1) is independent of any definition of shearing strain. However, it plays a role in relating experimental and theoretical results.

Physical interpretation of $\gamma_{xy}, \gamma_{xz}, \gamma_{yz}$. With respect to (x, y, z) axes, let the direction cosines of line 1 be $(1, 0, 0)$ and the direction cosines of line 2 be $(0, 1, 0)$. Then, if point P is coincident with the origin of (x, y, z) axes, line 1 lies along the x axis and line 2 lies along the y axis. Then, by Eq. (3–6.1),

$$\Gamma_{12} = \gamma_{xy} \qquad (3\text{–}6.2)$$

For small shearing strains, Eq. (3–6.2) reduces to

$$\Gamma_{12} = \gamma_{xy} \approx \gamma_{12} = \frac{\pi}{2} - \theta \qquad (3\text{–}6.3)$$

Hence, for small shearing strains, γ_{xy} represents the relative rotation between lines initially along the x and y axes. Similarly, γ_{xz}, γ_{yz} represent relative rotations between lines initially along the x and z axes and along the y and z axes, respectively, provided the shearing strain is small.

Problem. Express Eq. (3–6.1) in terms of ϵ_E [see Eq. (3–4.3)].

3-7 The Strain Tensor

The theory of strain becomes more systematic if the quantities $\gamma_{yz}, \gamma_{zx}, \gamma_{xy}$ are supplemented by other quantities $\gamma_{zy}, \gamma_{xz}, \gamma_{yx}$ that are defined as follows:

$$\gamma_{yz} = \gamma_{zy}, \qquad \gamma_{zx} = \gamma_{xz}, \qquad \gamma_{xy} = \gamma_{yx} \qquad (3\text{–}7.1)$$

Then the formula for the strain of a line element that lies in the direction (l, m, n) [Eq. (3–4.2)] may be written as follows:

$$\mathcal{M} = \epsilon = \epsilon_x l^2 + \tfrac{1}{2}\gamma_{xy} lm + \tfrac{1}{2}\gamma_{xz} ln + \tfrac{1}{2}\gamma_{yx} lm + \epsilon_y m^2 + \tfrac{1}{2}\gamma_{yz} mn$$
$$+ \tfrac{1}{2}\gamma_{zy} mn + \tfrac{1}{2}\gamma_{zx} ln + \epsilon_z n^2 \qquad (3\text{–}7.2)$$

The right side of this equation is a quadratic form in the variables (l, m, n), with the following matrix of coefficients:

$$\begin{pmatrix} \epsilon_x & \frac{1}{2}\gamma_{xy} & \frac{1}{2}\gamma_{xz} \\ \frac{1}{2}\gamma_{yx} & \epsilon_y & \frac{1}{2}\gamma_{yz} \\ \frac{1}{2}\gamma_{zx} & \frac{1}{2}\gamma_{zy} & \epsilon_z \end{pmatrix} \tag{3-7.3}$$

Equation (3–7.3) is analogous to Eq. (2–3.1). Accordingly, this matrix (array of elements) is called the *strain tensor*. The terms in the matrix are called the components of the strain tensor. Since the matrix [Eq. (3–7.3)] is symmetric with respect to its principal diagonal, it follows in a manner analogous to that of Art. 2–5 that ϵ defined by Eq. (3–7.2) possesses three stationary real values.[9] These stationary real values are called *principal values*, or since we are treating strains, *principal strains*. A physical interpretation of principal strains is presented in the next article.

Transformation of strain components. Analogous to the transformation of stress components, the components $\epsilon_{\alpha\beta}$ of the strain tensor relative to axes (x, y, z) obey the following law of transformation for $x \to X, y \to Y, z \to Z$ [see Art. 2–4 and Eq. (2–9.5)].

$$\epsilon'_{mn} = \epsilon_{\alpha\beta}a_{m\alpha}a_{n\beta} \tag{3-7.4}$$

where ϵ'_{mn} denotes strain components relative to axes (X, Y, Z) and a_{ij} denotes the direction cosines between axes X_i and x_j. (See also Appendix, Chapter 3, for definitions of $\epsilon_{\alpha\beta}$.) Alternatively, we may write

$$\epsilon_{mn} = \epsilon'_{\alpha\beta}a_{\alpha m}a_{\beta n} \tag{3-7.5}$$

Equations (3–7.4) and (3–7.5) represent the law of transformation of stress components from one system of rectangular cartesian coordinate axes to another. (See Arts. 1–17 and 1–18.)

3-8 Principal Strains

Since the following results are purely algebraic, they may be developed in an abstract form that is applicable to any quadratic form whose coefficients form a symmetric matrix. For example, the results are applicable to the theories of stress, strain, moments of inertia, and normal coordinates of vibrating systems.[10] The following development is geometric in nature. It is completely analogous to the theory of principal stress (see Art. 2–5).

The strain ϵ of a line element in an arbitrary direction (l, m, n) is given by Eq. (3–4.2). For some particular direction, ϵ takes a maximum value; for another direction, it takes a minimum value. There is a third direction for which ϵ is stationary, although it is neither a maximum nor a minimum.

---

[9]For a general treatment see C. Lanczos, *Applied Analysis* (Englewood Cliffs, N. J.: Prentice-Hall, Inc., 1956).

[10]See Courant and Hilbert, *Methods of Mathematical Physics*, Vol. 1 (New York: Interscience Publishers, 1953), Chap. 1.

These three stationary values of ϵ are denoted by ϵ_1, ϵ_2, ϵ_3. They are called the *principal strains* at the given point. The *initial* directions of the line elements that experience the principal strains are called the *principal directions*. These three directions are mutually perpendicular to each other. The shearing strains between line elements in the principal directions are zero. In other words, line elements in the principal direction remain perpendicular under the deformation. These conclusions are valid for all continuous deformations, regardless of the magnitudes of the displacements and the rotations.

Since the strain tensor [Eq. (3–7.3)] is analogous to the stress tensor [Eq. (2–3.1)] the principal strains are the roots of the following cubic equation in ϵ [see Eq. (2–5.2)].

$$\begin{vmatrix} \epsilon_x - \epsilon & \frac{1}{2}\gamma_{xy} & \frac{1}{2}\gamma_{xz} \\ \frac{1}{2}\gamma_{yx} & \epsilon_y - \epsilon & \frac{1}{2}\gamma_{yz} \\ \frac{1}{2}\gamma_{zx} & \frac{1}{2}\gamma_{zy} & \epsilon_z - \epsilon \end{vmatrix} = 0 \qquad (3\text{–}8.1)$$

Expansion of this determinant yields

$$\epsilon^3 - J_1\epsilon^2 + J_2\epsilon - J_3 = 0 \qquad (3\text{–}8.2)$$

where

$$J_1 = \epsilon_x + \epsilon_y + \epsilon_z$$

$$J_2 = \epsilon_x\epsilon_y + \epsilon_x\epsilon_z + \epsilon_y\epsilon_z - \tfrac{1}{4}\gamma_{xy}^2 - \tfrac{1}{4}\gamma_{xz}^2 - \tfrac{1}{4}\gamma_{yz}^2 \qquad (3\text{–}8.3)$$

$$J_3 = \begin{vmatrix} \epsilon_x & \frac{1}{2}\gamma_{xy} & \frac{1}{2}\gamma_{xz} \\ \frac{1}{2}\gamma_{yx} & \epsilon_y & \frac{1}{2}\gamma_{yz} \\ \frac{1}{2}\gamma_{zx} & \frac{1}{2}\gamma_{zy} & \epsilon_z \end{vmatrix}$$

Since $\gamma_{xy} = \gamma_{yx}$, $\gamma_{xz} = \gamma_{zx}$, $\gamma_{yz} = \gamma_{zy}$, that is, since the elements of Eq. (3–8.1) are symmetric with respect to the main diagonal, the three roots ϵ_1, ϵ_2, ϵ_3 of Eq. (3–8.2) are real. Hence, we can write down three systems (one system for each of ϵ_1, ϵ_2, ϵ_3) of the form

$$(\epsilon_x - \epsilon_i)l + \tfrac{1}{2}\gamma_{xy}m + \tfrac{1}{2}\gamma_{xz}n = 0$$

$$\tfrac{1}{2}\gamma_{yx}l + (\epsilon_y - \epsilon_i)m + \tfrac{1}{2}\gamma_{yz}n = 0 \qquad (3\text{–}8.4)$$

$$\tfrac{1}{2}\gamma_{zx}l + \tfrac{1}{2}\gamma_{zy}m + (\epsilon_z - \epsilon_i)n = 0; \qquad i = 1, 2, 3$$

With the relation $l^2 + m^2 + n^2 = 1$ and Eq. (3–8.4), all three directions corresponding to the extremal values of ϵ_x, ϵ_y, ϵ_z and the zero values of γ_{xy}, γ_{xz}, γ_{yz} are determined. The three mutually perpendicular directions, thus determined, are the principal directions referred to the undeformed body. Line elements in these directions rotate into the principal axes of strain referred to the deformed body.

It is shown in the theory of algebraic equations that the three roots of Eq. (3–8.2) satisfy the relations

$$J_1 = \epsilon_1 + \epsilon_2 + \epsilon_3$$

$$J_2 = \epsilon_1 \epsilon_2 + \epsilon_1 \epsilon_3 + \epsilon_2 \epsilon_3 \qquad (3\text{-}8.5)$$

$$J_3 = \epsilon_1 \epsilon_2 \epsilon_3$$

Equation (3–8.5) is a special case of Eq. (3–8.3) that results when the axes (x, y, z) are the principal axes of strain $(\gamma_{xy} = \gamma_{xz} = \gamma_{yz} = 0)$. Since the principal strains are independent of the coordinate system, Eq. (3–8.5) shows that the quantities J_1, J_2, J_3 are unchanged if the coordinate axes are translated or rotated. Consequently, the quantities J_1, J_2, J_3 are called the *invariants of the strain tensor*, or briefly, the *strain invariants*.

PROBLEM SET 3-8

1 Determine the principal strains for Prob. 2, Art. 3–3.

2 Noting the condition $l^2 + m^2 + n^2 = 1$, use the Lagrange multiplier method to seek extreme values of ϵ [Eq. (3–7.2)].

3 Show that for the case of plane strain $(\epsilon_z = \gamma_{xz} = \gamma_{yz} = 0)$ the strain tensor may be represented graphically by Mohr's circle (see Art. 2–7).

3-9 Volumetric Strain

Large-deflection definition. When a body is deformed, a volume element dV is deformed into a volume element dV^*. To be consistent with Eq. (3–4.1), we *define* the volumetric strain (or volumetric magnification factor) by the equation

$$e_L = \frac{1}{2}\left[\left(\frac{dV^*}{dV}\right)^2 - 1\right] \qquad (3\text{-}9.1)$$

Since line elements in the principal directions remain perpendicular to each other under the deformation, an infinitesimal rectangular parallelepiped with edges in the principal directions remains a rectangular parallelepiped under the deformation. Consequently, Eqs. (3–4.1) and (3–9.1) yield the result

$$\left(\frac{dV^*}{dV}\right)^2 = (1 + 2\epsilon_{1L})(1 + 2\epsilon_{2L})(1 + 2\epsilon_{3L}) \qquad (3\text{-}9.2)$$

where $\epsilon_{1L}, \epsilon_{2L}, \epsilon_{3L}$ are the principal strains.

By means of Eqs. (3–8.5) and (3–9.2), the volumetric strain e_L may be expressed as follows:

$$e_L = J_1 + 2J_2 + 4J_3 \qquad (3\text{-}9.3)$$

Equation (3–9.3) determines the volumetric strain defined by Eq. (3–9.1) in terms of the components of the strain tensor, irrespective of the choice of the coordinate axes, since Eq. (3–8.3) defines J_1, J_2, J_3 in terms of the components of the strain tensor.

Engineering definition. In analogy with Eq. (3–4.3), we may also *define* volumetric strain by the equation

$$e_E = \frac{dV^* - dV}{dV} \tag{3-9.4}$$

Consequently, Eqs. (3–4.3) and (3–9.4) yield

$$\frac{dV^*}{dV} = (1 + \epsilon_{1E})(1 + \epsilon_{2E})(1 + \epsilon_{3E}) \tag{3-9.5}$$

where ϵ_{1E}, ϵ_{2E}, ϵ_{3E} denote the principal strains for small displacement theory. By means of Eqs. (3–9.4) and (3–9.5), we find

$$e_E = J_{1E} + J_{2E} + J_{3E} \tag{3-9.6}$$

where

$$J_{1E} = \epsilon_{1E} + \epsilon_{2E} + \epsilon_{3E}$$

$$J_{2E} = \epsilon_{1E}\epsilon_{2E} + \epsilon_{1E}\epsilon_{3E} + \epsilon_{2E}\epsilon_{3E} \tag{3-9.7}$$

$$J_{3E} = \epsilon_{1E}\epsilon_{2E}\epsilon_{3E}$$

Logarithmic volumetric strain. By Eqs. (3–4.8), (3–9.4), and (3–9.5), we may write

$$e_E = e^{\epsilon_{1n} + \epsilon_{2n} + \epsilon_{3n}} - 1 \tag{3-9.8}$$

where ϵ_{1n}, ϵ_{2n}, ϵ_{3n} are the natural principal strains. Hence, by analogy with Eq. (3–4.8), the logarithmic volumetric strain is

$$e_n = \log(1 + e_E) = \epsilon_{1n} + \epsilon_{2n} + \epsilon_{3n} \tag{3-9.9}$$

or

$$e_n = J_{1n} \tag{3-9.10}$$

where J_{1n} denotes the sum of the natural principal strains ϵ_{1n}, ϵ_{2n}, ϵ_{3n}.

If the principal strains are small, $\epsilon_L \to \epsilon_E \to \epsilon_n$ and $e_L \to e_E \to e_n \to J_1$.

3-10 Mean and Deviator Strain Tensor. Octahedral Strain

In analogy to the theory of stress, we define the mean strain ϵ_m by the relation (see Art. 2–6)

$$\epsilon_m = \frac{\epsilon_x + \epsilon_y + \epsilon_z}{3} = \frac{\epsilon_1 + \epsilon_2 + \epsilon_3}{3} = \frac{1}{3}J_1 \tag{3-10.1}$$

The strain tensor can be written in the form [see Eq. (3–7.3)]

$$D = D_m + D_d \tag{3-10.2}$$

where D symbolically represents the strain (deformation) tensor and where

$$D_m = \begin{pmatrix} \epsilon_m & 0 & 0 \\ 0 & \epsilon_m & 0 \\ 0 & 0 & \epsilon_m \end{pmatrix} = \epsilon_m D_1 \tag{3-10.3}$$

where

$$D_1 = \begin{pmatrix} 1 & 0 & 0 \\ 0 & 1 & 0 \\ 0 & 0 & 1 \end{pmatrix} \tag{3-10.4}$$

represents the unit tensor and where

$$D_d = \begin{pmatrix} e_x & \frac{1}{2}\gamma_{xy} & \frac{1}{2}\gamma_{xz} \\ \frac{1}{2}\gamma_{xy} & e_y & \frac{1}{2}\gamma_{yz} \\ \frac{1}{2}\gamma_{xz} & \frac{1}{2}\gamma_{yz} & e_z \end{pmatrix} \tag{3-10.5}$$

where

$$e_x = \epsilon_x - \epsilon_m, \qquad e_y = \epsilon_y - \epsilon_m, \qquad e_z = \epsilon_z - \epsilon_m \tag{3-10.6}$$

The strain tensor D_m is called the *mean strain tensor*. The tensor D_d is called the *deviator stain tensor*, in analogy to the stress tensor T_d [Eq. (2-6.4)]. Accordingly, the components $e_x, e_y, e_z, \frac{1}{2}\gamma_{xy}, \frac{1}{2}\gamma_{xz}, \frac{1}{2}\gamma_{yz}$ are called the components of the deviator strain tensor.

If (x, y, z) are principal axes of strain,

$$\epsilon_x = \epsilon_1, \quad \epsilon_y = \epsilon_2, \quad \epsilon_z = \epsilon_3; \qquad \gamma_{xy} = \gamma_{xz} = \gamma_{yz} = 0$$

and Eq. (3-10.2) is simplified accordingly. Then, application of Eq. (3-8.5) to Eqs. (3-10.3) and (3-10.5) yields the following invariants for D_m and D_d:

For D_m:

$$J_{1m} = J_1 = 3\epsilon_m$$
$$J_{2m} = \tfrac{1}{3}J_1^2 = 3\epsilon_m^2 \tag{3-10.7}$$
$$J_{3m} = \tfrac{1}{27}J_1^3 = \epsilon_m^3$$

For D_d:

$$J_{1d} = 0$$
$$J_{2d} = J_2 - \tfrac{1}{3}J_1^2$$
$$= -\tfrac{1}{6}[(\epsilon_1 - \epsilon_2)^2 + (\epsilon_2 - \epsilon_3)^2 + (\epsilon_3 - \epsilon_1)^2]$$
$$= -\tfrac{1}{6}[(e_1 - e_2)^2 + (e_2 - e_3)^2 + (e_3 - e_1)^2] \tag{3-10.8}$$
$$J_{3d} = \tfrac{1}{27}(2\epsilon_1 - \epsilon_2 - \epsilon_3)(2\epsilon_2 - \epsilon_3 - \epsilon_1)(2\epsilon_3 - \epsilon_1 - \epsilon_2)$$
$$= (\epsilon_1 - \epsilon_m)(\epsilon_2 - \epsilon_m)(\epsilon_3 - \epsilon_m)$$
$$= e_1 e_2 e_3$$

Octahedral strains. Analogous to the concept of octahedral stress, we have the concept of octahedral strain.

For example, consider the octahedral planes defined by normals with direction cosines which satisfy the relations $l^2 = m^2 = n^2 = \tfrac{1}{3}$, with respect to principal strain axes. Then, Eq. (3-4.2) or Eq. (3-4.5) yields the strain of a line element in the direction of the normal to the octahedral plane:

$$\epsilon_{oct} = \frac{\epsilon_1 + \epsilon_2 + \epsilon_3}{3} = \epsilon_m \qquad (3\text{-}10.9)$$

The strain ϵ_{oct} is called the octahedral strain. Similarly, the shearing strain between an octahedral plane and its normal is

$$\gamma_{oct} = \tfrac{2}{3}\sqrt{(\epsilon_1 - \epsilon_2)^2 + (\epsilon_1 - \epsilon_3)^2 + (\epsilon_2 - \epsilon_3)^2} \qquad (3\text{-}10.10)$$

The shearing strain γ_{oct} is called the octahedral shearing strain. It plays a significant role in certain theories of plasticity.[11]

Problem. Derive Eq. (3–10.10).

3-11 Rotation of a Volume Element

Consider an infinitesimal volume element surrounding any particle P of a continuous medium. Under a deformation, this infinitesimal volume is altered not only in position, but also in dimensions and shape. We define the "rotation of the volume element" to be the mean value of the rotations experienced by the set of infinitesimal line elements emanating from point P. Accordingly, in our present discussion, we are concerned with only rotations of line elements. Hence, we let the position P^* of the particle in the deformed medium coincide with its position P in the undeformed medium.

Initially, we consider the rotation of a single infinitesimal line element PQ. First, we let the line PQ lie in the (x, y) plane. After the deformation, the line coincides with the direction P^*Q^* (or PQ^*) not necessarily in the (x, y) plane. (See Fig. 3–11.1.)

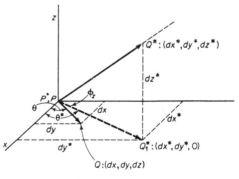

Figure 3-11.1

The orthogonal projection of the vector P^*Q^* on the (x, y) plane is $P^*Q_1^*$. The angle $\phi_z = \theta^* - \theta$ between lines PQ and $P^*Q_1^*$ is understood to be the rotation of line element PQ about the z axis. Accordingly, by Fig. 3–11.1, we have the relations

$$\tan \theta = \frac{dy}{dx}, \qquad \tan \theta^* = \frac{dy^*}{dx^*} \qquad (3\text{-}11.1)$$

Furthermore, the deformation is defined by the equations $x^* = x^*(x, y, z)$, $y^* = y^*(x, y, z)$, $z^* = z^*(x, y, z)$, with the understanding that (x^*, y^*, z^*)

---

[11]V. V. Sokolovski, *Theory of Plasticity* (in Russian) (Moscow: 1950). See also references given in Art. 2–6.

vanish at $x = y = z = 0$. Since vector $\mathbf{PQ}$ lies in the (x, y) plane, $\mathbf{PQ} = (dx, dy, 0)$. Taking the total differentials of (x^*, y^*, z^*), we have

$$dx^* = \frac{\partial x^*}{\partial x} dx + \frac{\partial x^*}{\partial y} dy + \frac{\partial x^*}{\partial z} dz$$

$$dy^* = \frac{\partial y^*}{\partial x} dx + \frac{\partial y^*}{\partial y} dy + \frac{\partial y^*}{\partial z} dz \qquad (3\text{-}11.2)$$

$$dz^* = \frac{\partial z^*}{\partial x} dx + \frac{\partial z^*}{\partial y} dy + \frac{\partial z^*}{\partial z} dz$$

Since $x^* = x + u$, $y^* = y + v$, $z^* = z + w$, Eqs. (3–11.2) yield

$$dx^* = (1 + u_x)\, dx + u_y\, dy + u_z\, dz$$
$$dy^* = v_x\, dx + (1 + v_y)\, dy + v_z\, dz \qquad (3\text{-}11.3)$$
$$dz^* = w_x\, dx + w_y\, dy + (1 + w_z)\, dz$$

where subscripts (x, y, z) on (u, v, w) denote partial derivatives.

Let us use temporarily the notation

$$e_x = u_x, \qquad\qquad e_y = v_y, \qquad\qquad e_z = w_z$$
$$e_{yz} = (w_y + v_z), \qquad e_{zx} = (u_z + w_x), \qquad e_{xy} = (v_x + u_y) \qquad (3\text{-}11.4)$$

Furthermore, let

$$\omega_x = \tfrac{1}{2}(w_y - v_z), \qquad \omega_y = \tfrac{1}{2}(u_z - w_x), \qquad \omega_z = \tfrac{1}{2}(v_x - u_y) \qquad (3\text{-}11.5)$$

Equations (3–11.3), (3–11.4), and (3–11.5) yield, with $\mathbf{PQ} = (dx, dy, 0)$,

$$dx^* = (1 + e_x)\, dx + (\tfrac{1}{2}e_{xy} - \omega_z)\, dy$$
$$dy^* = (\tfrac{1}{2}e_{xy} + \omega_z)\, dx + (1 + e_y)\, dy \qquad (3\text{-}11.6)$$

Consequently, Eqs. (3–11.1) and (3–11.6) yield the formula

$$\tan \theta^* = \frac{(\omega_z + \tfrac{1}{2}e_{xy}) + (1 + e_y) \tan \theta}{1 + e_x + (\tfrac{1}{2}e_{xy} - \omega_z) \tan \theta} \qquad (3\text{-}11.7)$$

The angle of rotation of the line element PQ about the z axis is $\phi_z = \theta^* - \theta$. Using the formula for the tangent of the difference of two angles,[12] we obtain

$$\tan \phi_z = \frac{\omega_z + \tfrac{1}{2}e_{xy} \cos 2\theta + \tfrac{1}{2}(e_y - e_x) \sin 2\theta}{1 + e_x \cos^2 \theta + e_y \sin^2 \theta + \tfrac{1}{2}e_{xy} \sin 2\theta} \qquad (3\text{-}11.8)$$

Equation (3–11.8) expresses the rotation ϕ_z of line element PQ about the z axis in terms of $\tan \phi_z$. If e_x, e_y, e_{xy}, and ω_z are small compared to 1, the numerator in Eq. (3–11.8) is a small quantity compared to 1. Also, the denominator is approximately 1. Hence, ϕ_z is a small angle; it is approxi-

---

[12]

$$\tan \phi_z = \frac{\tan \theta^* - \tan \theta}{1 + \tan \theta^* \tan \theta}$$

mately equal to its tangent. Consequently, to first powers in quantities small compared to 1, we may approximate Eq. (3–11.8) as follows:

$$\phi_z = \omega_z + \tfrac{1}{2}e_{xy}\cos 2\theta + \tfrac{1}{2}(e_y - e_x)\sin 2\theta \qquad (3\text{–}11.9)$$

The rotation of the volume element is defined to be the mean value of ϕ_z (denoted by $\bar{\phi}_z$). The mean value $\bar{\phi}_z$ is defined by

$$\bar{\phi}_z = \frac{1}{2\pi}\int_0^{2\pi} \phi_z\, d\theta \qquad (3\text{–}11.10)$$

Equations (3–11.9) and (3–11.10) yield

$$\bar{\phi}_z = \omega_z \qquad (3\text{–}11.11)$$

In an analogous manner, subject to the same restrictions as outlined above, it may be shown that the mean rotations $\bar{\phi}_x$ and $\bar{\phi}_y$ of the volume element about the x and y axes are ω_x and ω_y [see Eq. (3–11.5)]. Therefore, the quantities $(\omega_x, \omega_y, \omega_z)$ may be interpreted as the components of the rotation vector for a volume element, provided $e_x, e_y, e_z, \ldots, \omega_x, \omega_y, \omega_z$ [Eqs. (3–11.4) and (3–11.5)] are small compared to 1.

In Gibbs vector notation, Eq. (3–11.5) may be written

$$\boldsymbol{\omega} = \tfrac{1}{2}\operatorname{curl}\mathbf{q} \qquad (3\text{–}11.12)$$

in which $\boldsymbol{\omega}$ denotes the vector $(\omega_x, \omega_y, \omega_z)$ and $\mathbf{q}$ denotes the displacement vector (u, v, w). In other words, the rotation of a volume element is one-half the curl of the displacement vector. This conclusion, of course, is only an approximation; it is not valid if the rotations ϕ_x, ϕ_y, ϕ_z are large. Note that in determinant notation the curl of $\mathbf{q}$ is expressed as follows:

$$\operatorname{curl}\mathbf{q} = \begin{vmatrix} \mathbf{i} & \mathbf{j} & \mathbf{k} \\ \dfrac{\partial}{\partial x} & \dfrac{\partial}{\partial y} & \dfrac{\partial}{\partial z} \\ u & v & w \end{vmatrix} \qquad (3\text{–}11.13)$$

Hence,

$$\boldsymbol{\omega} = \frac{1}{2}\begin{vmatrix} \mathbf{i} & \mathbf{j} & \mathbf{k} \\ \dfrac{\partial}{\partial x} & \dfrac{\partial}{\partial y} & \dfrac{\partial}{\partial z} \\ u & v & w \end{vmatrix} \qquad (3\text{–}11.14)$$

Equation (3–11.14) serves as a device for recalling $\omega_x, \omega_y, \omega_z$ [Eqs. (3–11.5)].

3-12 Strain Components in Terms of $(\omega_x, \omega_y, \omega_z)$. Small-displacement Theory

Using the notation of Eqs. (3–11.4) and (3–11.5), we may rewrite Eqs. (3–3.4) in the form

$$\epsilon_x = u_x + \tfrac{1}{2}(u_x^2 + v_x^2 + w_x^2)$$
$$= e_x + \tfrac{1}{2}[e_x^2 + (\tfrac{1}{2}e_{xy} + \omega_z)^2 + (\tfrac{1}{2}e_{xz} - \omega_y)^2]$$
$$\epsilon_y = v_y + \tfrac{1}{2}(u_y^2 + v_y^2 + w_y^2)$$
$$= e_y + \tfrac{1}{2}[e_y^2 + (\tfrac{1}{2}e_{xy} - \omega_z)^2 + (\tfrac{1}{2}e_{yz} + \omega_x)^2]$$
$$\epsilon_z = w_z + \tfrac{1}{2}(u_z^2 + v_z^2 + w_z^2)$$
$$= e_z + \tfrac{1}{2}[e_z^2 + (\tfrac{1}{2}e_{xz} + \omega_y)^2 + (\tfrac{1}{2}e_{yz} - \omega_x)^2]$$
$$\gamma_{xy} = u_y + v_x + u_x u_y + v_x v_y + w_x w_y$$
$$= e_{xy} + e_x(\tfrac{1}{2}e_{xy} - \omega_z) + e_y(\tfrac{1}{2}e_{xy} + \omega_z) + (\tfrac{1}{2}e_{xz} - \omega_y)(\tfrac{1}{2}e_{yz} + \omega_x)$$
$$\gamma_{xz} = u_z + w_x + u_x u_z + v_x v_z + w_x w_z$$
$$= e_{xz} + e_x(\tfrac{1}{2}e_{xz} + \omega_y) + e_z(\tfrac{1}{2}e_{xz} - \omega_y) + (\tfrac{1}{2}e_{xy} + \omega_z)(\tfrac{1}{2}e_{yz} - \omega_x)$$
$$\gamma_{yz} = v_z + w_y + u_y u_z + v_y v_z + w_y w_z$$
$$= e_{yz} + e_y(\tfrac{1}{2}e_{yz} - \omega_x) + e_z(\tfrac{1}{2}e_{yz} + \omega_x) + (\tfrac{1}{2}e_{xy} - \omega_z)(\tfrac{1}{2}e_{xz} + \omega_y)$$

$$(3\text{-}12.1)$$

Equation (3–12.1) represents the strain components $\epsilon_x, \epsilon_y, \ldots$, in terms of the quantities $(\omega_x, \omega_y, \omega_z)$ and the quantities $e_x, e_y, \ldots$ [see Eqs. (3–11.4) and (3–11.5)]. To examine the reduction of Eq. (3–12.1) to the classical approximation of small-displacement theory, we rewrite the first of Eqs. (3–12.1) in the form

$$(1 + 2\epsilon_x) = (1 + e_x)^2 + (\tfrac{1}{2}e_{xy} + \omega_z)^2 + (\tfrac{1}{2}e_{xz} - \omega_y)^2 \qquad (3\text{-}12.2)$$

Next, we note that Eq. (3–12.2) is satisfied identically by the relations

$$\frac{1 + e_x}{\sqrt{1 + 2\epsilon_x}} = \cos \alpha_1$$

$$\frac{\tfrac{1}{2}e_{xy} + \omega_z}{\sqrt{1 + 2\epsilon_x}} = \sin \alpha_1 \cos \beta_1 \qquad (3\text{-}12.3)$$

$$\frac{\tfrac{1}{2}e_{xz} - \omega_y}{\sqrt{1 + 2\epsilon_x}} = \sin \alpha_1 \sin \beta_1$$

where $\cos \alpha_1 = l^*$ is the direction cosine with respect to the x axis of a line element with initial direction cosines $l = 1$, $m = n = 0$ in the undeformed state [see the first of Eqs. (3–5.7)]. Hence, the angle α_1 denotes a rotation. The angle β_1 is an intermediate variable of transformation. It does not enter into the principal results of the argument to follow.

Now, if the rotation α_1 is small, $l^* = \cos \alpha_1 \approx 1 - (\alpha_1^2/2)$. Thus, for small rotations, by the first of Eqs. (3–12.3), we obtain

$$\frac{1 + e_x}{\sqrt{1 + 2\epsilon_x}} \approx 1 - \frac{\alpha_1^2}{2} \qquad (3\text{-}12.4)$$

Proceeding in a similar manner, the second and third equations of Eq. (3–12.1) yield

$$\frac{1 + e_y}{\sqrt{1 + 2\epsilon_y}} \approx 1 - \frac{\alpha_2^2}{2}, \qquad \frac{1 + e_z}{\sqrt{1 + 2\epsilon_z}} \approx 1 - \frac{\alpha_3^2}{2} \qquad (3\text{-}12.5)$$

where (α_2, α_3) denote the angles of rotation of lines initially directed along the y and z axes, respectively.

For strains $(\epsilon_x, \epsilon_y, \epsilon_z)$ small compared to 1,

$$(1 + 2\epsilon_x)^{1/2} = 1 + \epsilon_x - \tfrac{1}{2}\epsilon_x^2 + \cdots \qquad (3\text{-}12.6)$$

$$\text{- - -, - - -,}$$

where the dashes denote similar expressions for $(1 + 2\epsilon_y)^{1/2}$, $(1 + 2\epsilon_z)^{1/2}$. Substituting Eqs. (3-12.6) into Eqs. (3-12.4) and (3-12.5), we obtain to second-degree terms in the rotations

$$\epsilon_x - e_x \approx \frac{\alpha_1^2}{2}$$

$$\epsilon_y - e_y \approx \frac{\alpha_2^2}{2} \qquad (3\text{-}12.7)$$

$$\epsilon_z - e_z \approx \frac{\alpha_3^2}{2}$$

Equation (3-12.7) indicate that if strains are small compared to 1, and if rotations are sufficiently small [so that Eqs. (3-12.4) and (3-12.5) are valid approximations], the differences between the strains $(\epsilon_x, \epsilon_y, \epsilon_z)$ and the quantities (e_x, e_y, e_z), respectively, are of the order of the squares of the angles of rotation.

To examine the reduction of the last three equations of Eqs. (3-12.1), we note that in a manner analogous to the relations (3-12.3) the second of Eqs. (3-12.1) yields the relations

$$\frac{\tfrac{1}{2}e_{xy} - \omega_z}{\sqrt{1 + 2\epsilon_y}} = \sin \alpha_2 \sin \beta_2$$

$$\frac{1 + e_y}{\sqrt{1 + 2\epsilon_y}} = \cos \alpha_2 \qquad (3\text{-}12.8)$$

$$\frac{\tfrac{1}{2}e_{yz} + \omega_x}{\sqrt{1 + 2\epsilon_y}} = \sin \alpha_2 \cos \beta_2$$

Then, by Eqs. (3-12.3) and (3-12.8) and the expression for γ_{xy} [see the fourth of Eqs. (3-12.1)], we find

$$\frac{\gamma_{xy}}{\sqrt{(1 + 2\epsilon_x)(1 + 2\epsilon_y)}} = \cos \alpha_1 \sin \alpha_2 \sin \beta_2 + \cos \alpha_2 \sin \alpha_1 \cos \beta_1$$

$$+ \sin \alpha_1 \sin \alpha_2 \sin \beta_1 \cos \beta_2 \qquad (3\text{-}12.9)$$

Now, if ϵ_x and ϵ_y are small compared to 1, and if the angles of rotation α_1 and α_2 are small, Eq. (3-12.9) yields the approximation

$$\gamma_{xy} \approx \alpha_2 \sin \beta_2 + \alpha_1 \cos \beta_1 + \alpha_1 \alpha_2 \sin \beta_1 \cos \beta_2 \qquad (3\text{-}12.10)$$

Also, Eqs. (3–12.3) and (3–12.8) yield

$$\frac{1}{2} e_{xy} + \omega_z \approx \alpha_1 \cos \beta_1$$
$$\frac{1}{2} e_{xy} - \omega_z \approx \alpha_2 \sin \beta_2 \qquad (3\text{-}12.11)$$

Finally, Eqs. (3–12.10) and (3–12.11) yield

$$\gamma_{xy} - e_{xy} \approx \alpha_1 \alpha_2 \sin \beta_1 \cos \beta_2 \qquad (3\text{-}12.12)$$

By an entirely similar argument, the last two of Eqs. (3–12.1) yield

$$\gamma_{xz} - e_{xz} \approx \alpha_1 \alpha_3 \cos \beta_1 \sin \beta_3$$
$$\gamma_{yz} - e_{yz} \approx \alpha_2 \alpha_3 \sin \beta_2 \cos \beta_3 \qquad (3\text{-}12.13)$$

Equations (3–12.12) and (3–12.13) show that for small strains and small rotations, $(\gamma_{xy}, \gamma_{xz}, \gamma_{yz})$ differ from (e_{xy}, e_{xz}, e_{yz}), respectively, by second-degree terms in the angles of rotations.

Consequently, the squares of the terms e_x, e_{xy}, e_{xz} can be neglected in the expression for ϵ_x [see Eq. (3–12.1)], since these terms yield second-degree terms in ϵ_x and fourth-degree terms in α_1, α_3. Hence,

$$\epsilon_x \approx e_x + \tfrac{1}{2}(e_{xy}\omega_z - e_{xz}\omega_y + \omega_y^2 + \omega_z^2) \qquad (3\text{-}12.14)$$

Furthermore, substitution for e_{xy}, e_{xz} [see Eqs. (3–12.11), (3–12.12), and (3–12.13)] yields square terms in the strains and cubic terms in the rotations. Hence, discarding these terms, we obtain the approximation

$$\epsilon_x \approx e_x + \tfrac{1}{2}(\omega_y^2 + \omega_z^2) \qquad (3\text{-}12.15)$$

By an analogous argument,

$$\epsilon_y \approx e_y + \tfrac{1}{2}(\omega_x^2 + \omega_z^2)$$
$$\epsilon_z \approx e_z + \tfrac{1}{2}(\omega_x^2 + \omega_y^2)$$
$$\gamma_{xy} \approx e_{xy} - \omega_x \omega_y \qquad (3\text{-}12.16)$$
$$\gamma_{xz} \approx e_{xz} - \omega_x \omega_z$$
$$\gamma_{yz} \approx e_{yz} - \omega_y \omega_z$$

Finally, if the squares and products of $\omega_x, \omega_y, \omega_z$ may be neglected with respect to the strains, the ω terms may be discarded from Eqs. (3–12.16).

Therefore, if the strains and the angles of rotation are small compared to 1, and if the squares of the rotations are small compared to the strains, we may neglect the quadratic terms in Eq. (3–12.1) in comparison to the linear terms. This is equivalent to discarding the quadratic terms in Eq. (3–3.4). Hence, we obtain the approximations

$$\epsilon_x \approx e_x = u_x = \frac{\partial u}{\partial x}$$

$$\epsilon_y \approx e_y = v_y = \frac{\partial v}{\partial y}$$

$$\epsilon_z \approx e_z = w_z = \frac{\partial w}{\partial z}$$

$$\gamma_{xy} \approx e_{xy} = v_x + u_y = \frac{\partial v}{\partial x} + \frac{\partial u}{\partial y}$$

$$\gamma_{xz} \approx e_{xz} = w_x + u_z = \frac{\partial w}{\partial x} + \frac{\partial u}{\partial z}$$

$$\gamma_{yz} \approx e_{yz} = w_y + v_z = \frac{\partial w}{\partial y} + \frac{\partial v}{\partial z}$$

(3–12.17)

These approximations, which are the basis of the classical theory of elasticity, imply that the strains and the rotations are small compared to unity, and the rotations are so small that quadratic terms in the rotations may be neglected in comparison to strains [see Eqs. (3–12.1) and (3–3.4)]. The latter conditions are not satisfied by flexible bodies, such as thin rods and plates. For these bodies, the angular displacement may greatly exceed the strains, and we are not justified in discarding the ω terms in Eqs. (3–12.1). Consequently, the classical small-deflection theory must be used with caution; it is applicable to massive bodies, but when applied to thin flexible bodies, it may give results that are seriously in error. For example, the use of Eqs. (3–12.17) may lead to serious errors in the theory of shells.[13]

Problem. Let $\epsilon_x = \epsilon_y = \epsilon_z = \gamma_{xy} = \gamma_{xz} = \gamma_{yz} = 0$, as given by Eqs. (3–12.17). Solve the resulting equations for (u, v, w); that is, derive the displacement components for a rigid-body displacement.

3-13 Special Types of Strain

Rigid displacements. The simplest type of displacement vector is $\mathbf{q} = c$, where c is a constant. This type of motion defines a translation of the body. There is a second group of rigid motions, called "rotations." These two groups (translations and rotations) combine to form the group of all rigid displacements, for any rigid displacement consists of an angular displacement about an arbitrary axis in a fixed direction, plus a translation that depends on the choice of this axis (see Chasles' theorem, Art. 3–1). We may fix the axis by requiring that it pass through the origin. For a rigid displacement, the vector $\mathbf{q}$ may be shown to be a linear function of the coordinates; however, it is not the most general linear point function. In fact since any rigid displacement

[13]A. E. H. Love, *Mathematical Theory of Elasticity,* 4th ed. (New York: Dover Publications, Inc., 1944).

can be effected by a screw motion,[14] there always exists a system of cylindrical coordinates such that $u = 0$, $v = cr$, $w = k$, where c and k are constants, and (u, v, w) are in the r, θ, z directions, respectively.

Simple extension. A type of displacement vector **q** which is a linear function of the coordinates is defined by

$$u = 0, \qquad v = 0, \qquad w = kz \qquad (3\text{-}13.1)$$

where k is a constant. This displacement is called a simple extension parallel to the z axis. Under the deformation, all line elements parallel to the z axis undergo the same strain k. If k is negative, the deformation is called a *contraction*.

Dilatation. The resultant of three simple extensions parallel to the three coordinates axes is called a *dilatation* along these axes. A dilatation along the coordinate axes is then defined by the displacement function

$$u = k_1 x, \qquad v = k_2 y, \qquad w = k_3 z \qquad (3\text{-}13.2)$$

A dilatation is said to be *simple* if all the k's are equal. In spherical coordinates, (r, θ, ϕ), the displacement function of a simple dilatation is

$$u = kr, \qquad v = 0, \qquad w = 0, \qquad k_1 = k_2 = k_3 = k \qquad (3\text{-}13.3)$$

where (u, v, w) are in the r, θ, ϕ directions, respectively. This type of deformation occurs when an isotropic body is subjected to uniform external pressure.

Another important type of dilatation is that for which

$$k_1 = k_2 = C \qquad \text{and} \qquad k_3 = K \neq C \qquad (3\text{-}13.4)$$

In cylindrical coordinates, the displacement function for this dilatation is

$$u = Cr, \qquad v = 0, \qquad w = Kz \qquad (3\text{-}13.5)$$

where (u, v, w) are in the (r, θ, z) directions, respectively. This type of deformation occurs when a cylindrical or prismatic bar is subjected to uniform tension or compression. In all cases, for real materials K and C have opposite signs. The ratio $-C/K$ is a characteristic constant of the material, called Poisson's ratio. Unlike Young's modulus, it is dimensionless. For most metals, Poisson's ratio lies in the range $\frac{1}{4}$ to $\frac{1}{3}$. For real materials Poisson's ratio lies in the range 0 to $\frac{1}{2}$.

Simple shear. A simple shear parallel to the xy plane and along the x axis is said to exist in a body when the displacement function is of the form

$$u = kz, \qquad v = 0, \qquad w = 0 \qquad (3\text{-}13.6)$$

The constant k is called the *shearing strain*. It is the tangent of the angle through which a line parallel to the z axis is turned by the deformation.

---

[14]E. Whittaker, *A Treatise on the Analytical Dynamics of Particles and Rigid Bodies*, 4th ed. (New York: Dover Publications, Inc., 1944).

Homogeneous strain. Disregarding an irrelevant translation, the several special types of strain that have been discussed, and any combination of them, are all included in the category of *homogeneous strain* defined by the general linear homogeneous displacement function

$$u = a_{11}x + a_{21}y + a_{31}z$$
$$v = a_{12}x + a_{22}y + a_{32}z \qquad (3\text{-}13.7)$$
$$w = a_{13}x + a_{23}y + a_{33}z$$

This type of strain is said to be homogeneous because the state of strain does not vary throughout the body; i.e., the components ϵ_x, ϵ_y, ϵ_z, $\frac{1}{2}\gamma_{xz}$, $\frac{1}{2}\gamma_{xy}$, $\frac{1}{2}\gamma_{yz}$ of the strain tensor are constants. We proceed to examine the geometrical characteristics of homogeneous strain.

Preservation of straight lines and planes. The general equation of a straight line is

$$x = a_1 + sb_1, \qquad y = a_2 + sb_2, \qquad z = a_3 + sb_3 \qquad (3\text{-}13.8)$$

in which $a_1, a_2, a_3, b_1, b_2, b_3$ are constants and s is a parameter. Under the deformation, this line is transformed into the line

$$X = x + u, \qquad Y = y + v, \qquad Z = z + w \qquad (3\text{-}13.9)$$

Hence, by Eq. (3-13.7) and (3-13.9),

$$X = (1 + a_{11})x + a_{21}y + a_{31}z$$
$$Y = a_{12}x + (1 + a_{22})y + a_{32}z \qquad (3\text{-}13.10)$$
$$Z = a_{13}x + a_{23}y + (1 + a_{33})z$$

Substitution of Eq. (3-13.8) into Eq. (3-13.10) yields

$$X = (a_1 + a_{11}a_1 + a_{21}a_2 + a_{31}a_3) + (b_1 + a_{11}b_1 + a_{21}b_2 + a_{31}b_3)s$$
$$Y = (a_2 + a_{12}a_1 + a_{22}a_2 + a_{32}a_3) + (b_2 + a_{12}b_1 + a_{22}b_2 + a_{32}b_3)s \qquad (3\text{-}13.11)$$
$$Z = (a_3 + a_{13}a_1 + a_{23}a_2 + a_{33}a_3) + (b_3 + a_{13}b_1 + a_{23}b_2 + a_{33}b_3)s$$

Equation (3-13.11) is a linear equation in s. Accordingly, it is the equation of a straight line. Thus, it is proved that straight lines [Eq. (3-13.8)] remain straight lines [Eq. (3-13.11)] under a homogeneous deformation. Since a plane is generated by all straight lines through two given non-skew straight lines, planes also remain planes under a homogeneous deformation.

Similarly, it may be shown that under a state of homogeneous strain parallel lines remain parallel; hence, parallel planes remain parallel, and any parallelepiped remains a parallelepiped, although its size and its angles may change.

Furthermore, under homogeneous strain a spherical surface within the body is deformed into another quadratic surface. For example, the spherical surface is deformed into an ellipsoidal surface, or a spherical surface, distinct from the initial spherical surface.

3-14 Compatibility Conditions of the Classical Theory of Small Displacements

The six strain components $\epsilon_x, \epsilon_y, \epsilon_z, \gamma_{xy}, \gamma_{xz}, \gamma_{yz}$ cannot be given arbitrarily as functions of x, y, z, since they are determined completely by the three displacement components (u, v, w). Hence, there must exist relations between the strain components since they are not independent functions.

For small displacements, Eqs. (3–12.17) yield the equations

$$\frac{\partial^2 \epsilon_x}{\partial y^2} = \frac{\partial^3 u}{\partial x \partial y^2}$$

$$\frac{\partial^2 \epsilon_y}{\partial x^2} = \frac{\partial^3 v}{\partial x^2 \partial y}$$

$$\frac{\partial^2 \gamma_{xy}}{\partial x \partial y} = \frac{\partial^3 u}{\partial x \partial y^2} + \frac{\partial^3 v}{\partial x^2 \partial y}$$

Hence,

$$\frac{\partial^2 \epsilon_x}{\partial y^2} + \frac{\partial^2 \epsilon_y}{\partial x^2} = \frac{\partial^2 \gamma_{xy}}{\partial x \partial y} \qquad (3\text{–}14.1)$$

Since Eqs. (3–12.17) are cyclically permutable in (x, y, z), the permutations $(x, y) \to (x, z)$ and $(x, z) \to (y, z)$ yield

$$\frac{\partial^2 \epsilon_x}{\partial z^2} + \frac{\partial^2 \epsilon_z}{\partial x^2} = \frac{\partial^2 \gamma_{xz}}{\partial x \partial z} \qquad (3\text{–}14.2)$$

$$\frac{\partial^2 \epsilon_y}{\partial z^2} + \frac{\partial^2 \epsilon_z}{\partial y^2} = \frac{\partial^2 \gamma_{yz}}{\partial y \partial z} \qquad (3\text{–}14.3)$$

Also, by Eqs. (3–12.17),

$$\frac{2\partial^2 \epsilon_x}{\partial y \partial z} = \frac{\partial}{\partial x}\left(-\frac{\partial \gamma_{yz}}{\partial x} + \frac{\partial \gamma_{xz}}{\partial y} + \frac{\partial \gamma_{xy}}{\partial z}\right) \qquad (3\text{–}14.4)$$

$$\frac{2\partial^2 \epsilon_y}{\partial x \partial z} = \frac{\partial}{\partial y}\left(-\frac{\partial \gamma_{xz}}{\partial y} + \frac{\partial \gamma_{yz}}{\partial x} + \frac{\partial \gamma_{xy}}{\partial z}\right) \qquad (3\text{–}14.5)$$

$$\frac{2\partial^2 \epsilon_z}{\partial x \partial y} = \frac{\partial}{\partial z}\left(-\frac{\partial \gamma_{xy}}{\partial z} + \frac{\partial \gamma_{xz}}{\partial y} + \frac{\partial \gamma_{yz}}{\partial x}\right) \qquad (3\text{–}14.6)$$

The differential relations given above are called the *conditions of compatibility*. The above demonstration proves the *necessity* of the conditions of compatibility. Various proofs have been given that they are also *sufficient* to insure the existence of functions (u, v, w) related to $(\epsilon_x, \epsilon_y, \ldots, \gamma_{yz})$ by Eq. (3–12.17).[15]

---

[15]See, for example, Love, *Mathematical Theory of Elasticity*.

PROBLEM SET 3-14

1 Neglecting quadratic terms in (u, v, w) in Eq. (3–3.4), [see Eq. (3–12.17)], determine whether or not $\epsilon_x - k(x^2 + y^2)$, $\epsilon_y - k(x^2 + y^2)$, $\gamma_{xy} = k'xyz$, $\epsilon_z = \gamma_{xz} = \gamma_{yz} = 0$ is a possible state of strain where k, k' are small positive constants.

2 Repeat Prob. 1 for

$$\epsilon_x = k(x^2 + y^2)z, \quad \epsilon_y = k(y^2 + z^2), \quad \gamma_{xy} = k'xyz,$$
$$\gamma_{xz} = k(x^2 + y^2), \quad \epsilon_z = \gamma_{yz} = 0$$

Review Problems

R-1 The classical theory of elasticity yields the following displacement components for a beam subjected to pure bending: $u = -k_1xy$, $v = k_2(x^2 + vy^2 - vz^2)$, $w = k_3vyz$. Compute the rotations of a volume element in the beam with respect to (x, y, z) axes, respectively.

R-2 The displacement components (u, v, w) are given by the relations $u = x - 2y$, $v = 3x + 2y$, $w = 5z$. Verify that this displacement vector is continuously possible for a deformable body. Determine the principal strains. Determine one of the principal axes of strain in the undeformed medium. In the deformed medium.

R-3 For a bar stretched by its own weight, the classical theory of elasticity yields the following displacement components:

$$u = -C_1zx, \quad v = -C_1zy, \quad w = \tfrac{1}{2}C_1(x^2 + y^2) + C_2z^2 + C_3$$

where C_1, C_2, C_3 are constants. Compute the rotations of a volume element in the body with respect to (x, y, z) axes, respectively.

R-4 A body is strained so that $\epsilon_x = \epsilon_y = \epsilon_z = \gamma_{xy} = \gamma_{xz} = \gamma_{yz} = e$, where e is a constant. Determine the principal strains. Hence, write down the three systems of equations which determine the principal directions.

R-5 The rectangular cartesian displacement components of an arbitrary point in a body are given by the relations

$$u = a_1x + a_2y + a_3z$$
$$v = b_1x + b_2y + b_3z$$
$$w = c_1x + c_2y + c_3z$$

Show that a spherical surface with center at the origin of coordinate system (x, y, z) is transformed into a quadratic surface. Show that if $\epsilon_x = \epsilon_y = \epsilon_z$, the spherical volume element enclosed in the spherical surface remains spherical under the deformation.

R-6 A body is strained so that $\epsilon_x = 0.002$, $\epsilon_y = -0.002$, $\epsilon_z = 0$, $\gamma_{xz} = 0.004$, $\gamma_{xy} = 0$, $\gamma_{yz} = 0$. Derive equations that determine the directions of the sides of a cubic element in the body whose angles are preserved under the strain.

R-7 Given: $\epsilon_x = A(L - x)$, $\epsilon_y = B(L - x)$, $\gamma_{xy} = 0$, $u = u(x, y)$, $v = v(x, y)$, $w = 0$, $A, B,$ and L are constants. Use linearized strain-displacement relations to determine the displacement components u and v for the case $u(0, 0) = v(0, 0) = 0$.

R-8 Let axes (x, y, z) be principal axes of strain. Let principal strains be $\epsilon_1, \epsilon_2, \epsilon_3$. Two perpendicular line elements (element 1 and element 2) lie in the octahedral plane in the first octant of the coordinate system. Element 1 is parallel to the (x, y) plane. Determine the direction cosines of elements 1 and 2. Determine Γ between elements 1 and 2 in terms of $(\epsilon_1, \epsilon_2, \epsilon_3)$. Determine the magnification of element 1 in terms of $\epsilon_1, \epsilon_2, \epsilon_3$.

R-9 The strains of a deformed body are defined by the equations $\epsilon_x = \nu C(l - z)$, $\epsilon_y = \nu C(l - z)$, $\epsilon_z = -C(l - z)$, $\gamma_{xy} = \gamma_{xz} = \gamma_{yz} = 0$; ν, C, l are constants, and C is small. Derive formulas for the displacement components (u, v, w).

R-10 The following strains have been measured at a point on the free (unloaded) surface of a body:

Direction	Angle ϕ	Strain
1	$0°$	0.002
2	$120°$	0.002
3	$240°$	−0.001

Determine the principal strains in the plane of the surface and the principal directions of strain.

Appendix: Theory of Strain in Index Notation

This appendix presents the theory of strain in index notation. For brevity, we do not discuss in detail the physical significance of the results (see Chapter 3). With some reference to the discussion of Chapter 3 and to Arts. 1–17 through 1–21, the reader may wish to develop the theory of strain directly in index notation, thus by-passing the algebraic development in Chapter 3.

A3-1 Strain of Any Line Element. Strain Components

The three components u_α of displacement, taken collectively [see Eqs. (3–2.5) and (3–2.6)], are called the displacement vector. A point (x, y, z) in index notation is denoted by x_i, where $x_i = (x_1, x_2, x_3)$ (Art. 1–17). Hence, when a body is deformed, a point $P: (x_1, x_2, x_3)$ is displaced to the point $P^*: (\xi_1, \xi_2, \xi_3)$. Therefore, the displacement u_α of point P is defined by

$$u_\alpha = \xi_\alpha - x_\alpha \qquad (A3\text{--}1.1)$$

Similarly, a point $Q: (x + dx)$ is displaced to the point $Q^*: (\xi + d\xi)$, where the notation $(x + dx)$ stands for $x_1 + dx_1, x_2 + dx_2, x_3 + dx_3$, and similarly for $(\xi + d\xi)$, The line element PQ has infinitesimal length ds, and line element P^*Q^* has infinitesimal length ds^*. In general, under the deformation line element PQ is elongated or shortened. Hence, $ds^* \neq ds$, except for a rigid-body displacement. Hence, let us calculate the difference $(ds^*)^2 - (ds)^2$. We assume that the displacement u_α is a known function of the coordinate x_α. (We may equally well assume that u_α is a known function of coordinates ξ_α; see Art. 3–3.) Letting the lengths of the vectors $PQ = (dx_1, dx_2, dx_3)$ and $P^*Q^* = (d\xi_1, d\xi_2, d\xi_3)$ be denoted by ds and ds^*, we write

$$ds^2 = dx_\alpha dx_\alpha = \delta_{\alpha\beta}\, dx_\alpha\, dx_\beta$$
$$(ds^*)^2 = d\xi_\alpha\, d\xi_\alpha = \delta_{\alpha\beta}\, d\xi_\alpha\, d\xi_\beta \tag{A3–1.2}$$

where $\delta_{\alpha\beta}$ denotes Kronecker's delta (Art. 1–20).

By Eq. (A3–1.1) and the definition of total differential, we write

$$d\xi_\alpha = \frac{\partial \xi_\alpha}{\partial x_\beta}\, dx_\beta \tag{A3–1.3}$$

Substitution of Eq. (A3–1.3) into Eq. (A3–1.2) yields

$$(ds^*)^2 - ds^2 = 2\epsilon_{\alpha\beta}\, dx_\alpha\, dx_\beta \tag{A3–1.4}$$

where

$$2\epsilon_{\alpha\beta} = \frac{\partial \xi_\theta}{\partial x_\alpha}\frac{\partial \xi_\theta}{\partial x_\beta} - \delta_{\alpha\beta} \tag{A3–1.5}$$

By Eq. (A3–1.1), we find

$$\frac{\partial \xi_\theta}{\partial x_\alpha}\frac{\partial \xi_\theta}{\partial x_\beta} = (\delta_{\theta\alpha} + u_{\theta,\alpha})(\delta_{\theta\beta} + u_{\theta,\beta})$$
$$= \delta_{\alpha\beta} + u_{\alpha,\beta} + u_{\beta,\alpha} + u_{\theta,\alpha}u_{\theta,\beta} \tag{A3–1.6}$$

where $u_{\alpha,\beta} = \partial u_\alpha/\partial x_\beta$.

Substituting Eq. (A3–1.6) into Eq. (A3–1.5) we find

$$\epsilon_{\alpha\beta} = \tfrac{1}{2}(u_{\alpha,\beta} + u_{\beta,\alpha} + u_{\theta,\alpha}u_{\theta,\beta}) \tag{A3–1.7}$$

The functions $\epsilon_{\alpha\beta}$ defined by Eq. (A3–1.7) are the *Lagrangian strain components*. Note that $\epsilon_{\alpha\beta} = \epsilon_{\beta\alpha}$. The quantities $\epsilon_{\alpha\beta}$ collectively are called the strain tensor. Letting $x_1 = x$, $x_2 = y$, $x_3 = z$, we note by Eqs. (3–3.4) and (A3–1.7) that

$$\epsilon_{11} = \epsilon_x, \qquad \epsilon_{22} = \epsilon_y, \qquad \epsilon_{33} = \epsilon_z,$$
$$2\epsilon_{12} = \gamma_{xy}, \qquad 2\epsilon_{13} = \gamma_{xz}, \qquad 2\epsilon_{23} = \gamma_{yz}$$

Noting that the unit vector in the direction of the infinitesimal vector dx_i is $n_i = dx_i/ds$, we find by Eq. (A3–1.4) (see Art. 3–4)

$$\epsilon_L = \mathcal{M} = \frac{1}{2}\left[\left(\frac{ds^*}{ds}\right)^2 - 1\right] = \epsilon_{\alpha\beta} n_\alpha n_\beta \tag{A3–1.8}$$

where ϵ_L is the definition of strain for large displacements. As noted in Art. 3–4, Eq. (A3–1.8) is not the usual engineering definition of strain ϵ_E. However, if ϵ_L is small compared to one, the difference in the definitions is small. For example, we may solve Eq. (A3–1.8) for ds^*/ds in terms of ϵ_L. Then, expanding the square root to *first powers* in ϵ_L, we find

$$\epsilon_L = \frac{ds^* - ds}{ds} = \epsilon_E \qquad (A3–1.9)$$

Thus, for small strains, to first-degree terms in ϵ_L, the definitions of ϵ_L and ϵ_E coincide.

In a manner similar to that employed in the derivation of Lagrangian strain components, it may be shown that the *Eulerian strain components* $\mathscr{E}_{\alpha\beta}$ are

$$\mathscr{E}_{\alpha\beta} = \tfrac{1}{2}(u_{\alpha,\beta} + u_{\beta,\alpha} - u_{\theta,\alpha}u_{\theta,\beta}) \qquad (A3–1.10)$$

where now $u_{\alpha,\beta} = \partial u_\alpha/\partial \xi_\beta$. [See also Eq. (3–3.9).]

Note that $ds^* = ds$ is a necessary and sufficient condition for a rigid-body displacement ($\mathscr{M} = 0$). Also, note that if the displacement u_α and its derivatives are small, quadratic terms in Eqs. (A3–1.7) and (A3–1.10) may be discarded. Then Eqs. (A3–1.7) and (A3–1.10) become identical in form, since to within higher-degree terms in the displacement, derivatives of the displacement relative to a point x_α or relative to a point ξ_α are equivalent.

Accordingly, for small displacements, we write simply

$$\epsilon_{\alpha\beta} = \tfrac{1}{2}(u_{\alpha,\beta} + u_{\beta,\alpha}) \qquad (A3–1.11)$$

Problem. Show that $\epsilon_{\alpha\beta}$ as defined by Eq. (A3–1.11) represents the components of a second order tensor.

A3-2 Definition of Shearing Strain

In theories of small deformation, the angular change that occurs between any two mutually perpendicular line elements in a medium that undergoes deformation is *defined* to be the shearing strain between the two given line elements. To examine the concept of shearing strain, we first derive expressions for the direction cosines n_i^* of an infinitesimal line element PQ, where $P = P(x_1, x_2, x_3)$ and $Q = Q(x_1 + dx_1, x_2 + dx_2, x_3 + dx_3)$, in the deformed state in terms of its original direction cosine n_i and the displacement components u_i of point P.

Under deformation, the line element dx_α deforms into the line element dx_α^*, the lengths of these line elements being ds and ds^*, respectively. By definition of direction cosines, the direction cosines n_α^* of dx_α^* are

$$n_\alpha^* = \frac{dx_\alpha^*}{ds^*} \qquad (a)$$

Analogously, the direction cosines n_α of dx_α are

$$n_\alpha = \frac{dx_\alpha}{ds} \qquad (b)$$

Alternatively, we may write Eq. (a) in the form

$$n_\alpha^* = \frac{dx_\alpha^*}{ds^*}\frac{ds}{ds} = \frac{dx_\alpha^*}{ds}\frac{ds}{ds^*} \tag{c}$$

By the chain rule of differentiation we may write

$$\frac{dx_\alpha^*}{ds} = \frac{\partial x_\alpha^*}{\partial x_\beta}\frac{dx_\beta}{ds} \tag{d}$$

and by Eq. (A3–1.1), with $\xi_\alpha = x_\alpha^*$, we may write

$$\frac{\partial x_\alpha^*}{\partial x_\beta} = \delta_{\alpha\beta} + \frac{\partial u_\alpha}{\partial x_\beta} = \delta_{\alpha\beta} + u_{\alpha,\beta} \tag{e}$$

where $\delta_{\alpha\beta}$ is the Kronecker delta (Art. 1–20) and $u_{\alpha,\beta} = \partial u_\alpha / \partial x_\beta$. Accordingly, by Eqs. (b), (d), and (e), we obtain

$$\frac{dx_\alpha^*}{ds} = (\delta_{\alpha\beta} + u_{\alpha,\beta})n_\beta \tag{f}$$

Also, by Eq. (A3–1.8)

$$\frac{ds}{ds^*} = \frac{1}{\sqrt{1 + 2\mathcal{M}_i}} \tag{g}$$

where $\mathcal{M}_i$ denotes the magnification factor of line element PQ. Consequently, by Eqs. (c), (f), and (g), we obtain the following expressions for the direction cosines n_α^*:

$$n_\alpha^* \sqrt{1 + 2\mathcal{M}_i} = (\delta_{\alpha\beta} + u_{\alpha,\beta})n_\beta \tag{A3–2.1}$$

where subscript notation, β denotes partial differentiation with respect to x_β.

Next, we consider two infinitesimal line elements PA and PB of lengths ds_1 and ds_2, emanating from point P in the body and forming angle θ. Under a deformation the two line elements pass into the line elements P^*A^* and P^*B^* with lengths ds_1^* and ds_2^* and with subtended angle θ^*. In general, the plane PAB is nonparallel to plane $P^*A^*B^*$.

Let m_α and n_α denote the direction cosines of lines PA and PB, respectively, with reference to axes x_α. Hence, by the scalar product of vectors, the angle θ^* is defined by the relation

$$\cos\theta^* = m_\alpha^* n_\alpha^* \tag{h}$$

By Eq. (A3–2.1), the direction cosines m_α^* and n_α^* may be expressed in terms of m_α and n_α, respectively. Thus, substituting Eq. (A3–2.1) into Eq. (h) and utilizing the relation $\cos\theta = m_\alpha n_\alpha$, we obtain, after employing the notation of Eq. (A3–1.7),

$$\Gamma_{12} = \sqrt{(1 + 2\mathcal{M}_1)(1 + 2\mathcal{M}_2)}\cos\theta^* = \cos\theta + 2\epsilon_{\alpha\beta}m_\alpha n_\beta \tag{A3–2.2}$$

where subscripts 1 and 2 on $\mathcal{M}$ refer to lines PA and PB, respectively. Accordingly, Eq. (A3–2.2) defines the angle θ^* subtended by the deformed line elements P^*A^*, P^*B^*, that initially subtend angle θ. If the initial angle is $\theta = 90°$, $\cos \theta = 0$. Then,

$$\Gamma_{12} = 2\epsilon_{\alpha\beta} m_\alpha n_\beta \qquad (A3-2.3)$$

Equation (A3–2.3) forms the basis for definition of shearing strain (Art. 3–6). For example, in theories of large deformation, the quantity

$$\Gamma_{12} = \sqrt{(1 + 2\mathcal{M}_1)(1 + 2\mathcal{M}_2)} \cos \theta^*$$

is *defined* to be the shearing strain between two given line elements PA and PB that initially are perpendicular to one another. If the elongations of lines PA and PB are small (that is, if $\mathcal{M}_1$ and $\mathcal{M}_2$ are small compared to one), we note that $\Gamma_{12} \approx \cos \theta^*$. Furthermore, for small relative rotations between PA and PB, θ^* is approximately $\pi/2$. Hence,

$$\Gamma_{12} \approx \cos \theta^* = \sin\left(\frac{\pi}{2} - \theta^*\right) \approx \frac{\pi}{2} - \theta^*$$

Then, the definition of shearing strain (Γ_{12}) employed in large-deformation theory does not differ appreciably from the conventional engineering definition of shearing strain, $\gamma_{12} = (\pi/2) - \theta^*$. (See also Art. 3–6.)

A3-3   Tensor Character of $\epsilon_{\alpha\beta}$. The Strain Tensor

In this article we consider the laws of transformation of Eq. (A3–1.7), under a transformation from rectangular cartesian coordinates x_α to rectangular cartesian coordinates X_α.

Let a medium undergo a deformation. Then the extension of an infinitesimal line element ds in the medium is characterized by the relation [see Eq. (A3–1.4)]

$$(ds^*)^2 - (ds)^2 = 2\epsilon_{\alpha\beta} \, dx_\alpha \, dx_\beta \qquad (a)$$

where the components $\epsilon_{\alpha\beta}$ are functions of x_α.

Since $(ds^*)^2 - (ds)^2$ represents the physical extension of line ds, it remains invariant under a transformation of coordinates. Hence, we may also write

$$(ds^*)^2 - (ds)^2 = 2E_{\gamma\delta} \, dX_\gamma \, dX_\delta \qquad (b)$$

where the components $E_{\gamma\delta}$ are functions of X_α. The components $E_{\gamma\delta}$ are symmetrical components which determine the quantity $(ds^*)^2 - (ds)^2$ in terms of X_α coordinates.

Now under a transformation of coordinates from x_α to X_α, dx_α transforms according to the rule [see Eq. (1–18.12)]

$$dx_\alpha = a_{\gamma\alpha} \, dX_\gamma \qquad (c)$$

Substituting Eq. (c) into Eq. (a) and equating the resulting expression to Eq. (b) we obtain

$$E_{\gamma\delta} \, dX_\gamma \, dX_\delta = \epsilon_{\alpha\beta} a_{\gamma\alpha} a_{\delta\beta} \, dX_\gamma \, dX_\delta$$

or

$$(E_{\gamma\delta} - \epsilon_{\alpha\beta} a_{\gamma\alpha} a_{\delta\beta}) \, dX_\gamma \, dX_\delta = 0 \qquad \text{(d)}$$

Since dX_γ is arbitrary and since both $E_{\gamma\delta}$ and $\epsilon_{\alpha\beta}$ are symmetric, Eq. (e) is satisfied identically[1] if

$$E_{\gamma\delta} = \epsilon_{\alpha\beta} a_{\gamma\alpha} a_{\delta\beta} \qquad \text{(A3–3.1)}$$

Accordingly, $\epsilon_{\alpha\beta}$ transforms according to the rules of transformation of a second-order tensor [see Eq. (1–18.14)]. For this reason, the following matrix (i.e. the array of elements $\epsilon_{\alpha\beta}$; $\epsilon_{\alpha\beta} = \epsilon_{\beta\alpha}$) is called the *strain tensor*.

$$\begin{pmatrix} \epsilon_{11} & \epsilon_{12} & \epsilon_{13} \\ \epsilon_{12} & \epsilon_{22} & \epsilon_{23} \\ \epsilon_{13} & \epsilon_{23} & \epsilon_{33} \end{pmatrix} \qquad \text{(A3–3.2)}$$

Individual elements of this matrix are called *components of the strain tensor*. If the six components of the strain tensor are known, the deformation of the medium is defined by Eq. (A3–1.8). Since the right-hand side of Eq. (A3–1.8) is a quadratic form in the variables n_α, Eq. (A3–3.2) is the matrix of co-efficients of the quadratic form (see Art. 1–21), which defines the deformation of the medium. Since the matrix is symmetric with respect to its principal diagonal (the diagonal containing $\epsilon_{11}, \epsilon_{22}, \epsilon_{33}$), by the theory of quadratic forms,[2] it follows that $\mathcal{M}_i$ defined by Eq. (A3–1.8) possesses three stationary real values. In the theory of quadratic forms, these stationary real values are called *principal values;* in the theory of strain, they are called *principal strains.*

A3-4 Determination of Principal Strains. Principal Axes

The determination of principal strains reduces to the problem of com-puting the directions for which the strain ϵ_L (or ϵ_E) assumes extremal values (Art. 3–8).

Hence, let us consider the law of transformation of the strain tensor $\epsilon_{\alpha\beta}$. By Eq. (A3–3.1), under a transformation from rectangular cartesian coordinates x_α to rectangular cartesian coordinates X_α, the components $E_{\gamma\delta}$ of the strain tensor $\epsilon_{\alpha\beta}$ in the coordinate system X_γ are

$$E_{\gamma\delta} = \epsilon_{\alpha\beta} a_{\gamma\alpha} a_{\delta\beta} \qquad \text{(a)}$$

where $a_{\alpha\beta}$ are the direction cosines between axes X_α and x_β.

Expanding Eq. (a), we obtain

---

[1] J. L. Synge and A. Schild, *Tensor Calculus* (Toronto: University of Toronto Press, 1956), p. 20.

[2] G. Birkhoff and S. Maclane, *A Survey of Modern Algebra*, rev. ed. (New York: The Macmillan Company, 1953), pp. 266 ff. See also Art. 1–21.

$$E_{11} = \epsilon_{11}a_{11}^2 + \epsilon_{22}a_{12}^2 + \epsilon_{33}a_{13}^2 + 2\epsilon_{12}a_{11}a_{12} + 2\epsilon_{13}a_{11}a_{13} + 2\epsilon_{23}a_{12}a_{13}$$

$$E_{22} = \epsilon_{11}a_{21}^2 + \epsilon_{22}a_{22}^2 + \epsilon_{33}a_{23}^2 + 2\epsilon_{12}a_{21}a_{22} + 2\epsilon_{13}a_{21}a_{23} + 2\epsilon_{23}a_{22}a_{23}$$

$$E_{33} = \epsilon_{11}a_{31}^2 + \epsilon_{22}a_{32}^2 + \epsilon_{33}a_{33}^2 + 2\epsilon_{12}a_{31}a_{32} + 2\epsilon_{13}a_{31}a_{33} + 2\epsilon_{23}a_{32}a_{33}$$

$$E_{12} = \epsilon_{11}a_{11}a_{21} + \epsilon_{22}a_{12}a_{22} + \epsilon_{33}a_{13}a_{23} + \epsilon_{12}(a_{11}a_{22} + a_{12}a_{21})$$
$$+ \epsilon_{13}(a_{11}a_{23} + a_{13}a_{21}) + \epsilon_{23}(a_{12}a_{23} + a_{13}a_{22}) \qquad \text{(A3–4.1)}$$

$$E_{13} = \epsilon_{11}a_{11}a_{31} + \epsilon_{22}a_{12}a_{32} + \epsilon_{33}a_{13}a_{33} + \epsilon_{12}(a_{11}a_{32} + a_{12}a_{31})$$
$$+ \epsilon_{13}(a_{11}a_{33} + a_{13}a_{31}) + \epsilon_{23}(a_{12}a_{33} + a_{13}a_{32})$$

$$E_{23} = \epsilon_{11}a_{21}a_{31} + \epsilon_{22}a_{22}a_{32} + \epsilon_{33}a_{23}a_{33} + \epsilon_{12}(a_{21}a_{32} + a_{22}a_{31})$$
$$+ \epsilon_{13}(a_{21}a_{33} + a_{23}a_{31}) + \epsilon_{23}(a_{22}a_{33} + a_{23}a_{32})$$

Now let the X_1 axis be parallel to the direction for which the strain $\epsilon_L = \epsilon_E + \frac{1}{2}\epsilon_E^2$ (see Art. 3–4) takes an extremal value. By Eq. (A3–1.8), Eq. (b) of Art. (A3–3), and Eq. (A3–4.1), we obtain

$$\epsilon_L = \epsilon_E + \tfrac{1}{2}\epsilon_E^2 = E_{11} \qquad \text{(b)}$$

Consequently, we see that the problem of determining an extremal value for the strain ϵ_L (or ϵ_E) is equivalent to the computation of an extremal value of the strain component E_{11}. In turn, the problem of computing an extremal value of the component E_{11} reduces to the determination of the initial direction (a_{11}, a_{12}, a_{13}) of the infinitesimal line element for which E_{11} attains an extremal value under a deformation. Thus, we seek stationary values of E_{11} (i.e., values for which $\partial E_{11}/\partial a_{1\alpha} = 0$) under the restriction that $a_{11}^2 + a_{12}^2 + a_{13}^2 = 1$.

The extremal values of ϵ_L are called the *principal values of the deformation* or simply the *principal strains*. Again, the initial directions $(a_{\alpha\beta})$ along which ϵ_L attains stationary values are called the *principal directions* (or *axes*) or strain.

We will see that there are three initially mutually orthogonal principal directions for which ϵ_L takes extremal values. Furthermore, it will be shown that in the deformed position the shearing strains between principal axes vanish. Hence, under the deformation principal axes remain mutually orthogonal. Accordingly, at each point in a body there exists a set of three mutually orthogonal principal axes which remain mutually orthogonal under a deformation.

As noted above, the mathematical problem of determining the extremal of E_{11} essentially consists of determining the directions (a_{11}, a_{12}, a_{13}) for which

$$\frac{\partial E_{11}}{\partial a_{11}} = \frac{\partial E_{11}}{\partial a_{12}} = \frac{\partial E_{11}}{\partial a_{13}} = 0, \qquad \text{(c)}$$

where

$$a_{11}^2 + a_{12}^2 + a_{13}^2 - 1 = 0 \qquad \text{(d)}$$

We may solve this problem straight away by eliminating one of the $a_{\alpha\beta}$

between Eqs. (c) and (d). Thus, the problem may be reduced to seeking extremal values of E_{11} as a function of two variables (say a_{11} and a_{12}). However, this procedure of elimination is rather complicated algebraically, since Eq. (d) is of second degree. Consequently, rather than proceed directly into these difficulties, we seek extremals of E_{11} by a more elegant symmetrical technique called the *Lagrange multiplier method*.[3]

For this purpose, we consider the function

$$H = E_{11} - L(a_{11}^2 + a_{12}^2 + a_{13}^2 - 1) \qquad \text{(e)}$$

where L is an undetermined constant called the Lagrange multiplier. In the manner of Lagrange, we ignore initially the condition of Eq. (d). Thus, we seek the direction for which H attains an extremal value. This direction is a function of L. Since it provides a stationary value of H, it also provides a stationary value for E_{11} in the region restricted by the condition $a_{11}^2 + a_{12}^2 + a_{13}^2 - 1 = 0$. This follows from the fact that extremal values of H and E_{11} coincide in the region $a_{11}^2 + a_{12}^2 + a_{13}^2 = 1$ [see Eq. (e)].

Substituting the expression E_{11} [Eq. (A3-4.1)] into Eq. (e) and setting partial derivatives of H with respect to a_{11}, a_{12}, a_{13} equal to zero, we obtain

$$(\epsilon_{11} - L)a_{11} + \epsilon_{12}a_{12} + \epsilon_{13}a_{13} = 0$$
$$\epsilon_{12}a_{11} + (\epsilon_{22} - L)a_{12} + \epsilon_{23}a_{13} = 0 \qquad \text{(A3-4.2)}$$
$$\epsilon_{13}a_{11} + \epsilon_{23}a_{12} + (\epsilon_{33} - L)a_{13} = 0$$

Equations (A3-4.2) are a set of three homogeneous linear algebraic equations in (a_{11}, a_{12}, a_{13}). Since $a_{11}^2 + a_{12}^2 + a_{13}^2 = 1$, the trivial solution $a_{11} = a_{12} = a_{13} = 0$ is excluded. Hence, by the theory of linear algebraic equations,[4] Eqs. (A3-4.2) possess a solution if, and only if, the determinant of the coefficients of (a_{11}, a_{12}, a_{13}) vanishes identically.

Thus, we obtain the result

$$F(L) = \begin{vmatrix} (\epsilon_{11} - L) & \epsilon_{12} & \epsilon_{13} \\ \epsilon_{12} & (\epsilon_{22} - L) & \epsilon_{23} \\ \epsilon_{13} & \epsilon_{23} & (\epsilon_{33} - L) \end{vmatrix} = 0 \qquad \text{(A3-4.3)}$$

Equation (A3-4.3) is a third-degree algebraic equation in the Lagrange multiplier L. Inspection of Eq. (A3-4.3) shows that the highest-degree term in L is $-L^3$. Hence, for large positive values of L, $F(L)$ is negative. For large negative values of L, $F(L)$ is positive. Hence, since $F(L)$ is a continuous cubic function of L, it must pass through the value zero at least once for real values of L. Consequently, Eq. (A3-4.3) possesses at least one real root, say L_1.

---

[3] R. Courant, *Differential and Integral Calculus*, Vol. II (New York: Interscience Publishers, Inc., 1950), p. 188.

[4] I. S and E. S. Sokolnikoff, *Higher Mathematics for Engineers and Physicists* (New York: McGraw-Hill Book Company, Inc., 1941), p. 120. See also Art. 1–21.

Substitution of L_1 into Eqs. (A3–4.2) yields the following relations for the principal direction ξ_i corresponding to the root L_1.

$$(\epsilon_{11} - L_1)\xi_1 + \epsilon_{12}\xi_2 + \epsilon_{13}\xi_3 = 0$$

$$\epsilon_{12}\xi_1 + (\epsilon_{22} - L_1)\xi_2 + \epsilon_{23}\xi_3 = 0 \qquad \text{(f)}$$

$$\epsilon_{13}\xi_1 + \epsilon_{23}\xi_2 + (\epsilon_{33} - L_1)\xi_3 = 0$$

where

$$\xi_1^2 + \xi_2^2 + \xi_3^2 = 1 \qquad \text{(g)}$$

Multiplying the first, second, and third of Eqs. (f) by ξ_1, ξ_2, ξ_3, respectively, adding and utilizing Eq. (g), we obtain

$$L_1 = \epsilon_{\alpha\beta}\xi_\alpha\xi_\beta \qquad \text{(h)}$$

Comparison of Eq. (h) and the first of Eqs. (A3–4.1) shows that

$$L_1 = \text{Extremal } E_{11} \qquad \text{(A3–4.4)}$$

Therefore, the value L_1 of the Lagrange multiplier L also corresponds to an extremal value of ϵ_L [see Eq. (b)].

Furthermore, it follows from the fourth and fifth of Eqs. (A3–4.1), Eq. (f), and the orthogonality conditions [see Eqs. (1–18.2) and (1–18.3)] for coordinate axes X_α that

$$E_{12} = E_{13} = 0 \qquad \text{(i)}$$

Equation (i) signifies that the shearing strains between line elements directed along (X_1, X_2) axes and along (X_1, X_3) axes vanish identically. However, by the last of Eqs. (A3–4.1) and by Eqs. (f), we note that $E_{23} \neq 0$. Furthermore, the condition that E_{11} attains an extremal value in the direction of axis X_1 does not ensure that the strain ϵ_L takes on extremal values in the directions of axes X_2, X_3.

Hence, having established the existence of one real root ($L_1 = $ Extremal E_{11}) for Eq. (A3–4.3), we now proceed to examine the two remaining roots. Accordingly, we consider a second transformation to coordinate axes Y_α which leaves E_{11} invariant; that is, we consider a rotation of axes with respect to axis X_α. Thus, we let $Y_1 = X_1$ under a rotation through an angle θ with respect to axis X_1. The direction cosines of this transformation are given in

TABLE A

	X_1	X_2	X_3
Y_1	1	0	0
Y_2	0	$\cos\theta$	$\sin\theta$
Y_3	0	$-\sin\theta$	$\cos\theta$

Table A. Let the strain components in the coordinate system Y_α be distinguished by a prime from those in the X_α system. Then, by Eqs. (A3–4.1), we have

$$E'_{11} = E_{11}$$

$$E'_{22} = E_{22} \cos^2 \theta + E_{33} \sin^2 \theta + E_{23} \sin 2\theta$$

$$E'_{33} = E_{22} \sin^2 \theta + E_{33} \cos^2 \theta - E_{23} \sin 2\theta \qquad \text{(A3–4.5)}$$

$$E'_{12} = E'_{13} = 0$$

$$E'_{23} = (E_{33} - E_{22}) \sin \theta \cos \theta + E_{23} \cos 2\theta$$

By Eq. (A3–4.5), the strain components $E'_{\alpha\beta}$ are expressed as functions of the rotation θ. Hence, we seek the values of θ for which E'_{22} and E'_{33} are stationary. Differentiation of E'_{22} with respect to θ yields the condition

$$\tan 2\theta = \frac{2E_{23}}{E_{22} - E_{33}} \qquad \text{(A3–4.6)}$$

Accordingly, E'_{22} is a real extremal value for θ determined by Eq. (A3–4.6). Similarly, the value of θ given by Eq. (A3–4.6) yields a stationary real value of E'_{33}. Thus, we have shown that the strain ϵ_L attains stationary real values in three mutually orthogonal directions; that is, Eq. (A3–4.3) possesses three real roots, L_1, L_2, L_3, these roots being equal to the extremal values E'_{11}, E'_{22}, E'_{33}. Furthermore, substitution of Eq. (A3–4.6) into the last of Eqs. (A3–4.5) shows that $E'_{23} = 0$. Consequently, all the shearing strains between line elements in the principal directions (axes) vanish. Furthermore, the extremal values of the strain ϵ_L in the direction of the principal axes are determined by substitution of the extremal values $E'_{11}, E'_{22}, E'_{33}$ into Eq. (b).

The three sets of direction cosines $\xi_\alpha, \eta_\alpha, \zeta_\alpha$ of the three principal axes in the undeformed medium may be determined by solving Eqs. (A3–4.2) with L equal to L_1, L_2, L_3, respectively, subject to the restriction that $\xi_\alpha \xi_\alpha = \eta_\alpha \eta_\alpha = \zeta_\alpha \zeta_\alpha = 1$. With $\xi_\alpha, \eta_\alpha, \zeta_\alpha$ known, the principal directions $\xi_\alpha^*, \eta_\alpha^*, \zeta_\alpha^*$ in the undeformed medium may be computed by means of Eqs. (A3–2.1), provided u_α is known.

Since the shearing strains between line elements directed along principal axes vanish, we have shown that at each point in a medium which undergoes deformation there exists a set of three directions which are mutually orthogonal before and after the deformation.

4
STRESS-STRAIN
RELATIONS OF ELASTICITY

In the preceding chapters we have developed certain geometrical and dynamical concepts in the general theory of the behavior of continuous media. In this chapter we restrict these concepts to elastic solid bodies. We consider first certain general concepts and definitions. To simplify the mathematical treatment we restrict the major portion of our work to small strains and small rotations.[1]

4-1 Concept of Elasticity

We shall assume that the stress at every point P in the body depends at all times solely on the simultaneous deformation in the immediate neighborhood of the point P. In general, the stress in a solid body depends more or less not only on the force that acts at any instant, but also on the previous history or deformation of the body. For example, the stress at point P may depend on residual stresses due to cold working or cold forming of the body. However, in this chapter we concern ourselves with the study of the behavior of those solid bodies (that is, those bodies composed of materials which possess large cohesive forces, in contrast to fluids, which can sustain only relatively small tension forces) that have the ability to instantly recover their original size and shape when the forces producing the deformation are removed. This property of recovery of initial size and shape is called *perfect elasticity*.

---

[1]For stress-strain relations in the large-deflection theory, see V. V. Novozhilov, *Foundations of the Nonlinear Theory of Elasticity* (Rochester, N. Y.: Graylock Press, 1953).

Generally, a physical body is acted on continuously by forces. For example, in the vicinity of the earth a body is acted on by the earth's gravitational force, even in the absence of other forces. Only in interstellar space does a body approach being free of the action of forces, although even there it is acted on by the gravitational attractions of the distant stars. Accordingly, the *zero state* or the *zero configuration* from which the deformations of the body are measured is arbitrary. However, once the zero configuration is specified, the strain of the body measured from the zero state determines the body's internal configuration.

Whenever a body exhibits the phenomenon of *hysteresis*—that is, of returning to its original size and shape only slowly or not at all—its behavior is not perfectly elastic. The study of bodies which recover their sizes and shapes only gradually is treated in the *theory of viscoelasticity*. The study of bodies which do not return to their original sizes is generally considered in the *theory of plasticity*.

Any body may be regarded as perfectly elastic provided it is not strained beyond a certain limiting value called the *elastic limit*. Accordingly, the theory of elasticity may be applied to any body provided the deformations do not exceed the elastic limit.

Finally, the complete description of the initial state of a body requires the specification of the temperature at every point in the body, as well as its initial configuration; for, in general, a change in temperature will produce a change in configuration. In turn, a change in configuration may or may not be accompanied by a change in temperature.

4-2 Strain Energy Density Function

The problem of equilibrium of a deformed solid body remains indeterminate until six equations, supplemental to the differential equations of motion and the strain-displacement equations, are established. These supplemental equations relate the components of the displacement vector to the components of the stress tensor, and they express the law according to which the material of a given body resists various forms of deformation. A theoretical explanation of this law would require an insight into the nature of the intermolecular forces which seek to keep the particles of a solid body at definite distances from one another—that is, an insight into the components of stress and strain within a solid body. This objective has been achieved only in the case of gases in states that are far removed from unstable states. However, in the case of elastic solids, the present state of scientific development offers no solution to this difficult problem. If relations between stress and strain interior to a body are found by experiment, it is always by inference from measurement of quantities that in general are not components of stress or strain (for example, average strains, cubic compression, extension of a line element on the surface of the body, etc.). Hence, at the present time, the relation between stress and strain is established mainly by direct experiment. However, some general properties inherent in this relation can be explained theoretically. The law of conservation of energy forms the basis for the theoretical treatment of stress-strain relations.

Let us assume initially that the process of deformation is adiabatic;[2] that is, no heat is lost or gained in the system during the deformation. Furthermore, let the work expended on changing the volume and the form of an arbitrary infinitesimal element of the body be independent of the manner in which the transition from the zero state (undeformed state) to the final state (strained state) is realized. This condition is an alternative definition of elasticity. We assume, in other words, that the role of dissipative (nonconservative) forces in the process of interaction of the particles of the body is negligible compared to the role of the conservative forces.[3] A body which satisfies this assumption must return to its initial dimensions and form after the load is removed; that is, the body is *perfectly elastic*.

Under the above restrictions, the work required to deform a differential element dV of an elastic body can be expressed in the form $U(\epsilon_x, \epsilon_y, \epsilon_z, \gamma_{xy}, \gamma_{xz}, \gamma_{yz}) \, dV$; that is, it is equal to the product of the initial volume dV of the element and a certain function U of the six strain components. This function is called the *strain energy density;* it depends on the physical properties of the material, but is independent of the form and the size of the body.

4-3 Relation of Stress Components to Strain Energy Density Function for an Adiabatic Deformation Process

We limit the following analysis to strains small compared to one. Also, the major results are restricted to small rotations.

Let S be a closed surface within the body, and let V be the volume enclosed by S. Suppose that the body is in a deformed equilibrium state. We might also suppose that the body is in a process of deformation.[4] However, it may be shown that the resulting relation between the stress components and the strain energy density function remains unchanged. Let dW denote the work that the external forces perform on volume V during the deformation. The change of internal energy of the volume due to the deformation is

---

[2]The subsequent analysis holds approximately, however, for isothermal processes. See A. E. H. Love, *Mathematical Theory of Elasticity*, 4th ed. (New York: Dover Publications, Inc., 1944), Arts. 62 and 65.

[3]The role of dissipative forces is of major importance in the study of plasticity. See R. Hill, *Mathematical Theory of Plasticity* (Oxford: Clarendon Press, 1950).

[4]Love, *Mathematical Theory of Elasticity*, Arts. 61 and 62.

denoted by dI. If the deformation is adiabatic, the law of conservation of energy yields[5] $dW = dI$. Now $I = \iiint U\, dV$, where U is the strain energy density. Hence, $dI = d[\iiint U\, dV]$, or

$$dW = d\left[\int \int \int U\, dV\right] \tag{a}$$

The work dW is the sum of the work dW_B of the body forces that act on volume V and the work dW_S of the surface forces that act on surface S. With the notation introduced in the theory of stress (Chapter 2), the work dW_B is

$$dW_B = \int \int \int (X\, du + Y\, dv + Z\, dw)\, dV \tag{b}$$

where (u, v, w) are the components of the displacement vector. Similarly, the work dW_S is

$$dW_S = \int \int (\sigma_{Px}\, du + \sigma_{Py}\, dv + \sigma_{Pz}\, dw)\, dS$$

With Eq. (2–3.10), this equation may be written in the form

$$dW_S = \int \int [(\sigma_x l + \tau_{xy} m + \tau_{xz} n)\, du + (\tau_{xy} l + \sigma_y m + \tau_{yz} n)\, dv$$
$$+ (\tau_{xz} l + \tau_{yz} m + \sigma_z n)\, dw]\, dS$$

By the divergence theorem (Art. 1–9), this integral may be transformed into the following volume integral:

$$dW_S = \int \int \int \left[\frac{\partial(\sigma_x\, du)}{\partial x} + \frac{\partial(\tau_{xy}\, du)}{\partial y} + \frac{\partial(\tau_{xz}\, du)}{\partial z} + \frac{\partial(\tau_{xy}\, dv)}{\partial x} + \frac{\partial(\sigma_y\, dv)}{\partial y}\right.$$
$$\left. + \frac{\partial(\tau_{yz}\, dv)}{\partial z} + \frac{\partial(\tau_{xz}\, dw)}{\partial x} + \frac{\partial(\tau_{yz}\, dw)}{\partial y} + \frac{\partial(\sigma_z\, dw)}{\partial z}\right] dV \tag{c}$$

Performing the differentiations indicated in Eq. (c), by Eqs. (a), (b), (c), (2–8.4), and (3–12.17), we obtain

$$\int \int \int (dU)\, dV$$
$$= \int \int \int (\sigma_x\, d\epsilon_x + \sigma_y\, d\epsilon_y + \sigma_z\, d\epsilon_z + \tau_{xy}\, d\gamma_{xy} + \tau_{xz}\, d\gamma_{xz} + \tau_{yz}\, d\gamma_{yz})\, dV$$

Hence,

$$dU = \sigma_x\, d\epsilon_x + \sigma_y\, d\epsilon_y + \sigma_z\, d\epsilon_z + \tau_{xy}\, d\gamma_{xy} + \tau_{xz}\, d\gamma_{xz} + \tau_{yz}\, d\gamma_{yz} \tag{4–3.1}$$

Also, by the rule for the total differential,

$$dU = \frac{\partial U}{\partial \epsilon_x}\, d\epsilon_x + \frac{\partial U}{\partial \epsilon_y}\, d\epsilon_y + \cdots + \frac{\partial U}{\partial \gamma_{yz}}\, d\gamma_{yz} \tag{4–3.2}$$

---

[5] A. B. Pippard, *The Elements of Classical Thermodynamics* (London: Cambridge University Press, 1960).

Comparison of Eqs. (4–3.1) and (4–3.2) yields the relations

$$\sigma_x = \frac{\partial U}{\partial \epsilon_x}, \qquad \sigma_y = \frac{\partial U}{\partial \epsilon_y}, \qquad \sigma_z = \frac{\partial U}{\partial \epsilon_z}$$

$$\tau_{xy} = \frac{\partial U}{\partial \gamma_{xy}}, \qquad \tau_{xz} = \frac{\partial U}{\partial \gamma_{xz}}, \qquad \tau_{yz} = \frac{\partial U}{\partial \gamma_{yz}} \tag{4–3.3}$$

Equations (4–3.3) provide a great simplification of the problem of deter-mining stress components in the small-deflection theory of elasticity, since, instead of seeking six unknown functions $(\sigma_x, \ldots, \tau_{yz})$, we need seek only one function U. In general, U is a function of six strain components (Art. 4–2). However, a further simplification results if the material is isotropic (Art. 4–5). Then, since the directions of principal strains have no bearing on the strain energy density, U is a function of the principal strains ϵ_1, ϵ_2, ϵ_3. Then, by Eqs. (4–3.3), the principal stresses are

$$\sigma_1 = \frac{\partial U}{\partial \epsilon_1}, \qquad \sigma_2 = \frac{\partial U}{\partial \epsilon_2}, \qquad \sigma_3 = \frac{\partial U}{\partial \epsilon_3} \tag{4–3.4}$$

The principal stresses and strains are not affected by rotations of particles of the medium, and therefore Eq. (4–3.4) is valid, even though the displace-ments are large, provided that the strains are small compared to 1.

Problem. Show that Eqs. (4–3.3) are valid if we take $dW/dt = dK/dt + dI/dt$, where $K = \frac{1}{2} \int\int\int \rho(\dot{u}^2 + \dot{v}^2 + \dot{w}^2)\, dV$ denotes the kinetic energy of the system, and W and I are defined as in Art. 4–2. Dots above u, v, w denote time derivatives, and t denotes time. (*See also* Art. A4–1.)

4-4 Generalized Hooke's Law

In its most general form, Hooke's law asserts that each of the stress com-ponents is a linear function of the components of the strain tensor; that is,

$$\sigma_x = C_{11}\epsilon_x + C_{12}\epsilon_y + C_{13}\epsilon_z + C_{14}\gamma_{xy} + C_{15}\gamma_{xz} + C_{16}\gamma_{yz}$$

$$\sigma_y = C_{21}\epsilon_x + C_{22}\epsilon_y + C_{23}\epsilon_z + C_{24}\gamma_{xy} + C_{25}\gamma_{xz} + C_{26}\gamma_{yz}$$

$$\sigma_z = C_{31}\epsilon_x + C_{32}\epsilon_y + C_{33}\epsilon_z + C_{34}\gamma_{xy} + C_{35}\gamma_{xz} + C_{36}\gamma_{yz}$$

$$\tau_{xy} = C_{41}\epsilon_x + C_{42}\epsilon_y + C_{43}\epsilon_z + C_{44}\gamma_{xy} + C_{45}\gamma_{xz} + C_{46}\gamma_{yz} \tag{4–4.1}$$

$$\tau_{xz} = C_{51}\epsilon_x + C_{52}\epsilon_y + C_{53}\epsilon_z + C_{54}\gamma_{xy} + C_{55}\gamma_{xz} + C_{56}\gamma_{yz}$$

$$\tau_{yz} = C_{61}\epsilon_x + C_{62}\epsilon_y + C_{63}\epsilon_z + C_{64}\gamma_{xy} + C_{65}\gamma_{xz} + C_{66}\gamma_{yz}$$

where the thirty-six coefficients, $C_{11}, \ldots C_{66}$, are called *elastic constants* (*stiffnesses*).

In general, the coefficients C_{ij} are not constants, but may depend on loca-tion in the body as well as on time and temperature. Ordinarily the C_{ij}

decrease with increasing temperature. In index notation (Art. 1–17), Eq. (4–4.1) may be written in the form

$$\sigma_a = C_{\alpha\beta}\epsilon_\beta \qquad (\alpha, \beta = 1, 2, \ldots, 6) \tag{4-4.2}$$

where

$$\sigma_1 = \sigma_x, \quad \sigma_2 = \sigma_y, \quad \ldots, \quad \sigma_6 = \tau_{yz}$$
$$\epsilon_1 = \epsilon_x, \quad \epsilon_2 = \epsilon_y, \quad \ldots, \quad \epsilon_6 = \gamma_{yz} \tag{4-4.3}$$

In reality, Eq. (4–4.1) is no law, but merely an approximation that is valid for small strains, since any continuous function is approximately linear in a sufficiently small range of the variables. For a given temperature, time, and location in the body, the coefficients $C_{\alpha\beta}$ in Eq. (4–4.1) are constants that are characteristics of the material.

Equations (4–3.3) and (4–4.1) yield

$$\frac{\partial U}{\partial \epsilon_x} = \sigma_x = C_{11}\epsilon_x + \cdots + C_{16}\gamma_{yz}$$
$$\frac{\partial U}{\partial \epsilon_y} = \sigma_y = C_{21}\epsilon_x + \cdots + C_{26}\gamma_{yz} \tag{4-4.4}$$

$$\cdots\cdots\cdots\cdots\cdots\cdots\cdots\cdots\cdots$$

Hence, differentiation of Eq. (4–4.4) yields

$$\frac{\partial^2 U}{\partial \epsilon_x \partial \epsilon_y} = C_{12} = C_{21}, \qquad \frac{\partial^2 U}{\partial \epsilon_x \partial \epsilon_z} = C_{13} = C_{31}, \qquad \cdots$$
$$\frac{\partial^2 U}{\partial \epsilon_x \partial \gamma_{yz}} = C_{16} = C_{61}, \ldots \tag{4-4.5}$$

These equations show that $C_{12} = C_{21}, C_{13} = C_{31}, \ldots, C_{ik} = C_{ki}, \ldots, C_{56} = C_{65}$; that is, the elastic constants $C_{\alpha\beta}$ are symmetrical. Accordingly, there are only twenty-one distinct C's. In other words, the general anisotropic linearly elastic material has twenty-one elastic constants. In view of the preceding relation, the strain energy density of a general anisotropic material is [by integration[6] of Eqs. (4–4.4)]

$$U = \tfrac{1}{2}C_{11}\epsilon_x^2 + \tfrac{1}{2}C_{12}\epsilon_x\epsilon_y + \cdots + \tfrac{1}{2}C_{16}\epsilon_x\gamma_{yz}$$
$$+ \tfrac{1}{2}C_{12}\epsilon_x\epsilon_y + \tfrac{1}{2}C_{22}\epsilon_y^2 + \cdots + \tfrac{1}{2}C_{26}\epsilon_y\gamma_{yz}$$
$$+ \tfrac{1}{2}C_{13}\epsilon_x\epsilon_z + \tfrac{1}{2}C_{23}\epsilon_y\epsilon_z + \cdots + \tfrac{1}{2}C_{36}\epsilon_z\gamma_{yz} \tag{4-4.6}$$
$$+ \cdots$$
$$+ \tfrac{1}{2}C_{16}\epsilon_x\gamma_{yz} + \tfrac{1}{2}C_{26}\epsilon_y\gamma_{yz} + \cdots + \tfrac{1}{2}C_{66}\gamma_{yz}^2$$

---

[6]Here, we discard a constant term, since we are interested in derivatives of U. Furthermore, in agreement with Eq. (4–4.1), we assume that the stress components σ_α [see Eq. (4–4.3)] vanish identically with the strain components. Accordingly, linear terms in ϵ_β are discarded from Eq. (4–4.6). If the σ_α do not vanish with the ϵ_β (for example, the case of residual stresses), constant terms must be added to Eq. (4–4.1). In turn, these constants terms lead to linear terms in ϵ_β in Eq. (4–4.6).

In index notation, Eq. (4–4.6) may be written

$$U = \tfrac{1}{2} C_{\alpha\beta} \epsilon_\alpha \epsilon_\beta \qquad (m, n = 1, 2, \ldots, 6) \qquad (4\text{–}4.7)$$

In its general form, Eq. (4–4.6) is important in the study of crystals.[7]

Symmetry conditions. The elastic constants $C_{\alpha\beta}$ of Eqs. (4–4.1) may be denoted by the array (matrix)

$$
\begin{array}{cccc}
C_{11} & C_{12} & \ldots & C_{16} \\
C_{12} & C_{22} & \ldots & C_{26} \\
\multicolumn{4}{c}{\ldots\ldots\ldots\ldots\ldots} \\
C_{16} & C_{26} & \ldots & C_{66}
\end{array}
\qquad (4\text{–}4.8)
$$

In certain structural materials, special kinds of symmetry may exist. For example, the elastic constants may remain invariant under a coordinate transformation $x \to x$, $y \to y$, $z \to -z$. Such a transformation is called a *reflection* with respect to the (x, y) plane. The direction cosines of this transformation are defined by

$$l_1 = m_2 = 1, \qquad n_3 = -1$$
$$l_2 = l_3 = m_1 = m_3 = n_1 = n_2 = 0 \qquad (4\text{–}4.9)$$

(See Table of Direction Cosines, Art. 2–4.) Substitution of Eqs. (4–4.9) into Eqs. (A2–2.1) and (3–7.4) reveals that for a reflection with respect to the (x, y) plane

$$\sigma'_{11} = \sigma'_x = \sigma_{11} = \sigma_x, \qquad\qquad \sigma'_{22} = \sigma'_y = \sigma_{22} = \sigma_y,$$
$$\sigma'_{33} = \sigma'_z = \sigma_{33} = \sigma_z, \qquad\qquad \sigma'_{12} = \tau'_{xy} = \sigma_{12} = \tau_{xy} \qquad (4\text{–}4.10)$$
$$\sigma'_{23} = \tau'_{yz} = -\sigma_{23} = -\tau_{yz}, \qquad \sigma'_{13} = \tau'_{xz} = -\sigma_{13} = -\tau_{xz}$$

and

$$\epsilon'_{11} = \epsilon'_x = \epsilon_{11} = \epsilon_x, \qquad\qquad \epsilon'_{22} = \epsilon'_y = \epsilon_{22} = \epsilon_y$$
$$\epsilon'_{33} = \epsilon'_z = \epsilon_{33} = \epsilon_z, \qquad\qquad \epsilon'_{12} = \tfrac{1}{2}\gamma'_{xy} = \epsilon_{12} = \tfrac{1}{2}\gamma_{xy} \qquad (4\text{–}4.11)$$
$$\epsilon'_{23} = \tfrac{1}{2}\gamma'_{yz} = -\epsilon_{23} = -\tfrac{1}{2}\gamma_{yz}, \quad \epsilon'_{13} = \tfrac{1}{2}\gamma'_{xz} = -\epsilon_{13} = -\tfrac{1}{2}\gamma_{xz}$$

Hence, under the transformation of Eq. (4–4.9), the first of Eqs. (4–4.1) yields

$$\sigma'_x = C_{11}\epsilon'_x + C_{12}\epsilon'_y + C_{13}\epsilon'_z + C_{14}\gamma'_{xy} + C_{15}\gamma'_{xz} + C_{16}\gamma'_{yz} \qquad (4\text{–}4.12)$$

Substitution of Eqs. (4–4.10) and (4–4.11) into Eq. (4–4.12) yields

$$\sigma_x = \sigma'_x = C_{11}\epsilon_x + C_{12}\epsilon_y + C_{13}\epsilon_z + C_{14}\gamma_{xy} - C_{15}\gamma_{xz} - C_{16}\gamma_{yz} \qquad (4\text{–}4.13)$$

Comparison of the first of Eqs. (4–4.1) with Eq. (4–4.13) yields the conditions $C_{15} = -C_{15}$, $C_{16} = -C_{16}$, or $C_{15} = C_{16} = 0$. Similarly, considering $\sigma'_y, \ldots, \tau'_{yz}$, we find

---

[7] M. Planck, *Mechanics of Deformable Bodies* (New York: The Macmillan Company, 1932); Love, *Mathematical Theory of Elasticity*; J. F. Nye, *Physical Properties of Crystals* (London: Oxford University Press, 1957).

$$C_{25} = C_{26} = C_{35} = C_{36} = C_{45} = C_{46} = 0$$

Accordingly, the elastic constants for a material whose elastic properties are invariant under a reflection with respect to the (x, y) plane (that is, the body possesses a plane of elastic symmetry) are summarized by the matrix

$$
\begin{matrix}
C_{11} & C_{12} & C_{13} & C_{14} & 0 & 0 \\
C_{12} & C_{22} & C_{23} & C_{24} & 0 & 0 \\
C_{13} & C_{23} & C_{33} & C_{34} & 0 & 0 \\
C_{14} & C_{24} & C_{34} & C_{44} & 0 & 0 \\
0 & 0 & 0 & 0 & C_{55} & C_{56} \\
0 & 0 & 0 & 0 & C_{56} & C_{66}
\end{matrix}
\tag{4-4.14}
$$

If the material has two mutually orthogonal planes of elastic symmetry, it may be shown that $C_{14} = C_{24} = C_{34} = C_{56} = 0$. Then, Eq. (4-4.14) reduces to

$$
\begin{matrix}
C_{11} & C_{12} & C_{13} & 0 & 0 & 0 \\
C_{12} & C_{22} & C_{23} & 0 & 0 & 0 \\
C_{13} & C_{23} & C_{33} & 0 & 0 & 0 \\
0 & 0 & 0 & C_{44} & 0 & 0 \\
0 & 0 & 0 & 0 & C_{55} & 0 \\
0 & 0 & 0 & 0 & 0 & C_{66}
\end{matrix}
\tag{4-4.15}
$$

Equation (4-4.1) is simplified accordingly.

PROBLEM SET 4-4

1 Derive Eq. (4-4.6).

2 Derive Eq. (4-4.15).

3 Consider a solid body which has three mutually orthogonal planes of axial symmetry. Derive the matrix for the elastic constants C_{mn}.

4-5 Isotropic Media. Homogeneous Media

If the orientations of crystals and grains constituting the material of a solid body are distributed sufficiently randomly, any part of the body will display essentially the same material properties in all directions. If a solid body is composed of such randomly oriented crystals and grains, it is said to be *isotropic*. Thus, isotropy may be considered as a directional property of the material. Accordingly, if a material body is isotropic, its physical properties at a point P in the body are invariant under a rotation with respect to axes with origin at P. A medium is said to be *elastically isotropic* if its characteristic elastic constants are invariant under any rotation of coordinates.

If the material properties at a point in a medium depend on the direction considered, the body (material) is said to be *nonisotropic*, *ȧnisotropic*, or *aeolotropic*. Wood is an example of an anisotropic material.

If the material properties are identical for every point in a body, the body is said to be *homogeneous*. In other words, homogeneity implies that the physical properties of a body are invariant under a translation. Alternatively, a body whose material properties change from point to point is said to be nonhomogeneous. For example, since in general the elastic constants are functions of temperature, a body subjected to a nonuniform temperature distribution is nonhomogeneous. Accordingly, the property of nonhomogeneity is a scalar property; that is, it depends only on the location of a point in the body, not on any direction at the point. Consequently, a body may be nonhomogeneous, but isotropic. For example, consider a flat plate sandwich formed by a layer of aluminum bounded by layers of steel. If the point considered is in a steel layer, the material properties have certain values which are generally independent of direction. That is, the steel is essentially isotropic. Furthermore, if the temperature is approximately constant throughout the plate, the material properties do not change greatly from point to point. If the point considered is in the aluminum, the material properties differ from those of steel. Accordingly, taken as a complete body, the sandwich plate exhibits nonhomogeneity. However, at any point in the body, the properties are essentially independent of direction.[8]

Analogously, a body may be nonisotropic, but homogeneous. For example, the physical properties of a crystal depend on direction in the crystal, but the properties vary little from one point to another.[9]

If an elastic body is composed of isotropic materials, the strain energy density depends only on the principal strains (which are invariants), since for isotropic materials the elastic constants are invariants under arbitrary rotations [see Eq. (4–6.2)].

4-6 Strain Energy Density for Elastically Isotropic Medium under Adiabatic Conditions

The strain energy density of an elastically isotropic material depends only on the principal strains (ϵ_1, ϵ_2, ϵ_3). Accordingly, if the elasticity is linear, Eq. (4–4.6) yields for an adiabatic deformation

$$U = \tfrac{1}{2}C_{11}\epsilon_1^2 + \tfrac{1}{2}C_{12}\epsilon_1\epsilon_2 + \tfrac{1}{2}C_{13}\epsilon_1\epsilon_3 + \tfrac{1}{2}C_{12}\epsilon_1\epsilon_2 + \tfrac{1}{2}C_{22}\epsilon_2^2$$
$$+ \tfrac{1}{2}C_{23}\epsilon_2\epsilon_3 + \tfrac{1}{2}C_{13}\epsilon_1\epsilon_3 + \tfrac{1}{2}C_{23}\epsilon_2\epsilon_3 + \tfrac{1}{2}C_{33}\epsilon_3^2 \tag{4-6.1}$$

---

[8]An exception occurs at the boundaries between the aluminum layer and the steel layers. Here, the body is nonisotropic in nature.

[9]For an extensive discussion of anisotropy and nonhomogeneity in crystals, see Nye, *Physical Properties of Crystals*.

By symmetry, the naming of the principal axes is arbitrary. Hence, $C_{11} = C_{22} = C_{33} = C_1$, and $C_{23} = C_{13} = C_{12} = C_2$. Consequently, Eq. (4–6.1) contains only two distinct constants. Hence, for a linearly *elastic* isotropic material the strain energy density may be expressed in the form

$$U = \tfrac{1}{2}\lambda(\epsilon_1 + \epsilon_2 + \epsilon_3)^2 + G(\epsilon_1^2 + \epsilon_2^2 + \epsilon_3^2) \qquad (4\text{–}6.2)$$

where $\lambda = C_2$ and $G = (C_1 - C_2)/2$ are elastic constants called *Lamé's elastic constants*. If the material is homogeneous, λ and G are constants at all points. In terms of the strain invariants [see Eq. (3–8.5)], Eq. (4–6.2) may be written in the following form:

$$U = (\tfrac{1}{2}\lambda + G)J_1^2 - 2GJ_2 \qquad (4\text{–}6.3)$$

Returning to arbitrary orthogonal coordinates (x, y, z), and introducing the general definitions of J_1 and J_2 from Eq. (3–8.3), we obtain

$$U = \tfrac{1}{2}\lambda(\epsilon_x + \epsilon_y + \epsilon_z)^2 + G(\epsilon_x^2 + \epsilon_y^2 + \epsilon_z^2 + \tfrac{1}{2}\gamma_{xy}^2 + \tfrac{1}{2}\gamma_{xz}^2 + \tfrac{1}{2}\gamma_{yz}^2) \qquad (4\text{–}6.4)$$

Equations (4–3.3) and (4–6.4) now yield Hooke's law for a linearly elastic, isotropic material in the form

$$\sigma_x = \lambda e + 2G\epsilon_x, \qquad \sigma_y = \lambda e + 2G\epsilon_y, \qquad \sigma_z = \lambda e + 2G\epsilon_z,$$
$$\tau_{xy} = G\gamma_{xy}, \qquad \tau_{xz} = G\gamma_{xz}, \qquad \tau_{yz} = G\gamma_{yz} \qquad (4\text{–}6.5)$$

where $e = J_1$ is the classical small-displacement cubical strain; that is, $e = \epsilon_x + \epsilon_y + \epsilon_z$. Thus, we have shown that for isotropic linearly elastic media, the stress-strain law involves no more than two elastic constants. An analytic proof of the fact that no further reduction is possible on a theoretical basis can be constructed.[10]

Inverting Eqs. (4–6.5), we obtain

$$\epsilon_x = \frac{1}{E}[\sigma_x - \nu(\sigma_y + \sigma_z)], \qquad \epsilon_y = \frac{1}{E}[\sigma_y - \nu(\sigma_x + \sigma_z)],$$

$$\epsilon_z = \frac{1}{E}[\sigma_z - \nu(\sigma_x + \sigma_y)]$$

$$\gamma_{xy} = \frac{1}{G}\tau_{xy} = \frac{2(1 + \nu)}{E}\tau_{xy}, \qquad \gamma_{xz} = \frac{1}{G}\tau_{xz} = \frac{2(1 + \nu)}{E}\tau_{xz},$$

$$\gamma_{yz} = \frac{1}{G}\tau_{yz} = \frac{2(1 + \nu)}{E}\tau_{yz}$$

$$(4\text{–}6.6)$$

where

$$E = \frac{G(3\lambda + 2G)}{\lambda + G}, \qquad \nu = \frac{\lambda}{2(\lambda + G)} \qquad (4\text{–}6.7)$$

are elastic constants called Young's modulus and Poisson's ratio, respectively. (For a physical interpretation of E and ν, see Art. 4–7.)

---

[10]H. Jeffreys, *Cartesian Tensors* (London: Cambridge University Press, 1957). See also, Love, *Mathematical Theory of Elasticity*, Art. 69.

Substitution of Eqs. (4–6.6) into Eq. (4–6.4) yields the strain energy density in terms of components of stress. We obtain

$$U = \frac{1}{2E}[\sigma_x^2 + \sigma_y^2 + \sigma_z^2 - 2\nu(\sigma_x\sigma_y + \sigma_x\sigma_z + \sigma_y\sigma_z) + 2(1+\nu)(\tau_{xy}^2 + \tau_{xz}^2 + \tau_{yz}^2)]$$

(4–6.8)

If the axes (x, y, z) are directed along the principal axes of strain, then $\gamma_{xy} = \gamma_{xz} = \gamma_{yz} = 0$. Hence, by Eq. (4–6.5), $\tau_{xy} = \tau_{xz} = \tau_{yz} = 0$. Therefore, the axes (x, y, z) must lie along the principal axes of stress. Consequently, for an isotropic material, the principal axes of stress are coincident with the principal axes of strain. *Hence, when we deal with isotropic material, no distinction need be made between principal axes of stress and principal axes of strain.* Such axes are called simply *principal axes*.

PROBLEM SET 4-6

1 Derive Eqs. (4–6.2), (4–6.3), (4–6.4), (4–6.6), and (4–6.8).

2 For an isotropic elastic medium subjected to a hydrostatic state of stress, $\sigma_x = \sigma_y = \sigma_z = -p$, $\tau_{xy} = \tau_{xz} = \tau_{yz} = 0$, where p denotes pressure. Show that for this state of stress $p = -ke$, where e is the cubical strain and $k = E/[3(1 - 2\nu)]$ is called the bulk modulus. Discuss the cases $\nu > \frac{1}{2}$, $\nu < -1$. See also A. E. H. Love, *Mathematical Theory of Elasticity*, 4th ed. (New York: Dover Publications, Inc., 1944), Art. 70.

4-7 Special States of Stress

Simple tension. To interpret the Lamé constants λ and G, we consider a body in the following state of stress:

$$\sigma_x = \sigma_y = \tau_{xy} = \tau_{xz} = \tau_{yz} = 0, \qquad \sigma_z = \sigma = \text{constant}$$

When this state of stress exists in a cylindrical or prismatic bar whose axis is parallel to the z axis, the stress on the lateral boundary vanishes. On the ends, the normal stress is σ, and the shearing stress is zero. Hence, this is the state of stress in a bar under simple tension.

Equation (4–6.5) yields $\lambda e + 2G\epsilon_x = \lambda e + 2G\epsilon_y = \gamma_{xy} = \gamma_{xz} = \gamma_{yz} = 0$ and $\lambda e + 2G\epsilon_z = \sigma$. Solving the equations for the ϵ's, we obtain

$$\epsilon_x = \epsilon_y = -\frac{\lambda\sigma}{2G(3\lambda + 2G)}$$

(4–7.1)

$$\epsilon_z = \frac{(\lambda + G)\sigma}{G(3\lambda + 2G)}$$

It follows that

$$-\frac{\epsilon_x}{\epsilon_z} = -\frac{\epsilon_y}{\epsilon_z} = \frac{\lambda}{2(\lambda + G)}$$

(4–7.2)

The constants

$$E = \frac{G(3\lambda + 2G)}{\lambda + G} \quad \text{and} \quad \nu = \frac{\lambda}{2(\lambda + G)} \tag{4-7.3}$$

are called Young's modulus of elasticity and Poisson's ratio, respectively. In terms of ν and E, Eq. (4-7.1) becomes

$$\epsilon_x = \epsilon_y = -\frac{\nu\sigma}{E}, \quad \epsilon_z = \frac{\sigma}{E} \tag{4-7.4}$$

Solving Eqs. (4-7.3) for λ and G in terms of the measurable constants E and ν, we obtain

$$G = \frac{E}{2(1 + \nu)}, \quad \lambda = \frac{\nu E}{(1 + \nu)(1 - 2\nu)} \tag{4-7.5}$$

Integrating Eqs. (4-7.4) and disregarding an arbitrary rigid-body displacement, we obtain the displacement vector

$$u = -\frac{\nu\sigma}{E}x, \quad v = -\frac{\nu\sigma}{E}y, \quad w = \frac{\sigma}{E}z \tag{4-7.6}$$

Since u, v, w are linear functions of the coordinates x, y, z, this type of strain is homogeneous (See Art. 3–13.).

Pure shear. Consider the state of pure shear characterized by the stress components $\sigma_x = \sigma_y = \sigma_z = \tau_{xy} = \tau_{xz} = 0$, $\tau_{yz} = \tau = $ constant. For this state of stress, Eqs. (4–6.5) yield

$$\lambda e + 2G\epsilon_x = \lambda e + 2G\epsilon_y = \lambda e + 2G\epsilon_z = \gamma_{xy} = \gamma_{xz} = 0, \quad \gamma_{yz} = \frac{\tau}{G}$$

Solving these equations for the strain components, we obtain

$$\epsilon_x = \epsilon_y = \epsilon_z = \gamma_{xy} = \gamma_{xz} = 0,$$

$$\gamma_{yz} = \frac{\tau}{G}$$

These formulas show that a rectangular parallelepiped $ABCD$ (Fig. 4–7.1), whose faces are parallel to the coordinate planes, is sheared in the yz plane so that the right angle between the edges of the parallelepiped parallel to the y and z axes decreases by the amount γ_{yz}. For this reason, G is called the *shear modulus of elasticity.*

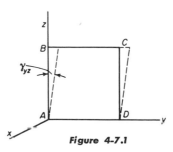

Figure 4-7.1

1 Derive Eqs. (4–7.1).

2 Derive the result that $\epsilon_x = \epsilon_y = \epsilon_z = \gamma_{xy} = \gamma_{xz} = 0$ for the state of pure shear.

3 Derive results equivalent to Eqs. (4–7.1)–(4–7.6) for the case of hydrostatic compression $\sigma_x = \sigma_y = \sigma_z = -p$.

4-8 Equations of Thermoelasticity for Isotropic Media

Consider an isotropic elastic body in an arbitrary zero configuration. Let the temperature of the body be increased by the small amount T. Since the body is isotropic, all infinitesimal line elements in the volume undergo equal expansions. Furthermore, all line elements maintain their initial directions. Accordingly, the strain components due to the temperature change T are, with respect to rectangular cartesian coordinates (x, y, z),

$$\epsilon'_x = \epsilon'_y = \epsilon'_z = kT, \qquad \gamma_{xy} = \gamma_{xz} = \gamma_{yz} = 0 \qquad (4\text{-}8.1)$$

or, in index notation,

$$\epsilon'_{ij} = kT\delta_{ij} \qquad (4\text{-}8.2)$$

where k denotes the linear coefficient of thermal expansion of the material and δ_{ij} denotes the Kronecker delta [Eq. (1–20.1)]. For a nonhomogeneous body, k may be a function of coordinates and of temperature; that is, $k = k(x, y, z, T)$.

Now let the body be subjected to forces which induce stresses σ_{ij} in the body. Accordingly, if ϵ_{ij} denote the strain components in the body after the application of the forces, the net change in strain produced by the forces is represented by the equations

$$\epsilon''_{ij} = \epsilon_{ij} - kT\delta_{ij} \qquad (4\text{-}8.3)$$

In general, T may depend on the location in the body and on time t. Hence, $T = T(x, y, z, t)$.

Substitution of Eqs. (4–8.3) into Eqs. (4–6.5) yields

$$\sigma_x = \lambda e + 2G\epsilon_x - cT, \quad \sigma_y = \lambda e + 2G\epsilon_y - cT, \quad \sigma_z = \lambda e + 2G\epsilon_z - cT$$
$$\tau_{xy} = G\gamma_{xy}, \qquad \tau_{xz} = G\gamma_{xz}, \qquad \tau_{yz} = G\gamma_{yz} \qquad (4\text{-}8.4)$$

where

$$c = (3\lambda + 2G)k \qquad (4\text{-}8.5)$$

Similarly, substitution of Eqs. (4–8.3) into Eq. (4–6.6) yields

$$\epsilon_x = \frac{1}{E}[\sigma_x - \nu(\sigma_y + \sigma_z)] + kT$$

$$\epsilon_y = \frac{1}{E}[\sigma_y - \nu(\sigma_x + \sigma_z)] + kT$$

$$\epsilon_z = \frac{1}{E}[\sigma_z - \nu(\sigma_x + \sigma_y)] + kT$$

$$\gamma_{xy} = \frac{2(1 + \nu)}{E}\tau_{xy} \qquad (4\text{-}8.6)$$

$$\gamma_{xz} = \frac{2(1 + \nu)}{E}\tau_{xz}$$

$$\gamma_{yz} = \frac{2(1 + \nu)}{E}\tau_{yz}$$

Finally, substituting Eqs. (4–8.6) into Eqs. (4–6.3) and (4–6.4), we find to first-degree terms in T

$$U = (\tfrac{1}{2}\lambda + G)J_1^2 - 2GJ_2 - cJ_1 T \qquad (4\text{–}8.7)$$

In terms of the strain components [see Eqs. (3–8.3)], we obtain

$$U = \tfrac{1}{2}\lambda(\epsilon_x + \epsilon_y + \epsilon_z)^2 + G(\epsilon_x^2 + \epsilon_y^2 + \epsilon_z^2 + \tfrac{1}{2}\gamma_{xy}^2 + \tfrac{1}{2}\gamma_{xz}^2 + \tfrac{1}{2}\gamma_{yz}^2) - c(\epsilon_x + \epsilon_y + \epsilon_z)T$$
$$(4\text{–}8.8)$$

Equations (4–8.7) and (4–8.8) are valid, provided that T is sufficiently small so that quadratic terms in T are negligible, and provided the material is isotropic.

Equations (4–8.4) and (4–8.6) are the basic stress-strain relations of classical thermoelasticity. For small temperature changes T, the strain energy density is modified by a temperature-dependent term which is proportional to the volumetric strain $e = J_1 = \epsilon_x + \epsilon_y + \epsilon_z$ [see Eqs. (4–8.7) and (4–8.8)].

4-9 Thermoelastic Compatibility Equations in Terms of Components of Stress and Temperature

Using the stress-strain relations [Eqs. (4–8.6)] we may write the strain compatibility relations [Eqs. (3–14.1) to (3–14.6)] in terms of stress components. Rewriting Eqs. (4–8.6), we obtain Hooke's law in the form:

$$\epsilon_x = \frac{1}{E}[(1+\nu)\sigma_x - I_1] + kT$$

$$\epsilon_y = \frac{1}{E}[(1+\nu)\sigma_y - I_1] + kT$$

$$\epsilon_z = \frac{1}{E}[(1+\nu)\sigma_z - I_1] + kT$$

$$\gamma_{xy} = \frac{2(1+\nu)}{E}\tau_{xy} \qquad (4\text{–}9.1)$$

$$\gamma_{xz} = \frac{2(1+\nu)}{E}\tau_{xz}$$

$$\gamma_{yz} = \frac{2(1+\nu)}{E}\gamma_{yz}$$

where $I_1 = \sigma_x + \sigma_y + \sigma_z$ is the first stress invariant [see (Eq. 2–5.4)], and where $T = T(x, y, z)$. Consider Eq. (3–14.1); namely,

$$\frac{\partial^2 \epsilon_x}{\partial y^2} + \frac{\partial^2 \epsilon_y}{\partial x^2} = \frac{\partial^2 \gamma_{xy}}{\partial x \partial y} \qquad \text{(a)}$$

Substitution of Eqs. (4–9.1) into Eq. (a) yields, for ν and E constant,

$$(1 + v)\left(\frac{\partial^2 \sigma_x}{\partial y^2} + \frac{\partial^2 \sigma_y}{\partial x^2}\right) - v\left(\frac{\partial^2 I_1}{\partial x^2} + \frac{\partial^2 I_1}{\partial y^2}\right)$$

$$= 2(1 + v)\frac{\partial^2 \tau_{xy}}{\partial x \, \partial y} - \frac{\partial^2 (EkT)}{\partial x^2} - \frac{\partial^2 (EkT)}{\partial y^2}$$

(b)

By Eq. (2–8.4), with the right-hand terms set equal to zero, we obtain

$$\frac{\partial \tau_{xy}}{\partial y} = -\frac{\partial \sigma_x}{\partial x} - \frac{\partial \tau_{xz}}{\partial z} - X$$

$$\frac{\partial \tau_{xy}}{\partial x} = -\frac{\partial \tau_{yz}}{\partial z} - \frac{\partial \sigma_y}{\partial y} - Y$$

Differentiation of the first of these equations by x and of the second by y yields

$$\frac{\partial^2 \tau_{xy}}{\partial y \, \partial x} = -\frac{\partial^2 \sigma_x}{\partial x^2} - \frac{\partial^2 \tau_{xz}}{\partial x \, \partial z} - \frac{\partial X}{\partial x}$$

$$\frac{\partial^2 \tau_{xy}}{\partial x \partial y} = -\frac{\partial^2 \tau_{yz}}{\partial y \, \partial z} - \frac{\partial^2 \sigma_y}{\partial y^2} - \frac{\partial Y}{\partial y}$$

Adding these equations, we obtain

$$2\frac{\partial^2 \tau_{xy}}{\partial x \partial y} = -\frac{\partial^2 \sigma_x}{\partial x^2} - \frac{\partial^2 \sigma_y}{\partial y^2} - \frac{\partial}{\partial z}\left(\frac{\partial \tau_{xz}}{\partial x} + \frac{\partial \tau_{yz}}{\partial y}\right) - \frac{\partial X}{\partial x} - \frac{\partial Y}{\partial y}$$

With the last of Eqs. (2–8.4), with $\ddot{w} = 0$, the above equation yields

$$2\frac{\partial^2 \tau_{xy}}{\partial x \, \partial y} = \frac{\partial^2 \sigma_z}{\partial z^2} - \frac{\partial^2 \sigma_x}{\partial x^2} - \frac{\partial^2 \sigma_y}{\partial y^2} + \frac{\partial Z}{\partial z} - \frac{\partial X}{\partial x} - \frac{\partial Y}{\partial y}$$

Substitution of this last equation into Eq. (b) yields, after simplification by the use of Eq. (2–5.4),

$$\nabla^2(I_1 + EkT) - \frac{\partial^2 (I_1 + EkT)}{\partial z^2} - (1 + v)\nabla^2 \sigma_z = (1 + v)\left(\frac{\partial Z}{\partial z} - \frac{\partial X}{\partial x} - \frac{\partial Y}{\partial y}\right)$$

(c)

where

$$\nabla^2 = \frac{\partial^2}{\partial x^2} + \frac{\partial^2}{\partial y^2} + \frac{\partial^2}{\partial z^2}$$

In a similar manner, by Eqs. (3–14.2) and (3–14.3), we obtain

$$\nabla^2(I_1 + EkT) - \frac{\partial^2 (I_1 + EkT)}{\partial x^2} - (1 + v)\nabla^2 \sigma_x$$

$$= (1 + v)\left(\frac{\partial X}{\partial x} - \frac{\partial Y}{\partial x} - \frac{\partial Z}{\partial z}\right)$$

(d)

$$\nabla^2(I_1 + EkT) - \frac{\partial^2 (I_1 + EkT)}{\partial y^2} - (1 + v)\nabla^2 \sigma_y$$

$$= (1 + v)\left(\frac{\partial Y}{\partial y} - \frac{\partial X}{\partial x} - \frac{\partial Z}{\partial z}\right)$$

Adding Eqs. (c) and (d), we get

$$(1 - \nu) \nabla^2 I_1 = -(1 + \nu) \left(\frac{\partial X}{\partial x} + \frac{\partial Y}{\partial y} + \frac{\partial Z}{\partial z} \right) - 2\nabla^2(EkT) \qquad \text{(e)}$$

Substitution of Eq. (e) into Eqs. (c) and (d) yields

$$\nabla^2 \sigma_x + \frac{1}{1 + \nu} \frac{\partial^2 (I_1 + EkT)}{\partial x^2}$$

$$= -\frac{\nu}{1 - \nu} \left(\frac{\partial X}{\partial x} + \frac{\partial Y}{\partial y} + \frac{\partial Z}{\partial z} \right) - 2 \frac{\partial X}{\partial x} - \frac{\nabla^2(EkT)}{1 - \nu}$$

$$\nabla^2 \sigma_y + \frac{1}{1 + \nu} \frac{\partial^2 (I_1 + EkT)}{\partial y^2}$$

$$= -\frac{\nu}{1 - \nu} \left(\frac{\partial X}{\partial x} + \frac{\partial Y}{\partial y} + \frac{\partial Z}{\partial z} \right) - 2 \frac{\partial Y}{\partial y} - \frac{\nabla^2(EkT)}{1 - \nu} \qquad \text{(4-9.2a)}$$

$$\nabla^2 \sigma_z + \frac{1}{1 + \nu} \frac{\partial^2 (I_1 + EkT)}{\partial z^2}$$

$$= -\frac{\nu}{1 - \nu} \left(\frac{\partial X}{\partial x} + \frac{\partial Y}{\partial y} + \frac{\partial Z}{\partial z} \right) - 2 \frac{\partial Z}{\partial z} - \frac{\nabla^2(EkT)}{1 - \nu}$$

In a similar manner, Eqs. (3–14.4), (3–14.5), and (3–14.6) yield

$$\nabla^2 \tau_{xy} + \frac{1}{1 + \nu} \frac{\partial^2 (I_1 + EkT)}{\partial x \, \partial y} = -\frac{\partial X}{\partial y} + \frac{\partial Y}{\partial x}$$

$$\nabla^2 \tau_{xz} + \frac{1}{1 + \nu} \frac{\partial^2 (I_1 + EkT)}{\partial x \, \partial z} = -\frac{\partial Z}{\partial x} + \frac{\partial X}{\partial z} \qquad \text{(4-9.2b)}$$

$$\nabla^2 \tau_{yz} + \frac{1}{1 + \nu} \frac{\partial^2 (I_1 + EkT)}{\partial y \, \partial z} = -\frac{\partial Y}{\partial z} + \frac{\partial Z}{\partial y}$$

If the body forces are constant throughout the body, the body-force terms on the right-hand side of Eqs. (4–9.2) are zero. We note that although Eqs. (4–9.2) were derived utilizing the equilibrium equations, they hold for dynamical problems, provided inertial forces are included in the body-force terms.

Equations (4–9.2) represent the thermoelastic strain compatibility conditions in terms of stress components and temperature. Since Hooke's law was used in their derivation, they are restricted to linearly elastic material. Furthermore, they are restricted to isotropic homogeneous materials, since it has been assumed that E and ν are constants and that the material is isotropic. In the absence of temperature T, Eqs. (4–9) are known as the *Beltrami-Michell compatibility relations*.

PROBLEM SET 4-9

1 Derive Eqs. (4–9.2b).

2 Let an isotropic homogeneous body be subjected to nonuniform temperature distribution. Assume that the body is free to expand thermally; that is, it is not subjected to geometrical constraints. Show that the most general temperature distribution T for a "stress-free" expansion of the body is given by the relation

$$kT = ax + by + cz + d$$

where k denotes the linear coefficient of thermal expansion and a, b, c, d are arbitrary constants.

4-10 Boundary Conditions

In addition to the equilibrium equations [Eq. (2–8.4)] and the compatibility conditions [Eq. (4–9.2)], the stress components on the surface of the body must be in equilibrium with the external forces acting on the surface (boundary). The equilibrium conditions at the boundary may be obtained from the theory of stress at a point. Equation (2–3.8) gives the stress σ_P on an oblique plane P through a point in a body. If the plane P is tangent to the surface of the body, σ_P is a stress on the boundary of the body. Hence, by Eq. (2–3.10),

$$\sigma_{Px} = l\sigma_x + m\tau_{xy} + n\tau_{xz}$$
$$\sigma_{Py} = l\tau_{xy} + m\sigma_y + n\tau_{yz} \qquad (4\text{--}10.1)$$
$$\sigma_{Pz} = l\tau_{xz} + m\tau_{yz} + n\sigma_z$$

where $\sigma_{Px}, \sigma_{Py}, \sigma_{Pz}$ denote the stress components of the surface stress vector at a point on the boundary, and l, m, n denote the direction cosines of the normal (positive outward) to the surface at this point. When Eqs. (2–3.10) pertain to a point on the boundary [Eq. (4–10.1)], they are called *boundary conditions*.

The solutions of elasticity problems require that the stress components satisfy equilibrium conditions [Eq. (2–8.4)], compatibility conditions [Eq. (4–9.2)], and boundary conditions [Eq. (4–10.1)]. In general, these conditions are usually sufficient to determine the stress components uniquely. However, if the body is in equilibrium, one cannot prescribe the body force (X, Y, Z) and the surface stress $(\sigma_{Px}, \sigma_{Py}, \sigma_{Pz})$ in a perfectly arbitrary way. For example, if a solution of the problem is to exist, the distribution of body forces and surface forces acting on the body must be such that the resultant force and the resultant moment vanish.

Since the basic equations of classical linear elasticity may be formulated either in terms of stresses or in terms of strains (through the use of stress-strain relations), instead of prescribing stresses acting on the boundary surface we could prescribe displacements u, v, w. Consequently, we may formulate the following fundamental boundary-value problems of elasticity:

1. *Determine the stress and the displacement in the interior of an elastic body in equilibrium when the body forces are prescribed and the distribution of forces acting on the surface of the body is known.*

2. *Determine the stress and the displacement in the interior of an elastic body in equilibrium when the body forces are prescribed and the displacements of the surface of the body are known.*

The general three-dimensional problem of elasticity presents formidable complications because of the difficulty of satisfying boundary conditions precisely. The majority of the general solutions of the boundary-value problems of three-dimensional elasticity amount to proofs of the existence of solutions. However, effective general methods have been developed for the solution of two-dimensional problems of elasticity.[11] Furthermore, solutions are often obtained in approximate form by employing Saint-Venant's principle—that is, by satisfying certain boundary conditions in integral form rather than in the pointwise manner required by the theory of elasticity.[12]

Roughly speaking, the usual engineering interpretation of Saint-Venant's principle may be summarized as follows:

Two statically equivalent force systems which act over a given small portion S on the surface of a body[13] *produce approximately the same stress and displacement at a point in the body sufficiently far removed from the region S over which the force systems act.*

4-11 Uniqueness Theorem for Equilibrium Problem of Elasticity

In the following articles, we seek solutions to the equilibrium problem of elasticity. However, before doing so, we prove the following theorem:[14]

If either the surface displacements or the surface stresses are given, the solution of the equilibrium problem is unique for the small-displacement theory of elasticity; that is, the state of stress (and strain) is determinable unequivocally.

In terms of principal axes and for isotropic material we observe that the strain energy density function U may be written in the form [Eq. (4–6.2)]

$$U = \tfrac{1}{2}\lambda(\epsilon_1 + \epsilon_2 + \epsilon_3)^2 + G(\epsilon_1^2 + \epsilon_2^2 + \epsilon_3^2)$$

---

[11]N. I. Muskhelishvili, *Some Basic Problems of the Mathematical Theory of Elasticity* (Groningen, Holland: P. Noordhoff, Ltd., 1953).

[12]Because of space limitations, rather than mislead the reader by discussing too briefly the implications of Saint-Venant's principle we refer to the following excellent papers: R. Von Mises, "On Saint-Venant's Principle, *"Bull. Amer. Math. Soc.*, Vol. 51 (1945), 555; E. Sternberg, "On Saint-Venant's Principle," *Quart. Appl. Math.*, Vol. 11 (1954), 393. See Also S. Timoshenko and J. Goodier, *Theory of Elasticity*, 2nd ed. (New York: McGraw-Hill Book Company, Inc., 1951), for a discussion of Saint-Venant's principle as often employed in engineering practice.

[13]That is, two force systems which have the same resultant, but not necessarily the same distribution over *S*.

[14]This theorem is due to Kirchhoff; see *J. F. Math.* (*Crelle*), Vol. 56, p. 859. See also Love, *Mathematical Theory of Elasticity*, pp. 170 , 176.

where $(\epsilon_1, \epsilon_2, \epsilon_3)$ denote principal strains and (λ, G) are Lamé constants. Hence, we observe that since $\lambda > 0$, $G > 0$ for real materials,

$$U \begin{cases} > 0 & \text{for nonzero } \epsilon_1, \epsilon_2, \epsilon_3 \\ = 0 & \text{if and only if } \epsilon_1 = \epsilon_2 = \epsilon_3 = 0 \end{cases} \qquad (4\text{--}11.1)$$

In other words, U is positive definite.[15]

Now let us assume that u', v', w' and u'', v'', w'' are two possible systems of nonsingular displacement components which satisfy the equilibrium equations [Eqs. (2–8.4), with $\ddot{u} = \ddot{v} = \ddot{w} = 0$] and the boundary conditions [Eqs. (4–10.1)]. We may express the equilibrium equations in terms of the function U by employing the relations given in Eqs. (4–3.3). For example, the first of Eqs. (2–8.4) may be written

$$\frac{\partial}{\partial x}\left(\frac{\partial U}{\partial \epsilon_x}\right) + \frac{\partial}{\partial y}\left(\frac{\partial U}{\partial \gamma_{xy}}\right) + \frac{\partial}{\partial z}\left(\frac{\partial U}{\partial \gamma_{xz}}\right) + X = 0 \qquad (4\text{--}11.2)$$

with similar expressions holding for the last two of Eqs. (2–8.4). Then, if we set

$$u = u' - u'', \qquad v = v' - v'', \qquad w = w' - w'' \qquad (4\text{--}11.3)$$

u, v, w is a system of displacements which satisfy the equations

$$\frac{\partial}{\partial x}\left(\frac{\partial U}{\partial \epsilon_x}\right) + \frac{\partial}{\partial y}\left(\frac{\partial U}{\partial \gamma_{xy}}\right) + \frac{\partial}{\partial z}\left(\frac{\partial U}{\partial \gamma_{xz}}\right) = 0, \quad \ldots, \quad \ldots \qquad (4\text{--}11.4)$$

where the ellipses denote two similar equations. Since Eqs. (4–11.4) hold at every point in the body, we may write

$$\iiint \left\{ u\left[\frac{\partial}{\partial x}\left(\frac{\partial U}{\partial \epsilon_x}\right) + \frac{\partial}{\partial y}\left(\frac{\partial U}{\partial \gamma_{xy}}\right) + \frac{\partial}{\partial z}\left(\frac{\partial U}{\partial \gamma_{xz}}\right)\right] \right.$$
$$+ v\left[\frac{\partial}{\partial x}\left(\frac{\partial U}{\partial \gamma_{xy}}\right) + \frac{\partial}{\partial y}\left(\frac{\partial U}{\partial \epsilon_y}\right) + \frac{\partial}{\partial z}\left(\frac{\partial U}{\partial \gamma_{yz}}\right)\right] \qquad (4\text{--}11.5)$$
$$+ \left. w\left[\frac{\partial}{\partial x}\left(\frac{\partial U}{\partial \gamma_{xz}}\right) + \frac{\partial}{\partial y}\left(\frac{\partial U}{\partial \gamma_{yz}}\right) + \frac{\partial}{\partial z}\left(\frac{\partial U}{\partial \epsilon_z}\right)\right] \right\} dx\, dy\, dz = 0$$

By the divergence theorem [Eq. (1–9.3)] we may transform Eq. (4–11.5) into the form [utilizing Eqs. (3–12.17)]

$$\iint \left[u\left(l\frac{\partial U}{\partial \epsilon_x} + m\frac{\partial U}{\partial \gamma_{xy}} + n\frac{\partial U}{\partial \gamma_{xz}}\right) + v\left(l\frac{\partial U}{\partial \gamma_{xy}} + m\frac{\partial U}{\partial \epsilon_y} + n\frac{\partial U}{\partial \gamma_{yz}}\right) \right.$$
$$\left. + w\left[l\frac{\partial U}{\partial \gamma_{xz}} + m\frac{\partial U}{\partial \gamma_{yz}} + n\frac{\partial U}{\partial \epsilon_z}\right)\right] dS$$
$$- \iiint \left[\frac{\partial U}{\partial \epsilon_x}\epsilon_x + \frac{\partial U}{\partial \epsilon_y}\epsilon_y + \frac{\partial U}{\partial \epsilon_z}\epsilon_z + \frac{\partial U}{\partial \gamma_{yz}}\gamma_{yz} \right. \qquad (4\text{--}11.6)$$
$$+ \left. \frac{\partial U}{\partial \gamma_{xz}}\gamma_{xz} + \frac{\partial U}{\partial \gamma_{xy}}\gamma_{xy}\right] dx\, dy\, dz = 0$$

---

[15] H. L. Langhaar, *Energy Methods in Applied Mechanics* (New York: John Wiley & Sons, Inc., 1962).

If boundary conditions are of the displacement type, $u = v = w = 0$ on S. If boundary conditions are of the stress type, the stress components calculated from u, v, w vanish on S (since each of sets u', v', w' and u'', v'', w'' yield the same stress components on S). In either case the double integral of Eq. (4-11.6) vanishes.

By Eqs. (4-4.4) and (4-4.6), we observe that the volume integral may be written in the form $\int \int \int 2U \, dx \, dy \, dz$. Hence, in order that Eq. (4-11.6) be satisfied, it follows that U must vanish, since by Eq. (4-11.1) U is either positive or zero. In order that U be zero, $\epsilon_1 = \epsilon_2 = \epsilon_3 = 0$. Hence, it follows that (u, v, w) represents a rigid-body displacement at most, and the assumed displacement sets (u', v', w') and (u'', v'', w'') can differ by a rigid-body displacement at most. However, when the boundary conditions are of the displacement type, (u, v, w) must vanish everywhere since they vanish at all points on S.

Accordingly, we conclude that the solution to the equilibrium problem is unique; that is, the stress and strain components are unique. In general, the displacement is unique to within an arbitrary rigid-body displacement (Art. 3-13).

4-12 Elementary Three-dimensional Problems of Elasticity. Semi-inverse Method

The solutions of an elasticity problem must satisfy not only the equations of equilibrium [Eqs. (2-8.4)] and the boundary conditions [Eqs. (4-10.1)], but also the compatibility conditions [Eqs. (3-14.1) through (3-14.6)]. With respect to rectangular cartesian coordinate axes (x, y, z), when expressed in terms of stress components, the compatibility equations contain only second derivatives of stress components and first derivatives of body forces [see Eqs. (4-9.2)]. If the body forces are constant, the compatibility equations contain only terms in second derivatives of stress components. Consequently, in a particular problem, if the equations of equilibrium and the boundary conditions are satisfied by stress components which are linear functions of (x, y, z), or constants, the compatibility equations are satisfied identically. Hence, these stress components are a solution to the elasticity problem. Furthermore, by the uniqueness theorem of elasticity (Art. 4-11), it follows that this solution is the only solution to the problem.

Semi-inverse method. Often a solution to an elasticity problem may be obtained without seeking simultaneous solutions to the equations of equilibrium, the compatibility conditions, and the boundary conditions. For example, one may attempt to seek solutions by making certain assumptions (guesses) about the components of stress, about the components of strain, or about the components of displacement, while leaving sufficient freedom in these assumptions so that the equations of elasticity may be satisfied. If the assumptions allow us to satisfy the elasticity equations, then by the uniqueness theorem, we have succeeded in obtaining *the* solution to the problem. This method was employed by Saint-Venent in his treatment of the torsion problem (Art. 7–2). Hence, it is often referred to as the Saint-Venant semi-inverse method.

Example 4–12.1. Hydrostatic State of Stress. In the absence of body forces, let a medium be subjected to the hydrostatic state

$$\sigma_x = \sigma_y = \sigma_z = -p, \qquad \tau_{xy} = \tau_{xz} = \tau_{yz} = 0 \tag{a}$$

where the constant p denotes pressure. Equations (a) automatically satisfy compatibility.

By Eqs. (a) and (4–6.6), we find

$$\epsilon_x = \epsilon_y = \epsilon_z = \frac{-p}{3\lambda + 2G} = -(1 - 2v)\frac{p}{E}$$
$$\gamma_{xy} = \gamma_{xz} = \gamma_{yz} = 0 \tag{b}$$

Equation (b) yields

$$e = \epsilon_x + \epsilon_y + \epsilon_z = -3(1 - 2v)\frac{p}{E} \tag{c}$$

where e denotes the volumetric strain. Substitution of Eqs. (b) into Eqs. (3–12.17) yields after integration

$$u = -\frac{p}{\lambda + 2G}x + ay + bz + c$$

$$v = -\frac{p}{\lambda + 2G}y - ax + dz + f \tag{d}$$

$$w = -\frac{p}{\lambda + 2G}z - bx - dy + g$$

where a, b, c, d, f, g are constants, which define a rigid-body displacement (see Art. 3–1 and problem of Art. 3–12). If we specify at the point $x = y = z = 0$ that $u = v = w = \omega_x = \omega_y = \omega_z = 0$, where $(\omega_x, \omega_y, \omega_z)$ denotes the rotation vector (see Art. 3–11), we obtain $a = b = c = d = f = g = 0$. Then, Eq. (d) reduces to

$$u = -\frac{p}{\lambda + 2G}x, \qquad v = -\frac{p}{\lambda + 2G}y \qquad w = -\frac{p}{\lambda + 2G}z \tag{e}$$

Equation (e) represents a simple dilatation (see Art. 3–13).

If the medium is incompressible, $e = 0$. Then, Eq. (c) yields $v = \frac{1}{2}$. Accordingly, for an incompressible medium Poisson's ratio is one-half.

4-13 Torsion of Shaft with Constant Circular Cross Section

Consider a solid cylinder with constant circular cross section A and with length L. Let the cylinder be subjected to axial twisting couples $\mathbf{M}$ applied at its ends; the vector which represents the couple is directed along the z axis, the axis of the shaft (see Fig. 4–13.1).

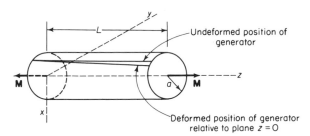

Fig. 4-13.1 Circular shaft subjected to twisting moment M.

Under the action of $\mathbf{M}$, an originally straight generator of the cylinder will deform into a helical curve. However, because of the symmetry of the cross section, it is reasonable to assume that plane cross sections of the cylinder normal to the z axis remain plane after the deformation. Furthermore, for small displacements a radius of a given section remains essentially straight and inextensible. In other words, the couple $\mathbf{M}$ causes each section to rotate approximately as a rigid body about the axis of the couple, that is, the axis of twist, z. Furthermore, if we measure the rotation θ of each section relative to the plane $z = 0$, the rotation θ of a given section will depend on its distance from the plane $z = 0$. For small deformations, a reasonable assumption is that the amount of rotation of a given section depends linearly on its distance z from the plane $z = 0$. Thus, the rotation θ of a section relative to the plane $z = 0$ is

$$\theta = \beta z \tag{4–13.1}$$

where β is the twist per unit length of the shaft. Under the assumption that plane sections remain plane and that Eq. (4–13.1) holds, we now seek to satisfy the equations of elasticity; that is, we employ the semi-inverse method of seeking the elasticity solution.

Since plane sections are assumed to remain plane, the displacement component w, parallel to the z axis, is taken to be zero. To calculate the (x, y) com-

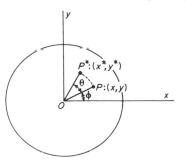

Figure 4-13.2

ponents u and v, consider a cross section distance z from the plane $z = 0$. Consider a point in the circular cross section (Fig. 4–13.2) with radial distance OP.

Under the deformation, radius OP rotates into the radius OP^*. In terms of the angular displacement θ of the radius, the displacement components (u, v) are

$$u = x^* - x = OP[\cos(\theta + \phi) - \cos\phi]$$
$$v = y^* - y = OP[\sin(\theta + \phi) - \sin\phi] \tag{4–13.2}$$

Expanding $\cos(\theta + \phi)$ and $\sin(\theta + \phi)$ and noting that $x = OP\cos\phi$, $y = OP\sin\phi$, we may write Eq. (4–13.2) in the form

$$u = x(\cos\theta - 1) - y\sin\theta$$
$$v = x\sin\theta + y(\cos\theta - 1) \tag{4–13.3}$$

Restricting the deformation to be small, we obtain (since then $\sin\theta \approx \theta$, $\cos\theta \approx 1$).

$$u = -y\theta, \qquad v = x\theta \tag{4–13.4}$$

to first-degree terms in θ.

Substitution of Eq. (4–13.1) into Eq. (4–13.4) yields

$$u = -\beta yz, \qquad v = \beta xz, \qquad w = 0 \tag{4–13.5}$$

On the basis of the foregoing assumptions, Eqs. (4–13.5) represent the displacement components of a circular shaft subjected to a twisting couple M.

Substitution of Eqs. (4–13.5) into Eqs. (3–12.17) yields the strain components

$$\epsilon_x = \epsilon_y = \epsilon_z = \gamma_{xy} = 0, \qquad \gamma_{xz} = -\beta y, \qquad \gamma_{yz} = \beta x \tag{4–13.6}$$

With Eqs. (4–13.6), Eqs. (4–6.5) yield the stress components

$$\sigma_x = \sigma_y = \sigma_z = \tau_{xy} = 0, \qquad \tau_{xz} = -\beta Gy, \qquad \tau_{yz} = \beta Gx \tag{4–13.7}$$

Since Eqs. (4–13.7) are linear in (x, y), they automatically satisfy compatibility [Eqs. (4–9.2)]. Furthermore, they satisfy equilibrium, provided the body forces are zero [Eqs. (2–8.4)].

To satisfy the boundary conditions, Eqs. (4–13.7) must yield no forces on the lateral boundary; on the ends, they must yield stresses such that the net moment is equal to M and the resultant force vanishes. Since the direction cosines of the unit normal to the lateral surface are $(l, m, 0)$, the first two of Eqs. (4–10.1) are satisfied identically. The last of Eqs. (4–10.1) yields

$$l\tau_{xz} + m\tau_{yz} = 0 \tag{4–13.8}$$

By Fig. (4–13.3),

$$l = \cos\phi = \frac{x}{a}, \qquad m = \sin\phi = \frac{y}{a} \tag{4–13.9}$$

Substitution of Eqs. (4–13.7) and (4–13.9) into Eq. (4–13.8) yields

$$-\frac{xy}{a} + \frac{xy}{a} = 0$$

Accordingly, the boundary conditions on the lateral boundary are satisfied.

On the ends, the stresses must be distributed so that the net moment is M. Since all stress components except τ_{yz}, τ_{xz} vanish, summation of forces on the end planes yield $F_x = F_y = F_z = 0$. Also summation of moments with respect to the z axis yields (Fig. 4–13.4)

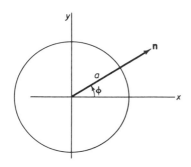

Figure 4-13.3   **Figure 4-13.4**

$$\Sigma M_z = M = \int_A (x\tau_{yz} - y\tau_{xz})\, dA \tag{4-13.10}$$

Substitution of Eqs. (4–13.7) into Eq. (4–13.10) yields

$$M = G\beta \int_A (x^2 + y^2)\, dA = G\beta \int_A r^2\, dA \tag{4-13.11}$$

Integration over the circular area yields

$$M = G\beta I_0 \tag{4-13.12}$$

where

$$I_0 = \frac{\pi}{2} a^4 \tag{4-13.12a}$$

is the polar moment of inertia of the circular cross section. Equation (4–13.12) relates the angular twist β per unit length of shaft to the applied moment M.

Since compatibility and equilibrium are satisfied, Eqs. (4–13.7) represent the solution of the elasticity problem, provided the stress components τ_{xz}, τ_{yz} are distributed over the end planes according to Eqs. (4–13.7). Since τ_{xz}, τ_{yz} are independent of z, the stress distribution is the same for all cross sections. Thus, the stress vector σ for any point P in a cross section is given by the relation

$$\sigma = -\mathbf{i}\beta Gy + \mathbf{j}\beta Gx \tag{4-13.13}$$

It lies in the plane of the section and is perpendicular to the radius vector $\mathbf{r}$ joining point P to the origin O.

By Eq. (4–13.13), the magnitude of σ is

$$\sigma = \beta G\sqrt{x^2 + y^2} = \beta G r \tag{4–13.14}$$

Hence, σ is a maximum for $r = a$; that is, σ attains a maximum value of $\beta G a$ on the lateral boundary of the shaft.

Review Problems

R-1 Displacement components are given by the formulas $u = 0$, $v = C_1 z$, $w = C_2 y$, where C_1 and C_2 are nonzero constants. What restrictions must be placed on C_1, C_2 in order that these displacement components may exist for a real body? Derive the strain components of the strain tensor. For small deflections, determine the state of stress that exists in the body if the body is linearly elastic and isotropic. Locate the principal axes of strain, the principal axes of stress.

R-2 Determine whether or not the following stress components are a possible solution of an elasticity problem in the absence of body forces.

$$\sigma_x = ayz, \qquad \tau_{xy} = dz^2$$
$$\sigma_y = bxz, \qquad \tau_{xz} = ey^2$$
$$\sigma_z = cxy. \qquad \tau_{yz} = fx^2$$

where a, b, c, d, e, f are constants.

R-3 The coordinate axes x and y on the free surface of a linearly elastic isotropic body are principal directions (see Fig. R4-3). At what angle θ must a strain gage be placed in order that direct measurement of the principal stress σ_x be made with this gage, i.e., so that $\sigma_x = K\epsilon_g$? Assume that the elastic constants of the material are known.

R-4 The stress components $\sigma_x = \sigma_z = \tau_{yz} = \tau_{xz} = 0$. Body forces are zero. The material is not necessarily elastic. Derive the most general formulas for the stress components σ_y, τ_{xy}.

R-5 Three strain gages are located on the free surface of a deformed body as shown in Fig. R4-5. The extensional strains measured by gages a, b, and c are ϵ_a, ϵ_b, and ϵ_c, respectively.

(a) Derive an expression for the strain components ϵ_x, ϵ_y, and γ_{xy} in terms of ϵ_a, ϵ_b, and ϵ_c.

(b) Assume that the material is linearly elastic and isotropic. Express the stress

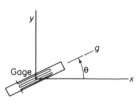

Figure R4-3

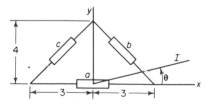

Figure R4-5

components σ_x, σ_y, and τ_{xy} on the surface in terms of ϵ_a, ϵ_b, ϵ_c and elastic constants ν and E.

(c) Assume that the direction I is a principal direction of strain. Express the angle θ in terms of ϵ_a, ϵ_b, and ϵ_c.

R-6 Show that the stress components

$$\sigma_y = \frac{E}{R} z + K, \qquad \sigma_x = \sigma_z = \tau_{xy} = \sigma_{xz} = \sigma_{yz} = 0$$

where E, R, and K are constants, satisfy the equilibrium equations and the boundary conditions for pure bending in the yz plane of a prismatic bar. Derive expressions for (x, y, z) displacement components (u, v, w) relative to one end of the bar. Are the compatibility conditions satisfied?

R-7 An elastic medium subjected to a state of stress σ_{ij} deforms incompressibly. Consider rectangular cartesian coordinate axes (x, y, z).

(a) Assume that $\sigma_x + \sigma_y + \sigma_z = 0$ and that $\epsilon_x = 0$, $\epsilon_y = 0$, $\epsilon_z = 0$. Determine the value of ν, Poisson's ratio, for the material.

(b) Assume that $\epsilon_z = 0$. Show that two values of ν are theoretically possible. Determine these two values of ν.

R-8 Consider a particle initially at the point (x, y, z) in a cylindrical shaft fixed at one end (see Fig. R4-8). When the bar is subjected to a couple **M** directed along the z axis, the radius to point (x, y) rotates about the z axis through an angle θz, where θ is the angle of twist per unit length of the bar. Assuming that the displacement is small, in terms of θ, x, y, and z derive the displacement components $u = x^* - x$, $v = y^* - y$. Assume that $w = \theta f(x, y)$, where w is the z component of displacement of the particle and $f(x, y)$ is a function of x and y. Derive formulas for the six strain components $\epsilon_x, \ldots, \gamma_{yz}$ in terms of θ, f, x, and y. Derive the corresponding

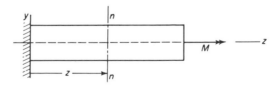

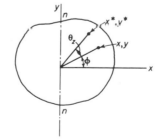

Figure R4-8

expressions for the six stress components in terms of f, θ, x, y, and G (the shear modulus). What is the equilibrium equation in terms of f? Neglect body forces.

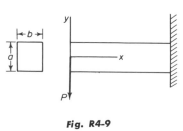

R-9 For the cantilever beam, it is assumed that the elementary beam formulas hold; that is (see Fig. R4-9),

$$\sigma_x = \frac{12Pxy}{a^3b}, \qquad \tau_{xy} = \frac{3P(a^2 - 4y^2)}{2a^3b},$$

$$\sigma_y = \sigma_z = \tau_{xz} = \tau_{yz} = 0$$

The material is elastic and deflections are small. Determine whether all the requirements of three-dimensional elasticity theory are satisfied by this solution. If not, what is violated?

Fig. R4-9

Appendix: Stress-strain Relations of Elasticity

In this appendix we present a brief development of the stress-strain relations of elasticity in index notation.

A4-1 Stress-strain Energy Density Function Relation

As in Art. 4–2, we assume the existence of a strain energy density function $U = U(\epsilon_{11}, \epsilon_{22}, \epsilon_{33}, \epsilon_{12}, \epsilon_{13}, \epsilon_{23})$, such that the work required to deform a differential element dV of an elastic body is $U\, dV$ (see Arts. 4–1 and 4–3). Hence, the rate of change of internal energy I of the body is

$$\dot{I} = \frac{d}{dt} \int \int \int U\, dV \tag{A4–1.1}$$

where the dot denotes time derivative.

If the deformation is adiabatic (or if the thermal effects are considered negligible) it follows by the first law of thermodynamics that

$$\dot{W} = \frac{d}{dt} \int \int \int U\, dV + \dot{K} \tag{A4–1.2}$$

where $\dot{W}$ denotes the time rate of work performed on the body by external forces and $\dot{K}$ denotes the time rate of change of kinetic energy K,

$$K = \frac{1}{2} \int \int \int \rho \dot{u}_\alpha \dot{u}_\alpha\, dV \tag{A4–1.3}$$

where $\dot{u}_\alpha$ denotes the time rate of change of the displacement vector u_α.

The work W of the external forces is the sum of the work W_B of the body forces ρB_α that act on the body and the work W_S of the surface forces p_α that act on the body (see Art. A2–4). Hence,

$$\dot{W} = \int_V \rho B_\alpha \dot{u}_\alpha\, dV + \int_S p_\alpha \dot{u}_\alpha\, dS \tag{A4–1.4}$$

Substituting Eqs. (A2–1.2) into Eq. (A4–1.4), transforming the surface integral in Eq. (A4–1.4) into a volume integral by the divergence theorem [Eq. (1–9.2)], and eliminating ρB_α by means of Eq. (A2–4.2), we obtain with Eqs. (A4–1.3) and (A3–1.11)

$$\dot{W} = \dot{K} + \int_V \sigma_{\alpha\beta} \dot{\epsilon}_{\alpha\beta} \, dV \tag{A4–1.5}$$

where

$$\dot{\epsilon}_{\alpha\beta} = \tfrac{1}{2}(\dot{u}_{\alpha,\beta} + \dot{u}_{\beta,\alpha}) \tag{A4–1.6}$$

Comparison of Eqs. (A4–1.2) and (A4–1.5) yields, since the integration must hold for arbitrary volumes,

$$\dot{U} = \sigma_{\alpha\beta} \dot{\epsilon}_{\alpha\beta} \tag{A4–1.7}$$

Temporarily, we employ the following notation:

$$s_1 = \sigma_{11}, \qquad s_2 = \sigma_{22}, \qquad s_3 = \sigma_{33}$$
$$s_4 = \sigma_{12}, \qquad s_5 = \sigma_{13}, \qquad s_6 = \sigma_{23}$$
$$e_1 = \epsilon_{11}, \qquad e_2 = \epsilon_{22}, \qquad e_3 = \epsilon_{33}$$
$$e_4 = 2\epsilon_{12}, \qquad e_5 = 2\epsilon_{13}, \qquad e_6 = 2\epsilon_{23}$$

Then Eq. (A4–1.7) may be written in the differential form $dU = s_\alpha \, de_\alpha$, $\alpha = 1, 2, 3, 4, 5, 6$. Also, by the rule for the total differential, $dU = (\partial U/\partial e_\alpha) de_\alpha$. Comparison of these two expressions for dU yields

$$s_\alpha = \frac{\partial U}{\partial e_\alpha} \qquad \text{or} \qquad \sigma_{\alpha\beta} = \frac{\partial U}{\partial \epsilon_{\alpha\beta}} \tag{A4–1.8}$$

Equations (A4–1.8) are equivalent to Eqs. (4–3.3).

A4-2 Generalized Hooke's Law

In its most general form, Hooke's law states that the components of the stress tensor are linearly related to the components of the strain tensor. Accordingly, if zero stress is to correspond to zero strain, we have for a general anisotropic body

$$\sigma_{\alpha\beta} = C_{\alpha\beta\gamma\delta} \epsilon_{\gamma\delta}, \qquad \alpha, \beta, \gamma, \delta = 1, \ldots, 6 \tag{A4–2.1}$$

where the coefficients $C_{\alpha\beta\gamma\delta}$ are characteristic constants of the body. Since $\sigma_{\alpha\beta} = \sigma_{\beta\alpha}$, it follows that the material constants $C_{\alpha\beta\gamma\delta}$ are symmetric in α, β. Hence, $C_{\alpha\beta\gamma\delta} = C_{\beta\alpha\gamma\delta}$. Furthermore, the $C_{\alpha\beta\gamma\delta}$ may be taken symmetrical with respect to γ, δ without loss of generality, since we may always effect symmetry by the substitution $\epsilon_{\gamma\delta} = \tfrac{1}{2}(\epsilon_{\gamma\delta} + \epsilon_{\delta\gamma})$. Furthermore, it follows by Eqs. (A4–1.8) and (A4–2.1) that

$$\frac{\partial^2 U}{\partial \epsilon_{\alpha\beta} \, \partial \epsilon_{\gamma\delta}} = C_{\alpha\beta\gamma\delta} \tag{A4–2.2}$$

Equation (A4–2.2) signifies that

$$C_{\alpha\beta\gamma\delta} = C_{\gamma\delta\alpha\beta} \tag{A4–2.3}$$

Equation (A4–2.3) indicates that at most twenty-one distinct elastic constants $C_{\alpha\beta\gamma\delta}$ characterize the general anisotropic body. Under a transformation of axes, the $C_{\alpha\beta\gamma\delta}$ transform according to the rules of a fourth-order isotropic tensor; that is, $C_{\alpha\beta\gamma\delta}$ is a fourth-order isotropic tensor (see Arts. 1–18 and 1–20).

For an isotropic body it may be shown (see Art. 4–6) that only two of the $C_{\alpha\beta\gamma\delta}$ are distinct.

5
BASIC EQUATIONS OF THE PLANE THEORY OF ELASTICITY

If a problem of elasticity is reducible to a two-dimensional problem, we say that it is a *plane problem* of elasticity. The corresponding theory is referred to as the *plane theory* of elasticity.

The equations of the plane theory of elasticity apply to the following two cases of equilibrium of elastic bodies, which are of considerable interest in practice: (1) *plane strain* (Art. 5–1) and (2) *deformation of a thin plate under forces applied to its boundary and acting in its plane* (Art. 5–2).

In the past decade or so, a considerable literature on the application of complex variables to the solution of plane problems has evolved. In fact, the complex variable method has been accepted to the extent that it is currently considered a routine approach to the plane problem of elasticity. However, we do not discuss the method in this book since to do so intelligently would require considerably more space. Furthermore, the method has been expounded extensively and authoritatively by Muskhelishvili and also by Sokolnikoff.[1]

5-1 Plane Strain

Definition. A body is in a state of plane strain, parallel to the (x, y) plane, if the displacement component w is zero, and if the components (u, v) are

---

[1]See N. I. Muskhelishvili, *Some Basic Problems of the Mathematical Theory of Elasticity* (Groningen, Holland: P. Noordhoff, Ltd., 1953) and I. S. Sokolnikoff, *Mathematical Theory of Elasticity* (New York: McGraw-Hill Book Company, Inc., 1956).

functions of (x, y) only. In view of this definition, the cubical strain for plane strain is

$$e = \frac{\partial u}{\partial x} + \frac{\partial v}{\partial y} \tag{5–1.1}$$

Hence, Eqs. (4–6.5) reduce to the following set:

$$\sigma_x = \lambda e + 2G\epsilon_x, \qquad \sigma_y = \lambda e + 2G\epsilon_y, \qquad \sigma_z = \lambda e$$

$$\tau_{xy} = G\gamma_{xy} = G\left(\frac{\partial v}{\partial x} + \frac{\partial u}{\partial y}\right), \qquad \tau_{xz} = \tau_{yz} = 0 \tag{5–1.2}$$

Equations (5–1.2) show that the stress components are functions of (x, y) only, since u, v, and hence e are functions of x, y only.

The equilibrium equations for plane strain [see Eqs. (2–8.4)] are

$$\frac{\partial \sigma_x}{\partial x} + \frac{\partial \tau_{xy}}{\partial y} + X = 0$$

$$\frac{\partial \tau_{xy}}{\partial x} + \frac{\partial \sigma_y}{\partial y} + Y = 0 \tag{5–1.3}$$

$$Z = 0$$

Consequently, in plane strain with respect to the (x, y) plane, the component of body force perpendicular to the (x, y) plane must vanish. Also, since σ_x, σ_y, τ_{xy} are functions of (x, y) only, the components X, Y of the body force are independent of z.

The strain-displacement relations [Eqs. (3–12.17)] reduce to the following form for plane strain:

$$\epsilon_x = \frac{\partial u}{\partial x}, \qquad \epsilon_y = \frac{\partial v}{\partial y}, \qquad \epsilon_z = 0$$

$$\gamma_{xy} = \frac{\partial u}{\partial y} + \frac{\partial v}{\partial x}, \qquad \gamma_{xz} = \gamma_{yz} = 0 \tag{5–1.4}$$

Hence, by Eqs. (4–6.6) and (5–1.4),

$$\sigma_z = \nu(\sigma_x + \sigma_y) \tag{5–1.5}$$

Thus, the static equations of elasticity for a body in plane strain with respect to the (x, y) plane reduce to the following set:

$$\frac{\partial \sigma_x}{\partial x} + \frac{\partial \tau_{xy}}{\partial y} + X = 0, \qquad \frac{\partial \tau_{xy}}{\partial x} + \frac{\partial \sigma_y}{\partial y} + Y = 0$$

$$\sigma_x = \lambda e + 2G\epsilon_x, \qquad \sigma_y = \lambda e + 2G\epsilon_y, \tag{5–1.6}$$

$$\sigma_z = \lambda e = \nu(\sigma_x + \sigma_y), \qquad \tau_{xy} = G\gamma_{xy}$$

In Eq. (5–1.6), it should be noted that σ_z is deduced from σ_x and σ_y [Eq. (5–1.5)]. Hence, the problem is reduced to determining three stress components σ_x, σ_y, τ_{xy}.

A state of plane strain can be maintained in a cylindrically shaped body by suitably applied forces. For example, by Eq. (5–1.5), we see that σ_z does not vanish in general. Hence, for a state of plane strain in a cylindrical body with the generators of the body parallel to the z axis, a tension or compression (σ_z) must be applied over the terminal sections formed by planes perpendicular to the z axis. Thus, the effect of σ_z is to keep constant the length of all longitudinal fibers of the body. In addition, the stress components σ_x and σ_y must attain values on the lateral surface of the body that are consistent with Eqs. (5–1.2) or Eqs. (5–1.6)

The solution of the plane strain problem of the cylindrical body may be used in conjunction with the auxiliary problem of a cylindrical body subjected to longitudinal terminal forces to solve the problem of deformation of a cylindrical body with terminal sections free of force. If the longitudinal terminal forces are equal in magnitude but opposite in sign to σ_z, the superposition of the results clears the terminal sections of the cylinder of force. However, the resulting deformation of the body is not necessarily a plane deformation. In general, the solution of the auxiliary problem involves the deformation of a cylinder by longitudinal end forces that produce a net axial force and a net couple (pure bending); see Probs. R-1 and R-2 at the end of Chapter 7.

5-2 Generalized Plane Stress

For certain kinds of loading, the equations of plane theory of elasticity apply to thin plates. We define a thin plate to be a prismatic member (for example, a cylinder) of very small length or *thickness h*. The middle surface of the plate, located halfway between its ends and parallel to them, is taken as the (x, y) plane (see Fig. 5–2.1).

We assume that the faces (upper and lower ends) are free from external stresses and that the stresses that act on the edges

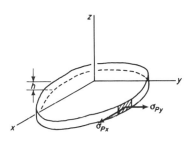

Figure 5-2.1

of the plate are parallel to the faces and are distributed symmetrically with respect to the middle surface. Similar restrictions apply to the body forces. By symmetry, note that points that are originally in the middle surface of the plate lie in the middle surface after deformation. Also, since the plate is assumed thin, the displacement component w is small, and variations of the displacement components u, v through the thickness are small. Consequently, satisfactory results are obtained, if we treat the equilibrium problem of the plate in terms of mean values $\bar{u}$, $\bar{v}$, and $\bar{w}$ of displacement components (u, v, w) defined as follows:

$$\bar{u}(x, y) = \frac{1}{h} \int_{-h/2}^{h/2} u(x, y, z) \, dz, \qquad \bar{v}(x, y) = \frac{1}{h} \int_{-h/2}^{h/2} v(x, y, z) \, dz$$

$$\bar{w}(x, y) = \frac{1}{h} \int_{-h/2}^{h/2} w(x, y, z) \, dz \tag{5-2.1}$$

where bars over letters denote mean values. In turn, substitution of Eqs. (5–2.1) into Eqs. (3–12.17) yields mean strains $\bar{\epsilon}_x, \bar{\epsilon}_y, \bar{\epsilon}_z, \bar{\gamma}_{xy}, \bar{\gamma}_{yz}, \bar{\gamma}_{xz}$.

Since it is assumed that $\tau_{xz} = \tau_{yz} = \sigma_z = 0$ on the ends, that is, $z = \pm h/2$, in the absence of body forces, it follows from the last of Eqs. (2–8.4) that for $z = \pm h/2$, $\partial \sigma_z / \partial z = 0$. This follows from the fact that since $\tau_{xz} = 0$ for $z = \pm h/2$, $\partial \tau_{xz} / \partial x = 0$ for $z = \pm h/2$, and since $\tau_{yz} = 0$ for $z = \pm h/2$, $\partial \tau_{yz} / \partial y = 0$ for $z = \pm h/2$.

Hence, σ_z is not only zero for $z = \pm h/2$, but also its derivative with respect to z vanishes. Therefore, since the plate is thin, σ_z is small throughout the plate. These observations lead us naturally to the *approximation* that $\sigma_z = 0$ everywhere.

Analogously, we define mean values of stress components $(\sigma_x, \sigma_y, \tau_{xy})$ as follows:

$$\bar{\sigma}_x = \frac{1}{h} \int_{-h/2}^{h/2} \sigma_x \, dz, \quad \bar{\sigma}_y = \frac{1}{h} \int_{-h/2}^{h/2} \sigma_y \, dz, \quad \bar{\tau}_{xy} = \frac{1}{h} \int_{-h/2}^{h/2} \tau_{xy} \, dz \tag{5-2.2}$$

Furthermore, derivatives with respect to z of the mean values of τ_{xz} and τ_{yz} vanish; that is,

$$\frac{\partial}{\partial z}(\bar{\tau}_{xz}) = \frac{1}{h} \frac{\partial}{\partial z} \int_{-h/2}^{h/2} \tau_{xz} \, dz = \frac{1}{h} \tau_{xz} \Big|_{-h/2}^{h/2} = 0$$

$$\frac{\partial}{\partial z}(\bar{\tau}_{yz}) = \frac{1}{h} \frac{\partial}{\partial z} \int_{-h/2}^{h/2} \tau_{yz} \, dz = \frac{1}{h} \tau_{yz} \Big|_{-h/2}^{h/2} = 0 \tag{5-2.3}$$

Also, mean values of body forces are defined as follows:

$$\bar{X} = \frac{1}{h} \int_{-h/2}^{h/2} X \, dz, \quad \bar{Y} = \frac{1}{h} \int_{-h/2}^{h/2} Y \, dz, \quad \bar{Z} = \frac{1}{h} \int_{-h/2}^{h/2} Z \, dz = 0 \tag{5-2.4}$$

Substitution of Eqs. (5–2.2), (5–2.3), and (5–2.4) into the first two of Eqs. (2–8.4) yields after integration with respect to z (neglecting acceleration effects)

$$\frac{\partial \bar{\sigma}_x}{\partial x} + \frac{\partial \bar{\tau}_{xy}}{\partial y} + \bar{X} = 0, \qquad \frac{\partial \bar{\tau}_{xy}}{\partial x} + \frac{\partial \bar{\sigma}_y}{\partial y} + \bar{Y} = 0 \tag{5-2.5}$$

From the stress-strain relations [Eqs. (4–6.5)], it follows from $\sigma_z = \lambda e + 2G\epsilon_z = 0$ that

$$\epsilon_z = -\frac{\lambda}{\lambda + 2G}(\epsilon_x + \epsilon_y) \tag{5-2.6}$$

Substituting Eq. (5–2.6) into the first and second of Eqs. (4–6.5), we obtain

$$\sigma_x = \frac{2\lambda G}{\lambda + 2G}(\epsilon_x + \epsilon_y) + 2G\epsilon_x, \qquad \sigma_y = \frac{2\lambda G}{\lambda + 2G}(\epsilon_x + \epsilon_y) + 2G\epsilon_y \tag{5-2.7}$$

The fourth of Eqs. (4–6.5) is

$$\tau_{xy} = G\left(\frac{\partial u}{\partial y} + \frac{\partial v}{\partial x}\right) \tag{5–2.8}$$

Taking the mean values of Eqs. (5–2.7) and (5–2.8), we obtain

$$\bar{\sigma}_x = \bar{\lambda}(\bar{\epsilon}_x + \bar{\epsilon}_y) + 2G\bar{\epsilon}_x = \bar{\lambda}\bar{e} + 2G\bar{\epsilon}_x$$

$$\bar{\sigma}_y = \bar{\lambda}(\bar{\epsilon}_x + \bar{\epsilon}_y) + 2G\bar{\epsilon}_y = \bar{\lambda}\bar{e} + 2G\bar{\epsilon}_y \tag{5–2.9}$$

$$\bar{\tau}_{xy} = G\left(\frac{\partial \bar{u}}{\partial y} + \frac{\partial \bar{v}}{\partial x}\right),$$

where

$$\bar{\lambda} = \frac{2\lambda G}{\lambda + 2G} = \frac{\nu E}{1 - \nu^2}, \quad \bar{\epsilon}_x = \frac{1}{h}\int_{-h/2}^{h/2} \epsilon_x\, dz, \quad \bar{\epsilon}_y = \frac{1}{h}\int_{-h/2}^{h/2} \epsilon_y\, dz \tag{5–2.10}$$

Comparison of Eqs. (5–2.5) and (5–2.9) with Eqs. (5–1.6) shows that the mean values of displacement components (u, v) and the mean values of the stress components $(\sigma_x, \sigma_y, \tau_{xy})$ satisfy the same equations which govern the case of plane strain, the only difference being that λ is replaced by $\bar{\lambda}$ defined by Eq. (5–2.10). Additionally, the stress components σ_{Px}, σ_{Py} on the boundary of the plate are replaced by their mean values $\bar{\sigma}_{Px}$, $\bar{\sigma}_{Py}$ [see Eqs. (4–10.1)].

Taking note of these facts, we may write the equations of generalized plane stress without bars over the symbols. We merely keep in mind that components of stress, strain, and displacement are mean values and that λ is replaced by

$$\bar{\lambda} = \frac{2\lambda G}{\lambda + 2G} = \frac{\nu E}{1 - \nu^2}$$

Thus, we see that for plane strain and for generalized plane stress we are led to the study of the following system of equations:

$$\frac{\partial \sigma_x}{\partial x} + \frac{\partial \tau_{xy}}{\partial y} + X = 0, \quad \frac{\partial \tau_{xy}}{\partial x} + \frac{\partial \sigma_y}{\partial y} + Y = 0 \tag{5–2.11}$$

$$\sigma_x = \lambda e + 2G\epsilon_x, \quad \sigma_y = \lambda e + 2G\epsilon_y, \quad \tau_{xy} = G\left(\frac{\partial u}{\partial y} + \frac{\partial v}{\partial x}\right) = G\gamma_{xy} \tag{5–2.12}$$

where

$$e = \frac{\partial u}{\partial x} + \frac{\partial v}{\partial y} \tag{5–2.13}$$

Equations (5–2.11) may be written entirely in terms of strain components by substitution of Eqs. (5–2.12) into Eqs. (5–2.11). Equations (5–2.11) may also be written entirely in terms of displacement components by substitution of Eqs. (5–2.13) and (3–12.17) into Eqs. (5–2.12) and substitution of the result into Eq. (5–2.11).

A more specialized state of stress, called *plane stress*, is obtained if we set $\sigma_z = \tau_{xz} = \tau_{yz} = Z = 0$ everywhere. Then the equilibrium equations are given by Eqs. (5–1.3).

Although in generalized plane stress, the mean values of the displacement components are independent of z, in a state of plane stress the displacement components u, v, w are not in general independent of z. In particular, we note that ϵ_z does not vanish and that it is defined by Eq. (5–2.6)

Furthermore, we observe that, in a plate, a state of plane stress requires the body forces and the tractions at the edges to be distributed in certain special ways. It does not, however, require tractions on the faces of the plate.

Finally, we also remark that the average values of displacement in any problem of plane stress are the same as if the problem were one of generalized plane stress. Accordingly, the solution of problems of plane strain may be employed to examine effects produced by certain distributions of forces which do not produce plane strain states since any such problem can be solved by treating it as a plane strain problem, and by replacing λ by $\bar{\lambda}$ in the results. For example, this technique may be employed in problems of equilibrium of a thin plate deformed by forces applied in the plane of the plate. Although the actual values of stress and displacement are not determined by this procedure (unless the forces actually produce a state of plane stress), the average values across the thickness of the plate are obtained. Moreover, average values are the usual quantities measured experimentally.

5-3 Compatibility Equation in Terms of Stress Components

The equations of plane elasticity comprise Eqs. (5–2.11) and one supplementary condition (the compatibility condition) which insures that there exist two displacement components (u, v) related to the three stress components $(\sigma_x, \sigma_y, \tau_{xy})$ through Eqs. (5–2.12). The compatibility equation may be derived from Eqs. (4–9.2) or from Eqs. (3–14.1) through (3–14.6).

Plane strain. Consider the state of plane strain. Such a state is defined by the conditions that ϵ_x, ϵ_y, γ_{xy} are independent of z, and $\epsilon_z = \gamma_{xz} = \gamma_{yz} = 0$. Hence, the compatibility conditions reduce to the single equation [Eq. (3–14.1)].

$$\frac{\partial^2 \epsilon_x}{\partial y^2} + \frac{\partial^2 \epsilon_y}{\partial x^2} = \frac{\partial^2 \gamma_{xy}}{\partial x \, \partial y} \tag{5-3.1}$$

Also, Eqs. (4–6.6) (with Eqs. 5–1.5) become

$$\epsilon_x = \frac{1}{2G}\left[\sigma_x - \frac{\lambda}{2(\lambda + G)}(\sigma_x + \sigma_y)\right]$$

$$\epsilon_y = \frac{1}{2G}\left[\sigma_y - \frac{\lambda}{2(\lambda + G)}(\sigma_x + \sigma_y)\right] \tag{5-3.2}$$

$$\gamma_{xy} = \frac{1}{G}\tau_{xy}$$

Substitution of Eqs. (5–3.2) into Eq. (5–3.1) yields

$$\frac{\partial^2 \sigma_x}{\partial y^2} + \frac{\partial^2 \sigma_y}{\partial x^2} - \nu \nabla^2(\sigma_x + \sigma_y) = 2\frac{\partial^2 \tau_{xy}}{\partial x\, \partial y} \tag{a}$$

Equations (2–8.4) yield

$$-2\frac{\partial^2 \tau_{xy}}{\partial x\, \partial y} = \frac{\partial^2 \sigma_x}{\partial x^2} + \frac{\partial^2 \sigma_y}{\partial y^2} + \frac{\partial X}{\partial x} + \frac{\partial Y}{\partial y} \tag{b}$$

Substitution of Eq. (b) into Eq. (a) yields after simplification

$$\nabla^2(\sigma_x + \sigma_y) = -\frac{2(\lambda + G)}{\lambda + 2G}\left(\frac{\partial X}{\partial x} + \frac{\partial Y}{\partial y}\right)$$

$$= -\frac{1}{1 - \nu}\left(\frac{\partial X}{\partial x} + \frac{\partial Y}{\partial y}\right) \tag{5-3.3}$$

Equations (5–2.11) and (5–3.3) represent the equations of plane strain. The equations of generalized plane stress are obtained from these equations if mean values of stress and body force are used, and if λ is replaced by

$$\bar{\lambda} = \frac{2\lambda G}{\lambda + 2G} = \frac{\nu E}{1 - \nu^2}$$

Generalized plane stress. For generalized plane stress, $\sigma_z = 0$. Hence, by the third of Eqs. (4–6.5),

$$\epsilon_z = -\frac{\nu}{1 - \nu}(\epsilon_x + \epsilon_y) = -\frac{\nu}{1 - \nu}(u_x + v_y) \tag{5-3.4}$$

By Eq. (5–3.4) we may eliminate ϵ_z from the first two of Eqs. (4–6.5). Then, on taking mean values, we obtain

$$\bar{\sigma}_x = \bar{\lambda}\bar{e} + 2G\bar{\epsilon}_x, \qquad \bar{\sigma}_y = \bar{\lambda}\bar{e} + 2G\bar{\epsilon}_y, \qquad \bar{\tau}_{xy} = G\bar{\gamma}_{xy}$$

$$\bar{e} = \bar{\epsilon}_x + \bar{\epsilon}_y, \qquad \bar{\lambda} = \frac{2G\nu}{1 - \nu} \tag{5-3.5}$$

The inverse relations are

$$E\bar{\epsilon}_x = \bar{\sigma}_x - \nu\bar{\sigma}_y, \qquad E\bar{\epsilon}_y = \bar{\sigma}_y - \nu\bar{\sigma}_x, \qquad G\bar{\gamma}_{xy} = \bar{\tau}_{xy} \tag{5-3.6}$$

The mean strain components evidently satisfy the compatibility conditions [Eq. (3–14.1) or Eq. (5–3.1)]. With Eq. (5–3.6), Eq. (5–3.1) may be expressed in terms of stress, as follows:

$$\nabla^2(\sigma_x + \sigma_y) = -(1 + \nu)\left(\frac{\partial X}{\partial x} + \frac{\partial Y}{\partial y}\right) \tag{5-3.7}$$

In view of the principle of superposition, body forces can be eliminated from consideration, if a particular solution is found. We must then solve a problem with no body forces, but with altered boundary conditions. For constant body forces or centrifugal body forces, particular solutions are easily found. Consequently, let us consider cases in which body forces are absent. Then the compatibility conditions for generalized plane stress and plane strain [Eqs. (5–3.3) and (5–3.7)] are identical. The stress-strain relations are the same in both cases, except that $\bar{\lambda}$ replaces λ in problems of generalized plane stress.

In terms of the Airy stress function F (see Art. 5–4), the problem, in either case, reduces to the solution $\nabla^2 \nabla^2 F = 0$. Furthermore, by the principle of superposition, any solution of an axial stress problem may be superimposed on a plane strain solution. For the general plane orthogonal curvilinear coordinate system the defining equation for F is obtained by specializing the expression for ∇^2 for the plane; that is, by setting $h_3 = 1$ and $\partial/\partial w = 0$ [see Art. 1–16 and Eq. (1–16.13)].

5-4 Airy Stress Function

Simply connected regions. For the plane theory of elasticity, the equilibrium equations [Eqs. (2–8.4)] reduce to the following two equations:

$$\frac{\partial \sigma_x}{\partial x} + \frac{\partial \tau_{xy}}{\partial y} + X = 0, \qquad \frac{\partial \tau_{xy}}{\partial x} + \frac{\partial \sigma_y}{\partial y} + Y = 0 \qquad (5\text{–}4.1)$$

As noted in Art. 5–3, we may initially ignore body forces (X, Y) and seek solutions to Eqs. (5–4.1) modified accordingly. Then, the effects of body forces may be superimposed. However, in the case of body forces derivable from a potential function V $(\nabla^2 V = 0)$, such that

$$X = -\frac{\partial V}{\partial x}, \qquad Y = -\frac{\partial V}{\partial y} \qquad (5\text{–}4.2)$$

we may incorporate the effects of body force directly. Thus, Eqs. (5–4.1) and (5–4.2) yield

$$\frac{\partial \sigma'_x}{\partial x} + \frac{\partial \tau_{xy}}{\partial y} = 0, \qquad \frac{\partial \sigma'_y}{\partial y} + \frac{\partial \tau_{xy}}{\partial x} = 0 \qquad (5\text{–}4.3)$$

where

$$\sigma'_x = \sigma_x - V, \qquad \sigma'_y = \sigma_y - V \qquad (5\text{–}4.4)$$

Now, for simply connected regions, we note that the first of Eqs. (5–4.3) represents the necessary and sufficient condition that there exists a function $\phi(x, y)$ such that (see Art. 1–13)

$$\frac{\partial \phi}{\partial y} = \sigma'_x, \qquad \frac{\partial \phi}{\partial x} = -\tau_{xy} \qquad (5\text{–}4.5)$$

The second of Eqs. (5–4.3) represents the necessary and sufficient condition that there exists a function $\theta(x, y)$ such that

$$\frac{\partial \theta}{\partial x} = \sigma'_y, \qquad \frac{\partial \theta}{\partial y} = -\tau_{xy} \qquad (5\text{–}4.6)$$

Comparison of the two expressions for τ_{xy} shows that

$$\frac{\partial \phi}{\partial x} = \frac{\partial \theta}{\partial y} \qquad (5\text{–}4.7)$$

In turn, Eq. (5–4.7) is the necessary and sufficient condition that there exists a function $F(x, y)$ such that

$$\phi = \frac{\partial F}{\partial y}, \qquad \theta = \frac{\partial F}{\partial x} \tag{5–4.8}$$

Substitution of Eq. (5–4.8) into Eqs. (5–4.5) and (5–4.6) shows that there always exists a function F such that for body forces represented by Eqs. (5–4.2) stress components in the plane theory of elasticity may be expressed in the form

$$\sigma'_x = \frac{\partial^2 F}{\partial y^2}, \qquad \sigma'_y = \frac{\partial^2 F}{\partial x^2}, \qquad \tau_{xy} = -\frac{\partial^2 F}{\partial x \, \partial y}$$

Alternatively, by Eqs. (5–4.4), we have

$$\sigma_x = \frac{\partial^2 F}{\partial y^2} + V, \qquad \sigma_y = \frac{\partial^2 F}{\partial x^2} + V, \qquad \tau_{xy} = -\frac{\partial^2 F}{\partial x \, \partial y} \tag{5–4.9}$$

The function F is called the *Airy stress function*, in honor of G. B. Airy, who first noted this relation.

Since it was assumed that the stresses $\sigma_x, \sigma_y, \tau_{xy}$ are single-valued and continuous together with their second-order derivatives [note the compatibility equations in terms of stress components Eq. (5–3.3)], the function F must possess continuous derivatives up to and including fourth order. These derivatives, from the second order on up, must be single-valued functions throughout the region occupied by the body [see Eqs. (5–4.9)].

Conversely, if F has these properties, the functions $\sigma_x, \sigma_y, \tau_{xy}$ defined in terms of F by Eqs. (5–4.9) will satisfy Eq. (5–4.1), provided body forces are defined by Eqs. (5–4.2). Additionally, in order to insure that the stresses so determined correspond to an actual deformation, the compatibility conditions for the plane theory of elasticity must be satisfied. For body forces defined by Eq. (5–4.2) (or for constant body forces), this condition becomes [see Eqs. (5–3.3) or (5–3.7)]

$$\nabla^2(\sigma_x + \sigma_y) = 0 \tag{5–4.10}$$

Adding the first two of Eqs. (5–4.9), we note that

$$\sigma_x + \sigma_y = \nabla^2 F + 2V \tag{5–4.11}$$

Substitution of Eq. (5–4.11) into Eq. (5–4.10) yields (since $\nabla^2 V = 0$)

$$\nabla^2 \nabla^2 F = \frac{\partial^4 F}{\partial x^4} + 2\frac{\partial^4 F}{\partial x^2 \, \partial y^2} + \frac{\partial^4 F}{\partial y^4} = 0 \tag{5–4.12}$$

Equation (5–4.12) is the compatibility condition of the plane theory of elasticity with constant body forces or body forces derivable from a potential function [Eq. (5–4.2)] in terms of the stress function F.

Equations of the form of Eq. (5–4.12) are called *biharmonic*. Solutions of

Eq. (5–4.12) are called biharmonic functions.[2] Some well-known solutions to Eq. (5–4.12) are, in rectangular coordinates,

$$y, \quad y^2, \quad y^3, \quad x, \quad x^2, \quad x^3, \quad xy, \quad x^2y, \quad x^3y$$
$$x^2 - y^2, \quad xy^2, \quad x^4 - y^4, \quad x^2y^2 - \tfrac{1}{3}y^4, \quad \ldots$$
$$\cos \lambda y \cosh \lambda x, \quad \cosh \lambda y \cos \lambda x, \quad y \cos \lambda y \cosh \lambda x$$
$$y \cosh \lambda y \cos \lambda x, \quad x \cos \lambda y \cosh \lambda x, \quad x \cosh \lambda y \cos \lambda x$$

$$(5\text{–}4.13)$$

By the above analysis, the problem of plane elasticity has been reduced to seeking solutions to Eq. (5–4.12) such that the stress components [Eqs. (5–4.9)] satisfy the boundary conditions. A number of problems may be solved by using simple linear combinations of polynomials[3] in x and y.

Problem. Verify that the functions listed in Eq. (5–4.13) satisfy Eq. (5–4.12).

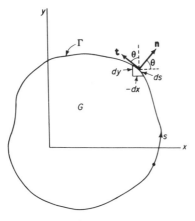

Figure 5-4.1

Boundary conditions. It is frequently convenient to have the stress boundary conditions [Eqs. (4–10.1)] expressed in terms of the Airy stress function. For simply connected regions, Eqs. (4–10.1) may be transformed as follows:

Consider region G: (x, y) bounded by the curve Γ (Fig. 5–4.1). The unit normal vector ($+$ outward) is

$$\mathbf{n} = (l, m, n) = \left(\frac{dy}{ds}, -\frac{dx}{ds}, 0\right)$$

$$(5\text{–}4.14)$$

where s denotes arc length measured from some arbitrary point P on Γ. The unit tangent vector to Γ is denoted by $\mathbf{t}$, the positive direction of $\mathbf{t}$ being such that $(\mathbf{n}, \mathbf{t})$ form a right-handed system.

For the plane theory of elasticity with respect to the (x, y) plane, the boundary conditions [Eqs. (4–10.1)] reduce to

$$\sigma_{Px} = l\sigma_x + m\tau_{xy}, \qquad \sigma_{Py} = l\tau_{xy} + n\sigma_y \qquad (5\text{–}4.15)$$

Substitution of Eqs. (5–4.14) into Eqs. (5–4.15) yields

$$\sigma_{Px} = \sigma_x \frac{dy}{ds} - \tau_{xy} \frac{dx}{ds}, \qquad \sigma_{Py} = \tau_{xy} \frac{dy}{ds} - \sigma_y \frac{dx}{ds} \qquad (5\text{–}4.16)$$

---

[2]J. C. Maxwell first noticed that the stress function must be biharmonic. See *The Scientific Papers of James Clerk Maxwell*, vol. 2 (New York: Dover Publications, Inc., 1890), p. 207.

[3]See S. Timoshenko and J. Goodier, *Theory of Elasticity*, 2nd ed. (New York: McGraw-Hill Book Company, Inc., 1951), Chap. 3.

By Eqs. (5–4.16), (5–4.5), and (5–4.6), we eliminate σ_x, σ_y, τ_{xy} to obtain

$$\sigma_{Px} = \frac{\partial \phi}{\partial y}\frac{dy}{ds} + \frac{\partial \phi}{\partial x}\frac{dx}{ds} = \frac{d\phi}{ds}$$

$$\sigma_{Py} = -\frac{\partial \theta}{\partial y}\frac{dy}{ds} - \frac{\partial \theta}{\partial x}\frac{dx}{ds} = -\frac{d\theta}{ds}$$

or multiplying by ds, we get

$$\sigma_{Px}\,ds = \frac{\partial \phi}{\partial x}\,dx + \frac{\partial \phi}{\partial y}\,dy = d\phi$$

$$-\sigma_{Py}\,ds = \frac{\partial \theta}{\partial x}\,dx + \frac{\partial \theta}{\partial y}\,dy = d\theta$$

(5–4.17)

Integration of Eq. (5–4.17) yields [with Eq. (5–4.8)]

$$\phi = \frac{\partial F}{\partial y} = \int \sigma_{Px}\,ds = \int_0^l \sigma_{Px}\,ds + C_1 = R_x + C_1$$

$$\theta = \frac{\partial F}{\partial x} = -\int \sigma_{Py}\,ds = -\int_0^l \sigma_{Py}\,ds + C_2 = -R_y + C_2$$

(5–4.18)

where (R_x, R_y) denote the (x, y) projections of the total force acting on Γ from 0 to l and (C_1, C_2) are constants. Equations (5–4.18) express the stress boundary conditions [Eqs. (4–10.1)] in terms of derivatives of the Airy stress function F.

The stress boundary conditions may be interpreted physically in terms of the net force and net moment at $s = l$ due to the stress distributed on the boundary from $s = 0$ to $s = l$. For example, recall that by definition the total differential dF of F is

$$dF = \frac{\partial F}{\partial x}\,dx + \frac{\partial F}{\partial y}\,dy$$

(5–4.19)

Substitution of Eqs. (5–4.18) into Eq. (5–4.19) yields (after integration)

$$F(l) = \int_0^l dF = \int_0^l (-R_y\,dx + R_x\,dy) + C_1(y - y_0) + C_2(x - x_0) + C_3$$

Since linear terms in F do not contribute to the stress components [Eq. (5–4.9) with $V = 0$], we take $C_1 = C_2 = C_3 = 0$. Then integration by parts yields [with Eqs. (5–4.18)]

$$F(l) = \int_0^l (-R_y\,dx + R_x\,dy)$$

$$= (-xR_y + yR_x)\Big|_0^l - \int_0^l (-x\,dR_y + y\,dR_x)$$

$$= -x_l\,R_y(l) + y_l\,R_x(l) + \int_0^l (x\sigma_{Py} - y\sigma_{Px})\,ds$$

$$= -\int_0^l (x_l - x)\sigma_{Py}\,ds + \int_0^l (y_l - y)\sigma_{Px}\,ds = M_l$$

(5–4.20)

where M_l denotes the moment with respect to $P: (s = l)$ of boundary forces on Γ from the point $P: (s = 0)$ to the point $P: (s = l)$. Thus, Eq. (5–4.20) shows that the value $F(l)$ of the Airy stress function at $s = l$, relative to its value at $s = 0$, is equal to the net moment of the boundary forces on Γ from the point $s = 0$ to the point $s = l$.

Equation (5–4.20) replaces one of the boundary conditions [Eqs. (5–4.18)]. To obtain a second equation, consider the directional derivative of the Airy stress function in the direction of $\mathbf{n}$ (Fig. 5–4.1) We have [see Art. 1–2 and Eqs. (5–4.14) and (5–4.18)]

$$
\begin{aligned}
\frac{dF(l)}{dn} &= \mathbf{n} \cdot \text{grad } F \\[2mm]
&= \left(\frac{dy}{ds}, -\frac{dx}{ds}\right) \cdot (-R_y(l), R_x(l)) \\[2mm]
&= -\left(\frac{dx}{ds}, \frac{dy}{ds}\right) \cdot \left[\int_0^l \sigma_{Px}\, ds, \int_0^l \sigma_{Py}\, ds\right] \\[2mm]
&= -\mathbf{t} \cdot \mathbf{R}
\end{aligned}
\tag{5–4.21}
$$

where $\mathbf{R}$ denotes the resultant external force acting on Γ from the point $s = 0$ to the point $s = l$. Hence, the normal derivative of F at point $s = l$ is equal to the negative of the projection of $\mathbf{R}$ on the tangent $\mathbf{t}$ to the curve Γ at point $s = l$.

Equations (5–4.20) and (5–4.21) serve as boundary conditions in terms of the Airy stress function F. If the boundary Γ is free of external forces Eqs. (5–4.20) and (5–4.21) yield

$$
F(l) = 0, \qquad \frac{dF(l)}{dn} = 0
\tag{5–4.22}
$$

Multiply connected regions. The above argument assumes that derivatives $G = G(x, y)$ of second order or higher of the Airy stress function are single-valued functions of (x, y). Hence, it is restricted to simply connected regions for which

$$
\frac{\partial Q}{\partial x} = \frac{\partial P}{\partial y}, \qquad P = \frac{\partial G}{\partial x}, \qquad Q = \frac{\partial G}{\partial y}
\tag{5–4.23}
$$

are necessary and sufficient conditions for the existence of G (see Art. 1–13). For multiply connected regions with bounding contours L_k (Fig. 5–4.2), the condition (5–4.23) is only a necessary condition for the existence of the single-valued functions $G(x, y)$. For a multiply connected region, in addition to Eq. (5–4.23), the conditions

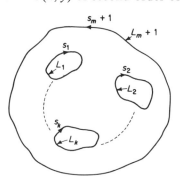

Fig. 5-4.2 Multiply connected region bounded by closed curves, L_k, $k = 1, 2, \ldots, m + 1$. Contour $L_m + 1$ contains all other contours.

$$J_k = \int_{L_k} P \, dx + Q \, dy = 0, \qquad k = 1, 2, \ldots, m \qquad (5\text{-}4.24)$$

are also required.

Accordingly, in order that the derivatives $G(x, y)$ of second order or higher of the Airy stress function $F(x, y)$ be single-valued, it is necessary and sufficient that in addition to Eq. (5–4.23), the following conditions[4] hold:

$$J_1 = J_2 = \ldots = J_k = J_m = 0 \qquad (5\text{-}4.25)$$

where J_k is defined by Eq. (5–4.24).

The defining equations for the Airy stress function [Eqs. (5–4.12), (5–4.20), (5–4.21), (5–4.25)] may be expressed for the general plane orthogonal curvilinear coordinate system by specializing the results of Art. 1–16 for the plane.

Equations (5–4.23) and (5–4.25) ensures the single valuedness of the stress components $\sigma_x, \sigma_y, \tau_{xy}$. However, they do not assure the existence of single-valued displacement components (u, v) since these components are obtained by an integration of stress (or strain) quantities, this integration process possibly yielding multivalued terms. Accordingly, if we require single-valued displacement, we must select the arbitrary functions (or constants) that result in the expressions for (u, v) in such a fashion that the single valuedness of displacement is assured. Although we ordinarily require that the displacement be single-valued, the concept of multivalued displacement components may be interpreted in a physical sense and finds an application through Volterra's theory of dislocations (see Love, *The Mathematical Theory of Elasticity*, pp. 221–28).

PROBLEM SET 5-4

1. In a state of plane strain relative to the (x, y) plane, the displacement component $w = 0$, and the displacement components u, v are functions of (x, y) only. Hence, the components of rotation $\omega_x = \omega_y = 0$ and $\omega = \omega_z$. For zero body forces, (set $V = 0$) we note that the equations of equilibrium are satisfied by Eqs. (5–4.9). Show that

$$\sigma_x + \sigma_y = 2(\lambda + G)e$$

where e is the volumetric strain or dilatation and where λ, G are the Lamé constants. Hence, show that in terms of dilatation and rotation the equations of equilibrium are

$$(\lambda + 2G)\frac{\partial e}{\partial x} - 2G\frac{\partial \omega}{\partial y} = 0, \qquad (\lambda + 2G)\frac{\partial e}{\partial y} - 2G\frac{\partial \omega}{\partial x} = 0$$

Thus show that e and ω are plane harmonic functions.

2. Since the dilatation e and rotation ω are plane harmonic functions (see Prob. 1), $(\lambda + 2G)e + i2G\omega$ is a function of the complex variable $x + iy$, where i is $\sqrt{-1}$.

[4]N. I. Muskhelishvili, *Some Basic Problems of the Mathematical Theory of Elasticity* (Groningen Holland: P. Noordhoff, Ltd., 1953), App. 2. Translated from the Russian by J. R. M. Radok.

Also, the Airy stress function F is related to e by $\nabla^2 F = 2(\lambda + G)e$, where

$$\nabla^2 = \frac{\partial^2}{\partial x^2} + \frac{\partial^2}{\partial y^2}$$

Introduce the new function $\xi + i\eta$ of $x + iy$ as follows:

$$\xi + i\eta = \int [(\lambda + 2G)e + i2G\omega]\, d(x + iy)$$

so that

$$\frac{\partial \xi}{\partial x} = \frac{\partial \eta}{\partial y} = (\lambda + 2G)e = \frac{\lambda + 2G}{2(\lambda + G)} \nabla^2 F, \qquad -\frac{\partial \xi}{\partial y} = \frac{\partial \eta}{\partial x} = 2G\omega$$

where F is Airy's stress function. Hence, show that

$$2G \frac{\partial u}{\partial x} = \frac{\partial^2 F}{\partial y^2} - \frac{\lambda}{2(\lambda + G)} \nabla^2 F = -\frac{\partial^2 F}{\partial x^2} + \frac{\partial \xi}{\partial x}$$

$$2G \frac{\partial v}{\partial y} = \frac{\partial^2 F}{\partial x^2} - \frac{\lambda}{2(\lambda + G)} \nabla^2 F = -\frac{\partial^2 F}{\partial y^2} + \frac{\partial \eta}{\partial y}$$

and that

$$2G \frac{\partial u}{\partial y} = -\frac{\partial^2 F}{\partial x \partial y} - 2G\omega = -\frac{\partial^2 F}{\partial x \partial y} + \frac{\partial \xi}{\partial y}$$

$$2G \frac{\partial v}{\partial x} = -\frac{\partial^2 F}{\partial x \partial y} + 2G\omega = -\frac{\partial^2 F}{\partial x \partial y} + \frac{\partial \eta}{\partial x}$$

and that there follows

$$2Gu = -\frac{\partial F}{\partial x} + \xi, \qquad 2Gv = -\frac{\partial F}{\partial y} + \eta$$

These equations define the displacement components u, v when F is known.

3. We recall that

$$e = \frac{\partial u}{\partial x} + \frac{\partial v}{\partial y}, \qquad 2\omega = \frac{\partial v}{\partial x} - \frac{\partial u}{\partial y}$$

These equations, with the definitions of ξ, η given in Prob. 2 yield after integration

$$u = \frac{\partial}{\partial x} \left[\frac{y\eta}{2(\lambda + 2G)} \right] + \frac{\partial}{\partial y} \left[\frac{y\xi}{2G} \right] + u'$$

$$v = \frac{\partial}{\partial y} \left[\frac{y\eta}{2(\lambda + 2G)} \right] - \frac{\partial}{\partial x} \left[\frac{y\xi}{2G} \right] + v'$$

where $v' + iu'$ is a function of $x + iy$. Let $u' = \partial f / \partial x$, $v' = \partial f / \partial y$, $\nabla^2 f = 0$. Show that

$$u = \frac{\xi}{2G} + \frac{\lambda + G}{2G(\lambda + 2G)} y \frac{\partial \xi}{\partial y} + \frac{\partial f}{\partial x}$$

$$v = \frac{\eta}{2(\lambda + 2G)} - \frac{\lambda + G}{2G(\lambda + 2G)} y \frac{\partial \eta}{\partial y} + \frac{\partial f}{\partial y}$$

These equations define u, v when e and ω are known.

4. With the information given in Probs. (2) and (3) show that

$$F = -2Gf + \frac{\lambda + G}{\lambda + 2G} y\eta$$

and that hence the formulas for u, v given in Probs. (2) and (3) are equivalent.

5. Express Eqs. (5–2.11) entirely in terms of strain components.

6. Express Eqs. (5–2.11) entirely in terms of displacement components.

7. Derive formulas that define the stress components τ_{xz}, τ_{yz} for generalized plane stress. (Note Eqs. 2–8.4 and 4–9.2 with body forces and temperature terms discarded.)

5-5 Polynomial Solutions of Two-dimensional Problems in Rectangular Cartesian Coordinates

For plane elasticity with constant body forces or with body forces derivable from a potential function, the compatibility relations reduce to the following single equation in terms of a stress function F (for simply connected regions):

$$\nabla^2 \nabla^2 F = 0 \tag{5–5.1}$$

where for plane rectangular cartesian coordinates (x, y),

$$\nabla^2 = \frac{\partial^2}{\partial x^2} + \frac{\partial^2}{\partial y^2} \tag{5–5.2}$$

For zero body forces, the stress components σ_x, σ_y, τ_{xy} are related to F by the following equations:

$$\sigma_x = \frac{\partial^2 F}{\partial y^2}, \qquad \sigma_y = \frac{\partial^2 F}{\partial x^2}, \qquad \tau_{xy} = -\frac{\partial^2 F}{\partial x\, \partial y} \tag{5–5.3}$$

In the absence of body forces, Eqs. (5–5.3) automatically satisfy equilibrium [Eqs. (5–2.11)]. Accordingly, any solution to Eq. (5–5.1) represents the solution of a certain problem of plane elasticity. For example, any of the terms of Eq. (5–4.13) represents a solution to Eq. (5–5.1). Hence, Eq. (5–4.13) represents a set of solutions of the problem of plane elasticity.

If the stress function F is taken in the form of a polynomial in x and y, we note [see Eqs. (5–5.3)] that nontrivial (nonzero) stress components are obtained only from a polynomial of second degree or higher in x and y. Furthermore, Eq. (5–5.1) is satisfied identically by polynomials of third degree in x and y. For polynomials of degree higher than three, Eq. (5–5.1) requires the coefficients of all terms of degree higher than three to satisfy a set of $n - 3$ auxiliary conditions, where n is the degree of the polynomial.

For discontinuous loads on boundaries, the polynomial method has severe theoretical limitations, since discontinuous boundary conditions are not representable by polynomials. For continuously varying loads, however, the polynomial method seems to be unlimited theoretically, although in practice the computations may quickly become prohibitive if boundary conditions are to be precisely satisfied. Furthermore, since the computations soon become laborious in any case, the polynomial method requires a systematic approach. One such approach has been proposed by Neou.[5]

Method of Neou. The method proposed by C. Y. Neou systematically reduces the Airy stress function F expressed in a general doubly infinite power series to the desirable polynomial form for special cases. The method proceeds as follows:

Let

$$F = \sum_{m=0}^{\infty} \sum_{n=0}^{\infty} A_{mn} x^m y^n \tag{5-5.4}$$

where $m, n = 0, 1, 2, \ldots$ and A_{mn} are undetermined coefficients which may be arranged in the following rectangular array:

$$
\begin{array}{cccccc}
A_{00} & A_{01} & A_{02} & A_{03} & A_{04} & \cdots \\
A_{10} & A_{11} & A_{12} & A_{13} & A_{14} & \cdots \\
A_{20} & A_{21} & A_{22} & A_{23} & A_{24} & \cdots \\
A_{30} & A_{31} & A_{32} & A_{33} & A_{34} & \cdots \\
A_{40} & A_{41} & A_{42} & A_{43} & A_{44} & \cdots \\
\vdots & \vdots & \vdots & \vdots & \vdots &
\end{array}
\tag{5-5.5}
$$

Substitution of Eq. (5–5.4) into Eq. (5–5.3) yields

$$\sigma_x = \sum_{m=0}^{\infty} \sum_{n=2}^{\infty} n(n-1) A_{mn} x^m y^{n-2} \tag{5-5.6}$$

$$\sigma_y = \sum_{m=2}^{\infty} \sum_{n=0}^{\infty} m(m-1) A_{mn} x^{m-2} y^n \tag{5-5.7}$$

$$\sigma_{xy} = -\sum_{m=1}^{\infty} \sum_{n=1}^{\infty} mn A_{mn} x^{m-1} y^{n-1} \tag{5-5.8}$$

Since A_{00}, A_{01}, and A_{10} do not occur in Eqs. (5–5.6), (5–5.7), and (5–5.8), they may be omitted from Eq. (5–5.5).

Substitution of Eq. (5–5.4) into Eq. (5–5.1) yields

$$\sum_{m=4}^{\infty} \sum_{n=0}^{\infty} m(m-1)(m-2)(m-3) x^{m-4} y^n A_{mn}$$

$$+ 2 \sum_{m=2}^{\infty} \sum_{n=2}^{\infty} m(m-1) n(n-1) x^{m-2} y^{n-2} A_{mn}$$

$$+ \sum_{m=0}^{\infty} \sum_{n=4}^{\infty} n(n-1)(n-2)(n-3) x^m y^{n-4} A_{mn} = 0 \tag{5-5.9}$$

Collecting similar powers of x and y and writing Eq. (5–5.9) under one summation sign, we obtain

---

[5]C. Y. Neou, "Direct Method for Determining Airy Polynomial Stress Functions," *J. A. M.*, Vol. 24, no. 3 (September, 1957), p. 387.

$$\sum_{m=2}^{\infty} \sum_{n=2}^{\infty} [(m + 2)(m + 1)m(m - 1)A_{m+2,\,n-2} + 2m(m - 1)n(n - 1)A_{mn}$$

$$+ (n + 2)(n + 1)n(n - 1)A_{m-2,\,n+2}]x^{m-2}y^{n-2} = 0 \qquad (5\text{-}5.10)$$

Since Eq. (5–5.10) must be satisfied for all values of x and y,

$$(m + 2)(m + 1)m(m - 1)A_{m+2,\,n-2} + 2m(m - 1)n(n - 1)A_{mn}$$

$$+ (n + 2)(n + 1)n(n - 1)A_{m-2,\,n+2} = 0 \qquad (5\text{-}5.11)$$

Equation (5–5.11) establishes an interrelation among any three alternate coefficients in the diagonals of Eq. (5–5.5), running from lower left to upper right. For example, for $m = 2$ and $n = 2$, Eq. (5–5.11) yields

$$6A_{40} + A_{22} + 6A_{04} = 0$$

Similarly, other relations between the A_{mn} may be established by Eq. (5–5.11).

In the manner outlined above, the plane problem of elasticity with continuous boundary stress is reduced to the determination of A_{mn} [see Eqs. (5–5.4) and (5–5.5)] from the interdependence relations [Eq. (5–5.11)] and the prescribed boundary conditions.

Alternatively, the plane problem of elasticity may be solved by more general techniques such as transform methods[6] or by methods of complex variables.[7]

PROBLEM SET 5-5

1. Determine the interrelations between A_{mn} [Eq. (5–5.11)] for $(m = 4, n = 2)$, $(m = 3, n = 3)$, and $(m = 2, n = 4)$.

2. By the method of Neou, derive a polynomial in x and y for the Airy stress function F for the cantilever beam loaded as shown in Fig. P5-5.2. Hence, derive formulas for the stress components $\sigma_x, \sigma_y, \tau_{xy}$. What stress boundary conditions exist at $x = L$? Discuss the application of Saint-Venant's principle to this problem (see Art. 4–10).

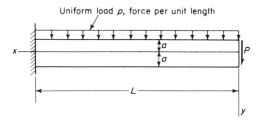

Uniform load p, force per unit length

Figure P5-5.2

---

[6]See A. E. Green, *Proc. Cambridge Phil. Soc.*, Vol. 41 (1945); A. C. Stevenson, *Phil. Mag.*, Vol. 34 (1943); Milne-Thomson, *J. London Math. Soc.*, Vol. 17 (1942). See also I. Sneddon, *Fourier Transforms* (New York: McGraw-Hill Book Company, Inc., 1951).
[7]Muskhclishvili, *Some Basic Problems of the Mathematical Theory of Elasticity.*

3. By the method of Neou, derive a polynomial in x and y for the Airy stress function F for the beam loaded as shown in Fig. P5–5.3. Hence, derive formulas for the stress components $\sigma_x, \sigma_y, \tau_{xy}$. Discuss the application of Saint-Venant's principle to this problem (see Art. 4–10).

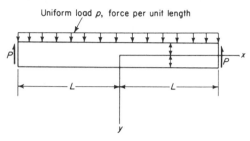

Uniform load p, force per unit length

Figure P5-5.3

5-6 Displacement Components for Plane Elasticity

When the plane elasticity stress components $\sigma_x, \sigma_y, \tau_{xy}$ are known, the strain components $\epsilon_x, \epsilon_y, \gamma_{xy}$ may be determined by Eqs. (5–3.6) for generalized plane stress or by Eqs. (5–3.2) for plane strain. Then, integration of the strain-displacement relations [Eqs. (5–1.4) for plane strain or Eqs. (5–1.4) with ϵ_z given by Eqs. (5–3.4) for generalized plane stress] yields the (x, y) displacement components (u, v). The integration of the strain-displacement relations yields an arbitrary rigid-body displacement (see Art. 3–13 and Example 4–12.1). Accordingly, complete specification of the displacement (u, v) requires that the rigid-body displacement of a point in the body be known. For example, in Example 4–12.1 it was specified that the point $x = y = z = 0$ be fixed and that the volumetric rotation for this point vanish. Consequently, the displacements and rotations of all other points and volume elements in the body were determined relative to the point and volume element at $x = y = z = 0$. Similarly, to fix the rigid-body displacement in the solution of the plane problem, it is necessary to specify the displacement of some point (say x_0, y_0) and the rotation of a line element (say a line element through point x_0, y_0).

Review Problems

R-1 Consider a beam in the region $-h/2 \leq y \leq h/2$, $-b/2 \leq z \leq b/2$, $0 \leq x \leq L$. Assume plane stress in the (x, y) plane, with zero body forces. The stress component normal to the plane perpendicular to the x axis is $\sigma_x = -My/I$ where $M = M(x)$ is a function of x only, and $I = bh^3/12$. Derive expressions for σ_y and τ_{xy}, subject to the boundary conditions $\tau_{xy} = 0$ for $y = \pm h/2$ and $\sigma_y = 0$ for $y = h/2$. What restrictions, if any, must be placed on M in order that the derived state of stress be compatible?

R-2 Let a thin plate with constant thickness and with mass density ρ rotate with constant angular velocity ω about the y axis (Fig. R5–2). Neglecting gravity, write down an expression for the inertia force X per unit volume (body force per unit volume) that acts on an arbitrary mass element of the plate. Write down the differential equations of equilibrium for the plate. Write the general solution of these equations in terms of Airy's stress function F. Show that the equation of compatibility is $\nabla^4 F = (1 - \nu)\rho\omega^2$, where ν is Poisson's ratio.

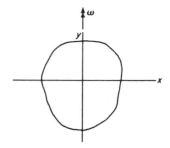

Figure R5-2

R-3 For a state of plane strain, $\sigma_x = f(y)$. Neglecting body forces, derive the most general equations for $\sigma_x, \sigma_y, \sigma_z,$ and τ_{xy}.

R-4 An infinite plate strip is bounded by the lines $y = \pm 1$. The stresses on the lines $y = \pm 1$ are $\sigma_y = \cos x$, $\tau_{xy} = 0$. There is no body force. By assuming an Airy stress function of the form $f(y) \cos x$, determine $\sigma_x, \sigma_y, \tau_{xy}$ as functions of (x, y).

R-5 The following stress-strain relations pertain to an anisotropic flat thin plate subjected to a state of generalized plane stress:

$$\epsilon_x = S_{11}\sigma_x + S_{12}\sigma_y$$
$$\epsilon_y = S_{12}\sigma_x + S_{22}\sigma_y$$
$$\gamma_{xy} = S_{33}\tau_{xy}, \qquad (x, y) = \text{rectangular cartesian coordinates}$$

where S_{11}, S_{22}, S_{33} are elastic constants and where $(\sigma_x, \sigma_y, \tau_{xy})$ and $(\epsilon_x, \epsilon_y, \gamma_{xy})$ are average values of stress and strain through the thickness. Let $\sigma_x, \sigma_y, \tau_{xy}$ be defined in terms of an Airy stress function F.

Show that the defining equation for the Airy stress function F is of the form

$$\left(\frac{\partial^2}{\partial x^2} + \alpha_1 \frac{\partial^2}{\partial y^2}\right)\left(\frac{\partial^2 F}{\partial x^2} + \alpha_2 \frac{\partial^2 F}{\partial y^2}\right) = 0 \qquad \text{(a)}$$

where a_1, a_2 are constants. For the case $S_{11} = S_{22} = 1/E$, $S_{12} = -\nu/E$, $S_{33} = 1/G$, show that Eq. (a) reduces to the biharmonic equation.

R-6 Let

$$F = ax^2 + by^3 + \sum_{n=1}^{\infty} A_n(y) \cos\left(\frac{n\pi x}{L}\right)$$

be an Airy stress function for a plane, isotropic plate, where a, b, L are constants, and $A_n(y)$ are functions of y. Derive the defining differential equation for the coefficients A_n.

Consider a plane rectangular region $-L \leq x \leq L$, $-C \leq y \leq C$. Assume that no net force or no net couple acts on the sections $x = \pm L$. Discuss how the arbitrary constants in the solution of the differential equation for $A_n(y)$ may be evaluated.

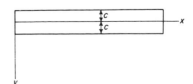

R-7 Consider a case of plane stress without body forces in the region $-c \leq y \leq +c, 0 \leq x \leq l$ (see Fig. R5–7). If the resultant of the

Figure R5-7

stresses in the x direction is zero, the elementary beam formula yields $\sigma_x = My/I$, i.e., σ_x is a linear function of y.

(a) Let $\sigma_x = F_{yy}$, $\sigma_y = F_{xx}$, $\tau_{xy} = -F_{xy}$. Write down the most general expression for $F(x, y)$ that satisfies the equations of equilibrium and yields σ_y as a linear function of y in the form $\sigma_x = yf(x)$.

(b) Assuming that the material is isotropic and linearly elastic, write the equation of compatibility for $F(x, y)$ as determined in (a).

(c) Determine the most general form of $F(x, y)$, which satisfies the equations of equilibrium and compatibility, and yields σ_x, linear in y.

(d) Derive expressions for the stress components using the stress function derived in (c).

(e) Assume that no load is applied along the line $y = c$. Show that the elementary formula can be correct, strictly speaking, only if the stresses are those produced in a cantilever with a concentrated vertical load at the end, and/or a moment applied at the end.

R-8 The general stress-strain-temperature relationship for an isotropic material is

$$\epsilon_x = \frac{1}{E}\sigma_x - \frac{\nu}{E}\sigma_y - \frac{\nu}{E}\sigma_z + \alpha T$$

$$\epsilon_y = -\frac{\nu}{E}\sigma_x + \frac{1}{E}\sigma_y - \frac{\nu}{E}\sigma_z + \alpha T$$

$$\epsilon_z = -\frac{\nu}{E}\sigma_x - \frac{\nu}{E}\sigma_y + \frac{1}{E}\sigma_z + \alpha T$$

$$\gamma_{yz} = \frac{1}{G}\tau_{yz}, \qquad \gamma_{xz} = \frac{1}{G}\tau_{xz}, \qquad \gamma_{xy} = \frac{1}{G}\tau_{xy}$$

Consider a body that is in a state of plane strain.

(a) Derive the "two-dimensional" Hooke's law expressing the strains $\epsilon_x, \epsilon_y, \ldots$ as functions of $\sigma_x, \sigma_y, \tau_{xy}$, and $T = T(x, y)$.

(b) Assuming that body forces are negligible, let $\sigma_x = F_{yy}$, $\sigma_y = F_{xx}$, $\tau_{xy} = -F_{xy}$ where F is a stress function. Derive the compatibility conditions in terms of T and F. Thus, show that $F(x, y)$ must be biharmonic, if $T(x, y)$ is harmonic.

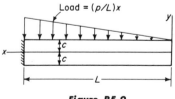

Figure R5-9

R-9 A cantilever beam is loaded as shown in Fig. R5-9.

(a) Derive expressions for the stresses in the beam using the stress function

$$\phi = C_1 xy + C_2 \frac{x^3}{6} + C_3 \frac{x^3 y}{6} + C_4 \frac{xy^3}{6}$$

$$+ C_5 \frac{x^3 y^3}{9} + C_6 \frac{xy^5}{20}$$

At the boundary $x = 0$ the solution is to satisfy the condition that the resultant force system vanishes (i.e., $F_x = F_y = M_z = 0$). What stress boundary conditions exist at $x = L$?

(b) Derive expressions for the displacement components u and v, assuming that the beam is in a state of plane stress and that it is fixed at the left end so that

$$u = (L, 0) = v(L, 0) = 0, \qquad \frac{\partial u}{\partial y}(L, 0) = 0$$

R-10 Express the equations of plane elasticity in terms of strain components only.

R-11 Express the equations of plane elasticity in terms of displacement components only.

R-12 Express the equations of plane elasticity in terms of stress components.

R-13 The skewed plate of unit thickness is loaded by uniformly distributed stresses S_1 and S_2 applied perpendicularly to the sides of the plate (see Fig. R5-13).
(a) Determine all conditions of equilibrium for the plate in terms of S_1, S_2, a, b, and θ.
(b) For $\theta = 90°$, derive an expression for the elongation of the diagonal AC under the action of S_1 and S_2. Assume that the material is homogeneous, isotropic, and linearly elastic, and that the displacements are small.

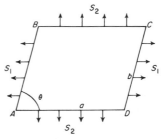

Figure R5-13

R-14 In Fig. R5-13, let S_1 and S_2 be applied so that they are directed parallel to the edges $AB(DC)$ and $AD(BC)$ of the skewed plate. Assuming that the plate is elastic derive expressions for the principal stresses and the principal strains in terms of S_1, S_2, a, b, θ, E, and ν, where E and ν denote Young's modulus and Poisson's ratio, respectively.

R-15 For a state of plane strain in an isotropic body, $\sigma_x = ay^2$, $\sigma_y = -ax^2$, $\tau_{xy} = 0$. The body forces and temperature are zero. Using small-displacement elasticity theory, compute the displacement components $u(x, y)$ and $v(x, y)$ (a is a constant).

R-16 A material is isotropic and elastic. Body forces and temperature are zero. All stress components are zero except τ_{xy}. Using small-displacement theory, determine the most general form for τ_{xy}.

6
PLANE ELASTICITY
IN POLAR COORDINATES

The use of polar coordinates is advantageous in problems involving boundaries formed by circular arcs or radially straight lines. Furthermore, certain problems of symmetry lend themselves well to polar coordinates. Accordingly, in this chapter we express the basic plane-elasticity equations in polar coordinates.

6-1 Equilibrium Equations in Polar Coordinates

Consider an element of volume bounded by the polar coordinate lines (r, θ) and $(r + dr, \theta + d\theta)$ (Fig. 6–1.1). Let the thickness of the element be one unit perpendicular to the (x, y) plane. Let the element be subjected to stress as shown (R and T denote body forces per unit volume in the radial and tangential directions, respectively). Since $d\theta$ is an infinitesimal angle, summations of forces in the radial and tangential directions yield for equilibrium

$$\frac{\partial \sigma_r}{\partial r} + \frac{1}{r}\frac{\partial \tau_{r\theta}}{\partial \theta} + \frac{\sigma_r - \sigma_\theta}{r} + R = 0$$

$$\frac{1}{r}\frac{\partial \sigma_\theta}{\partial \theta} + \frac{\partial \tau_{r\theta}}{\partial r} + \frac{2\tau_{r\theta}}{r} + T = 0$$

(6–1.1)

Equations (6–1.1) are the equilibrium equations for plane elasticity in polar coordinates. They are equivalent to Eqs. (5–2.11). Alternatively, Eqs. (6–1.1) may be derived by mathematically transforming Eq. (5–2.11) from (x, y) coordinates to (r, θ) coordinates by tensor theory (see also Appendix A).

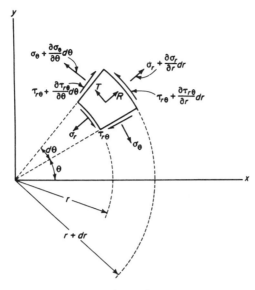

Figure 6-1.1

6-2 Stress Components in Terms of Airy Stress Function $F = F(r, \theta)$

To derive stress components in terms of the Airy stress function F, where F is considered to be a function of polar coordinates (r, θ), we may transform Eqs. (5–5.3)(in the absence of body forces) to polar coordinates as follows: By Fig. (6–1.1), we obtain the following relations between (x, y) and (r, θ):

$$r^2 = x^2 + y^2$$

$$x = r \cos \theta, \qquad y = r \sin \theta \qquad\qquad (6\text{–}2.1)$$

$$\tan \theta = \frac{y}{x}$$

Consider first the transformation of σ_x. By Eq. (5–5.3), we note that we require $\partial^2 F/\partial y^2$ in terms of (r, θ). By the chain rule of partial differentiation and Eq. (6–2.1), we have

$$\frac{\partial F}{\partial y} = \frac{\partial F}{\partial r}\frac{\partial r}{\partial y} + \frac{\partial F}{\partial \theta}\frac{\partial \theta}{\partial y} = \frac{\partial F}{\partial r}\sin\theta + \frac{1}{r}\frac{\partial F}{\partial \theta}\cos\theta$$

Similarly,

$$\frac{\partial^2 F}{\partial y^2} = \frac{\partial}{\partial y}\left(\frac{\partial F}{\partial y}\right)$$

$$= \frac{\partial^2 F}{\partial r^2}\sin^2\theta + \frac{2}{r}\frac{\partial^2 F}{\partial r\,\partial\theta}\sin\theta\cos\theta - \frac{2}{r^2}\frac{\partial F}{\partial\theta}\sin\theta\cos\theta$$

$$+ \frac{1}{r}\frac{\partial F}{\partial r}\cos^2\theta + \frac{1}{r^2}\frac{\partial^2 F}{\partial\theta^2}\cos^2\theta$$

Now, noting that as $\theta \to 0$, $\sigma_x \to \sigma_r$, $\cos \theta \to 1$, $\sin \theta \to 0$, we obtain

$$\sigma_r = \left. \frac{\partial^2 F}{\partial y^2} \right|_{\theta \to 0} = \frac{1}{r} \frac{\partial F}{\partial r} + \frac{1}{r^2} \frac{\partial^2 F}{\partial \theta^2}$$

Also, noting that as $\theta \to \pi/2$, $\sigma_x \to \sigma_\theta$, $\cos \theta \to 0$, $\sin \theta \to 1$, we find

$$\sigma_\theta = \left. \frac{\partial^2 F}{\partial y^2} \right|_{\theta \to \pi/2} = \frac{\partial^2 F}{\partial r^2}$$

In a similar manner, we may evaluate $\partial^2 F/\partial x\, \partial y$. Then, noting that as $\theta \to 0$, $\tau_{xy} \to \tau_{r\theta}$, we find

$$\tau_{r\theta} = -\left. \frac{\partial^2 F}{\partial x\, \partial y} \right|_{\theta \to 0} = -\frac{1}{r} \frac{\partial^2 F}{\partial r\, \partial \theta} + \frac{1}{r^2} \frac{\partial^2 F}{\partial \theta^2} = -\frac{\partial}{\partial r} \left(\frac{1}{r} \frac{\partial F}{\partial \theta} \right)$$

Accordingly, the stress components are given in terms of the Airy stress function $F(r, \theta)$ by the relations

$$\sigma_r = \frac{1}{r} \frac{\partial F}{\partial r} + \frac{1}{r^2} \frac{\partial^2 F}{\partial \theta^2}$$

$$\sigma_\theta = \frac{\partial^2 F}{\partial r^2} \tag{6-2.2}$$

$$\tau_{r\theta} = -\frac{\partial}{\partial r} \left(\frac{1}{r} \frac{\partial F}{\partial \theta} \right)$$

More generally, the preceding transformations may be carried out with respect to orthogonal curvilinear coordinates (Art. 1–16).

6-3 Compatibility Equation for Plane Elasticity in Terms of Polar Coordinates

Expressing the second derivative of F with respect to x in terms of polar coordinates and adding it the second derivative of F with respect to y derived in Art. 6–2, we obtain

$$\sigma_x + \sigma_y = \frac{\partial^2 F}{\partial x^2} + \frac{\partial^2 F}{\partial y^2} = \frac{\partial^2 F}{\partial r^2} + \frac{1}{r} \frac{\partial F}{\partial r} + \frac{1}{r^2} \frac{\partial^2 F}{\partial \theta^2} \tag{6-3.1}$$

Also, by Eqs. (6–2.2) we note that

$$\sigma_r + \sigma_\theta = \frac{\partial^2 F}{\partial r^2} + \frac{1}{r} \frac{\partial F}{\partial r} + \frac{1}{r^2} \frac{\partial^2 F}{\partial \theta^2} \tag{6-3.2}$$

Accordingly, by Eqs. (6–3.1), (6–3.2), and (5–5.1), we obtain the compatibility relation (for constant body forces, or body forces derivable from a potential function) in terms of polar coordinates (r, θ):

$$\nabla^2 \nabla^2 F = \left(\frac{\partial^2}{\partial r^2} + \frac{1}{r} \frac{\partial}{\partial r} + \frac{1}{r^2} \frac{\partial^2}{\partial \theta^2} \right) \left(\frac{\partial^2 F}{\partial r^2} + \frac{1}{r} \frac{\partial F}{\partial r} + \frac{1}{r^2} \frac{\partial^2 F}{\partial \theta^2} \right) = 0 \tag{6-3.3}$$

Accordingly, in polar coordinates [see Art. 1–16 and Eq. (1–16.13)]

$$\nabla^2 = \frac{\partial^2}{\partial r^2} + \frac{1}{r}\frac{\partial}{\partial r} + \frac{1}{r^2}\frac{\partial^2}{\partial \theta^2} \tag{6-3.4}$$

A solution of the compatibility equation $\nabla^2 \nabla^2 F = 0$ in polar coordinates has been derived by J. H. Michell,[1] for a certain class of plane problems. A modified form of the solution given by Michell[2] is

$$F = A_0 \log r + B_0 r^2 + C_0 r^2 \log r + D_0 r^2 \theta + A_0' \theta$$

$$+ \frac{A_1}{2} r\theta \sin \theta + (B_1 r^3 + A_1' r^{-1} + B_1' r \log r) \cos \theta$$

$$- \frac{C_1}{2} r\theta \cos \theta + (D_1 r^3 + C_1' r^{-1} + D_1' r \log r) \sin \theta \tag{6-3.5}$$

$$+ \sum_{n=2}^{\infty} (A_n r^n + B_n r^{n+2} + A_n' r^{-n} + B_n' r^{-n+2}) \cos n\theta$$

$$+ \sum_{n=2}^{\infty} (C_n r^n + D_n r^{n+2} + C_n' r^{-n} + D_n' r^{-n+2}) \sin n\theta$$

Problem. Consider a ring loaded as shown in Fig. P6-3.1. Show that the function

$$\phi = (Ar^2 + Br^4 + \frac{C}{r^2} + D) \cos 2\theta$$

$$+ Fr^2 + H \log r$$

satisfies $\nabla^2 \nabla^2 \phi = 0$. Determine the constants A, B, C, D, F, H to satisfy the stress boundary conditions. Hence, derive formulas for $\sigma_r, \sigma_\theta, \tau_{r\theta}$.

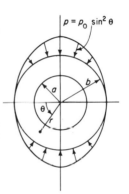

Figure P6-3.1

6-4 Axially Symmetric Problems

For axially symmetric problems, $F = F(r)$. Then, the equilibrium equations [see Eqs. (6–1.1)] reduce to

$$\frac{d\sigma_r}{dr} + \frac{1}{r}(\sigma_r - \sigma_\theta) + R = 0, \qquad T = 0 \tag{6-4.1}$$

Accordingly, for axially symmetric problems of equilibrium the tangential body force T is zero, and the two stress components $(\sigma_r, \sigma_\theta)$ and the radial body force R are functions of r only. Furthermore, the shearing stress $\tau_{r\theta}$ [see Eqs. (6–2.2)] is zero.

---

[1] J. H. Michell, *Proc. London Math. Soc.*, vol. 31 (1899), p. 100.

[2] The term $D_0 r^2 \theta$ was not given by Michell. Also, Michell included terms $r \cos \theta, r \sin \theta$ not included here. However, these terms yield zero stress components. See S. Timoshenko and J. Goodier, *Theory of Elasticity*, 2nd ed. (New York: McGraw-Hill Book Company, Inc., 1951), chap. 4. See also A. Timpe, *Z. Math. Physik*, vol. 52 (1905), p. 348, and *Math. Z.*, vol. 17 (1923), p. 189.

The compatibility relation simplifies to

$$\left(\frac{d^2}{dr^2} + \frac{1}{r}\frac{d}{dr}\right)\left(\frac{d^2 F}{dr^2} + \frac{1}{r}\frac{dF}{dr}\right) = 0 \qquad (6\text{-}4.2)$$

Equation (6-4.2) may be written in the form

$$\frac{1}{r}\frac{d}{dr}\left\{r\frac{d}{dr}\left[\frac{1}{r}\frac{d}{dr}\left(r\frac{dF}{dr}\right)\right]\right\} = 0 \qquad (6\text{-}4.3)$$

In this latter form, the Airy stress function F may be determined by direct integration. Accordingly, for problems of axial symmetry, integration of Eq. (6-3.4) yields the Airy stress function in the form

$$F = A \log r + Br^2 \log r + Cr^2 + D \qquad (6\text{-}4.4)$$

where A, B, C, and D are arbitrary constants of integration, which are determined by boundary conditions. However, in fact, the constant D does not enter into the formulas for the stress components, since they depend on derivatives of F. Thus, by Eqs. (6-2.2) and Eq. (6-4.4), we obtain

$$\sigma_r = \frac{1}{r}\frac{dF}{dr} = \frac{A}{r^2} + B(1 + 2\log r) + 2C$$
$$\sigma_\theta = \frac{d^2 F}{dr^2} = -\frac{A}{r^2} + B(3 + 2\log r) + 2C \qquad (6\text{-}4.5)$$

For a doubly connected region bounded by contours L_1 and L_2 and with the origin of coordinates (r, θ) inside the inner contour (Fig. 6-4.1), the requirement that the displacement be single-valued dictates that $B = 0$; see Example 6-4.2 and Prob. R-5 at the end of Chapter 6; see also remarks at end of Art. 5-4.

Example 6-4.1. Let $A = B = 0$ in Eqs. (6-4.5). Then, Eq. (6-4.5) yields

$$\sigma_r = \sigma_\theta = 2C \qquad (a)$$

Equation (a) represents the case of constant stress throughout the plane (see Fig. 6-4.2).

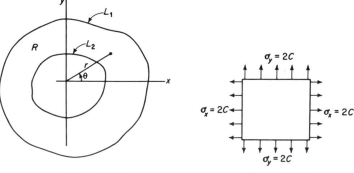

Figure 6-4.1   Figure 6-4.2

Example 6–4.2. Let $B = 0$ in Eqs. (6–4.5). Then,

$$\sigma_r = \frac{A}{r^2} + 2C, \qquad \sigma_\theta = -\frac{A}{r^2} + 2C \qquad \text{(b)}$$

Equation (b) may be used to represent the stress in a thick-walled cylinder with inner radius a and outer radius b and with internal pressure p_i and external pressure p_0 (Fig. 6–4.3). Then, the boundary conditions are

$$\sigma_r = -p_0 \qquad \text{for} \qquad r = b$$
$$\sigma_r = -p_i \qquad \text{for} \qquad r = a \qquad \text{(c)}$$

Substitution of Eqs. (c) into Eqs. (b) yields

$$A = \frac{a^2 b^2 (p_0 - p_i)}{b^2 - a^2}$$
$$2C = \frac{p_i a^2 - p_0 b^2}{b^2 - a^2} \qquad \text{(d)}$$

To investigate the variation of σ_r, σ_θ through the wall of the cylinder, consider the case $p_i = p$, $p_0 = 0$. Then Eqs. (b) and (d) yield

$$\sigma_r = -\frac{a^2 b^2 p}{(b^2 - a^2) r^2} + \frac{a^2 p}{b^2 - a^2}$$
$$\sigma_\theta = \frac{a^2 b^2 p}{(b^2 - a^2) r^2} + \frac{a^2 p}{b^2 - a^2} \qquad \text{(e)}$$

The change of $(\sigma_r, \sigma_\theta)$ with radial distance r is pictured in Fig. 6–4.4.

For other examples of axially symmetrical states of stress in polar coordinates see S. Timoshenko and J. Goodier, *Theory of Elasticity*, 2nd ed. (New York: McGraw-Hill Book Company, Inc., 1951), chap. 4. Other plane problems in polar coordinates are also discussed there.

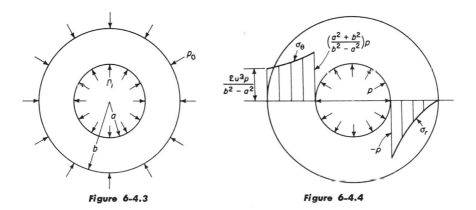

Figure 6-4.3   **Figure 6-4.4**

6-5 Strain Components in Polar Coordinates

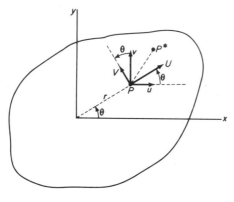

Consider a point P in a medium that undergoes a deformation (Fig. 6–5.1). Under the deformation, the point P moves to P^*. With respect to rectangular cartesian coordinates (x, y), the displacement components of point P are (u, v); with respect to polar coordinates, the displacement components are (U, V). Accordingly, by Fig. (6–5.1),

Figure 6-5.1

$$u = U \cos \theta - V \sin \theta$$
$$v = U \sin \theta + V \cos \theta \qquad (6\text{–}5.1)$$

Substitution of Eqs. (6–5.1) into Eq. (3–12.17) yields ϵ_x, ϵ_y, γ_{xy} in terms of U, V, and θ. For example, consider ϵ_x. By Eqs. (3–12.17) and the chain rule for partial differentiation,

$$\epsilon_x = \frac{\partial u}{\partial x} = \frac{\partial u}{\partial \theta} \frac{\partial \theta}{\partial x} + \frac{\partial u}{\partial r} \frac{\partial r}{\partial x} \qquad (6\text{–}5.2)$$

where, by Eqs. (6–5.1) and (6–2.1),

$$\frac{\partial u}{\partial \theta} = \frac{\partial U}{\partial \theta} \cos \theta - U \sin \theta - \frac{\partial V}{\partial \theta} \sin \theta - V \cos \theta$$

$$\frac{\partial u}{\partial r} = \frac{\partial U}{\partial r} \cos \theta - \frac{\partial V}{\partial r} \sin \theta$$

$$\frac{\partial \theta}{\partial x} = - \frac{\sin \theta}{r} \qquad (6\text{–}5.3)$$

$$\frac{\partial r}{\partial x} = \cos \theta$$

Accordingly, by Eqs. (6–5.2) and (6–5.3),

$$\epsilon_x = \left(-\frac{\partial U}{\partial \theta} \cos \theta + U \sin \theta + \frac{\partial V}{\partial \theta} \sin \theta + V \cos \theta \right) \frac{\sin \theta}{r}$$
$$+ \left(\frac{\partial U}{\partial r} \cos \theta - \frac{\partial V}{\partial r} \sin \theta \right) \cos \theta$$

Noting that as $\theta \to 0$, $\epsilon_x \to \epsilon_r$, $\sin \theta \to 0$, and $\cos \theta \to 1$, we obtain

$$\epsilon_r = \epsilon_x \Big|_{\theta \to 0} = \frac{\partial U}{\partial r}$$

Analogously, as $\theta \to \pi/2$, $\epsilon_x \to \epsilon_\theta$, $\sin \theta \to 1$, and $\cos \theta \to 0$. Hence,

$$\epsilon_\theta = \epsilon_x\Big|_{\theta \to 2/\pi} = \frac{1}{r}\frac{\partial V}{\partial \theta} + \frac{U}{r}$$

Finally, in a similar manner, we may express γ_{xy} as a function of U, V, and θ, and noting that $\gamma_{xy} \to \gamma_{r\theta}$ as $\theta \to 0$, we obtain

$$\gamma_{r\theta} = \gamma_{xy}\big|_{\theta \to 0} = \frac{\partial V}{\partial r} - \frac{V}{r} + \frac{1}{r}\frac{\partial U}{\partial \theta}$$

Accordingly, the strain components ϵ_r, ϵ_θ, $\gamma_{r\theta}$ with respect to polar coordinates (r, θ) are

$$\epsilon_r = \frac{\partial U}{\partial r}$$

$$\epsilon_\theta = \frac{U}{r} + \frac{1}{r}\frac{\partial V}{\partial \theta} \qquad (6\text{–}5.4)$$

$$\gamma_{r\theta} = \frac{1}{r}\frac{\partial U}{\partial \theta} + \frac{\partial V}{\partial r} - \frac{V}{r}$$

where $U = U(r, \theta)$, $V = V(r, \theta)$ are the radial and tangential displacement components (Fig. 6–5.1).

Alternatively, Eq. (6–5.4) may be derived by the method of Art. 3–3 (see also Appendix A and Prob. R–6).

Problem. Derive the last of Eqs. (6–5.4).

Review Problems

R-1 The stress function $F = Ar\,\theta \sin \theta$ yields the solution to the problem of a semi-infinite plate loaded by a concentrated force perpendicular to its straight-line boundary, where $0 < r$, $-\pi/2 \leq \theta \leq \pi/2$. Derive a formula for the maximum shearing stress at a point in the plate some distance from the load. Derive an equation for curves along which the maximum shearing stress is a constant and trace several of these curves on a sketch of the plate. Derive expressions for radial and tangential components of displacement.

R-2 The semi-infinite plate is loaded uniformly along the straight-line boundary $\theta = \pi$ (Fig. R6–2). Show that the stress components may be derived from the stress function $F = Cr^2(\theta - \sin \theta \cos \theta)$. Evaluate the stress components for $\theta = \pi/2$; for $\theta = 0$. Discuss any discrepancies in these components. Derive expressions for radial and tangential components of displacement.

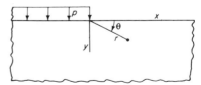

Figure R6-2

R-3 The line t is tangent to the centerline of a circular arc ring AB at point P(see Fig. R6–3). When the ring is loaded, point P undergoes radial and tangential displacement components (w, u). Derive an expression for $\tan (\phi^* - \phi)$, the tan of the angle through which line t rotates. Linearize this formula for small rotations, that is, for $\tan(\phi^* - \phi) \approx \phi^* - \phi$. Recall that $\tan(\phi^* - \phi) = (\tan\phi^* - \tan\phi)/(1 + \tan\phi^*\tan\phi)$.

Note that $u = u(\theta)$, $w = w(\theta)$. *Express the results in terms of a, w, u, and derivatives of w and u.*

R-4 A semi-infinite plate is loaded normally to its free boundary by a concentrated force P (Fig. R6–4). Assume that $\sigma_\theta = \tau_{r\theta} = 0$. Hence, show that $r\sigma_r = f(\theta)$, where $f(\theta)$ is a function of θ alone. Derive the formula for $f(\theta)$. Hence, express σ_r as a known function of r, θ, and the load P. Derive expressions for radial and tangential components of displacement.

Figure R6-3   Figure R6-4

R-5 Derive expressions for the radial and tangential components (U, V) of displacement for the problem of Example 6–4.2.

R-6 Consider two orthogonal line elements, ds_1 and ds_2, one radial and one tangential (Fig. R6–6) in a plane region R. Consider the following separate deformations: (a) all points in the body (region) undergo a radial displacement; $U = U_1(r)$, $V = V_1 = 0$ where U, V denote radial and tangential components of displacement, (b) all points undergo a displacement such that $U = U_2(\theta)$, $V = V_2(r, \theta)$. Derive expressions for the strain components ϵ_r, ϵ_θ, $\gamma_{r\theta}$ corresponding to the deformations (a) and (b). Superimpose the results of deformations (a) and (b) to arrive at Eqs. (6–5.4).

R-7 The stress function for a single concentrated force P acting perpendicular to the straight boundary of a semi-infinite plate is

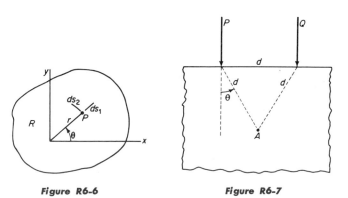

Figure R6-6   Figure R6-7

$$F = -\frac{P}{\pi} r\theta \sin \theta$$

By the method of superposition derive expressions for the principal stresses and the maximum shear at point A for the semi-infinite plate loaded as shown in Fig. R6-7 for the cases $Q = P$ and $Q = 2P$.

R-8 A long mine tunnel of radius a is cut in deep rock. Before the rock is cut, the rock is subjected to uniform pressure p. Considering the rock to be an infinite, homogeneous elastic medium with elastic constants E and ν, determine the radial displacement at the surface of the tunnel due to the excavation.

R-9 For a state of plane stress expressed in polar coordinates, assume that all stress components except σ_r are zero. (a) In the absence of body forces and acceleration, show that $r\sigma_r = f(\theta)$, where $f(\theta)$ is an arbitrary function of θ. (b) Derive a general formula for $f(\theta)$. (c) Apply the results of parts (a) and (b) to the problem of a cantilever wedge loaded in its plane by a concentrated force P applied at its tip (Fig. R6-9); that is, express σ_r as a completely determined function of r and θ. Discuss the boundary conditions at the support.

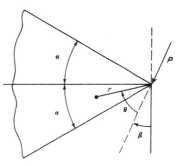

Figure R6-9

7

PRISMATIC BAR
SUBJECTED TO END LOAD

In this chapter we consider the formulation of the classical problem of cylindrical elastic bars subjected to forces acting on the end planes of the bar. After developing the general theory, we examine bars of certain typical cross sections by elementary means. First, we consider the classical problem of torsion of prismatic bars after Saint-Venant. Next, we treat briefly the problem of bending of prismatic bars. The latter theory is again due principally to Saint-Venant.

7-1 General Problem of Three-dimensional Elastic Bars Subjected to Transverse End Loads

Consider a cylindrical bar made of linearly elastic, homogeneous, isotropic material. Let the bar occupy the region bounded by a cylindrical lateral surface S and by two end planes distance L apart and perpendicular to the surface S (Fig. 7–1.1). The lateral surface of the bar is free of external load. The end planes of the bar are subjected to forces which satisfy equilibrium conditions of the bar as a whole. If the body forces are zero, the following sets of equations apply:

(a) *Equilibrium equations:*

$$\frac{\partial \sigma_x}{\partial x} + \frac{\partial \tau_{xy}}{\partial y} + \frac{\partial \tau_{xz}}{\partial z} = 0$$

$$\frac{\partial \tau_{xy}}{\partial x} + \frac{\partial \sigma_y}{\partial y} + \frac{\partial \tau_{yz}}{\partial z} = 0 \qquad (7–1.1)$$

$$\frac{\partial \tau_{xz}}{\partial x} + \frac{\partial \tau_{yz}}{\partial y} + \frac{\partial \sigma_z}{\partial z} = 0$$

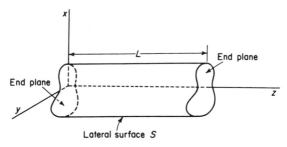

Figure 7-1.1

(b) *Stress-strain relations:*

$$\sigma_x = \lambda e + 2G\epsilon_x, \qquad \sigma_y = \lambda e + 2G\epsilon_y, \qquad \sigma_z = \lambda e + 2G\epsilon_z$$

$$\tau_{xy} = G\gamma_{xy}, \qquad \tau_{xz} = G\gamma_{xz}, \qquad \tau_{yz} = G\gamma_{yz} \tag{7-1.2}$$

or alternatively

$$\epsilon_x = \frac{1}{E}[\sigma_x - \nu(\sigma_y + \sigma_z)]$$

$$\epsilon_y = \frac{1}{E}[\sigma_y - \nu(\sigma_x + \sigma_z)]$$

$$\epsilon_z = \frac{1}{E}[\sigma_z - \nu(\sigma_x + \sigma_y)] \tag{7-1.3}$$

$$\gamma_{xy} = \frac{1}{G}\tau_{xy}, \qquad \gamma_{xz} = \frac{1}{G}\tau_{xz}, \qquad \gamma_{yz} = \frac{1}{G}\tau_{yz}$$

(c) *Boundary conditions:*

On lateral surfaces (direction cosines $l, m, n = l, m, 0$):

$$\sigma_{Px} = l\sigma_x + m\tau_{xy} = 0$$

$$\sigma_{Py} = l\tau_{xy} + m\sigma_y = 0 \tag{7-1.4a}$$

$$\sigma_{Pz} = l\tau_{xz} + m\tau_{yz} = 0$$

On ends ($z = 0, z = L$; direction cosines $l, m, n = 0, 0, \mp 1$):

$$\tau_{xz}, \tau_{yz} \text{ prescribed functions} \tag{7-1.4b}$$

such that

$$\Sigma F_x = P_x, \qquad \Sigma F_y = P_y, \qquad \Sigma M_z = M$$

where P_x, P_y denote (x, y) components of the resultant force and M denotes the moment of the resultant couple. The problem of solving the equations formulated in the above generality poses considerable mathematical diffi-culties, particularly if the solution sought is to permit reasonably simple calculations. Fortunately, in a large number of practical cases, it is unnecessary to consider the problem in such general terms. Even though in practice we rarely know the true distribution of forces that act in the end planes of the bar, we often know a force system which is statically equivalent to the actual force system. Accordingly, if we are considering a member with cross-sectional dimensions which are small compared to the length of the member, it may be adequate to merely ensure that the solution yields resultant forces and resultant moments which have given values at the ends of the bar. For example, by Saint-Venant's principle, the stress distribution in regions suffi-ciently far removed from the end planes will be little affected by different distribution of forces over the end planes, provided the resultant force and moment for all distributions considered are the same (Art. 4–10).

Finally, the stress component σ_{ij} must satisfy the Beltrami-Michell com-patibility equations (in the absence of body forces and for uniform temper-ature distribution)

$$\nabla^2 \sigma_{ij} + \frac{1}{1+\nu} \frac{\partial^2 I_1}{\partial x_i \, \partial x_j} = 0, \qquad i,j = 1, 2, 3 \qquad (7\text{–}1.5)$$

where

$$I_1 = \sigma_{11} + \sigma_{22} + \sigma_{33} = \sigma_x + \sigma_y + \sigma_z \qquad (7\text{–}1.6)$$

and

$$\nabla^2 = \frac{\partial^2}{\partial x^2} + \frac{\partial^2}{\partial y^2} + \frac{\partial^2}{\partial z^2} \qquad (7\text{–}1.7)$$

In the following discussion, we consider first the problem of twisting (torsion) of the bar by couples whose planes lie in the end planes of the bar. Then, we treat the problem of bending of the bar by transverse end forces. The problems of bars subjected to axial forces at the ends and to couples whose planes are perpendicular to the end planes of the bar are left as exer-cises (see Probs. R-1 and R-2 at the end of this chapter).

7-2 Torsion of Prismatic Bars. Saint-Venant's Solution. Warping Function

In Art. 4–13 we treated the problem of torsion of a bar with simply con-nected circular cross section by the semi-inverse method. By taking displace-ment components in the form

$$u = -\theta yz, \qquad v = \theta xz, \qquad w = 0 \qquad (7\text{–}2.1)$$

where (x, y, z) denote rectangular cartesian coordinates and θ denotes the angle of twist per unit length of the bar, we were able to satisfy the equations of elasticity exactly, provided the end shears were applied in a particular manner (Art. 4–13). However, if we proceed to apply Eqs. (7–2.1) to the torsion problem of a bar with simply connected noncircular cross section, we find that in general it is not possible to satisfy the boundary conditions on the lateral surface [See Eqs. (7–1.4) and Prob. R4–8]. Accordingly, Eqs.

(7–2.1) do not represent the solution to the torsion problem of bars with noncircular cross section. Hence, we are faced with the choice of either modifying Eqs. (7–2.1) or abandoning the semi-inverse method with regard to displacement components. For example, one may attempt to add more generality to Eqs. (7–2.1) (after Saint-Venant) or one may attempt to reformulate the problem in terms of stress components (after Prandtl). Initially, in this article, we modify Eqs. (7–2.1). In Art. 7–3 we return to the formulation of the problem in terms of stress components.

The concept of allowing a section distance z from the end $z = 0$ to rotate as a rigid body about the axis of twist (the z axis, Fig. 7–2.1) is analytically attractive. Accordingly, we retain the same form for u, v [see Eq. (7–2.1) and Art. 4–13]; however, we relax the condition $w = 0$.

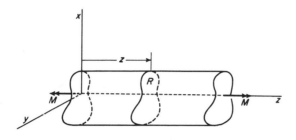

Figure 7-2.1

Since the end forces tend to twist the bar about the z axis, physically it seems reasonable that extension of the bar along its axis is of negligible importance. Hence, the dependency of w, the displacement component in the z direction, upon z appears to be of secondary importance. Physically the dependency of w upon coordinates (x, y) is difficult to guess. Accordingly, we do not attempt to specific an explicit relation between w and (x, y); rather we arbitrarily take (after Saint-Venant) w in the form $w = \theta \psi(x, y)$, where $\psi(x, y)$ is an arbitrary function of (x, y). Since $\psi(x, y)$ is a measure of how much a point in the plane $z = $ const. displaces in the z direction, it is called the *warping function*. Thus, for the small-displacement torsion problem of a bar with noncircular cross section, we take the displacement vector (u, v, w) in the form

$$u = -\theta z y, \qquad v = \theta z x, \qquad w = \theta \psi(x, y) \qquad (7\text{–}2.2)$$

We now proceed to determine whether or not the equations of elasticity may be satisfied by this assumption. In other words, we seek to determine the function $\psi(x, y)$ such that the equations of elasticity are satisfied.

For small-displacement theory, Eqs. (3–12.17) and (7–2.2) yield

$$\epsilon_x = \epsilon_y = \epsilon_z = \gamma_{xy} = 0$$

$$\gamma_{xz} = \theta\left(\frac{\partial \psi}{\partial x} - y\right), \qquad \gamma_{yz} = \theta\left(\frac{\partial \psi}{\partial y} + x\right) \qquad (7\text{-}2.3)$$

Substitution of Eqs. (7–2.3) into Eqs. (7–1.2) yields the stress components

$$\sigma_x = \sigma_y = \sigma_z = \tau_{xy} = 0$$

$$\tau_{xz} = G\theta\left(\frac{\partial \psi}{\partial x} - y\right), \qquad \tau_{yz} = G\theta\left(\frac{\partial \psi}{\partial y} + x\right) \qquad (7\text{-}2.4)$$

Now substitution of Eqs. (7–2.4) into Eqs. (7–1.1) yields for equilibrium

$$\frac{\partial^2 \psi}{\partial x^2} + \frac{\partial^2 \psi}{\partial y^2} = \nabla^2 \psi = 0 \qquad (7\text{-}2.5)$$

where now

$$\nabla^2 = \frac{\partial^2}{\partial x^2} + \frac{\partial^2}{\partial y^2}$$

Accordingly the assumption of displacement components in the form of Eqs. (7–2.2) yields the requirement that $\nabla^2 \psi = 0$, that is, that ψ be harmonic over the region R of the cross section of the bar (Fig. 7–2.1). Since we have assumed displacement components (u, v, w), compatibility conditions are automatically satisfied (Art. 3–14). Consequently, we have satisfied the equations of elasticity provided that we can find a harmonic function (warping function) ψ which by Eqs. (7–2.4) yields stress components which satisfy the boundary conditions [Eqs. (7–1.4)].

Substituting Eqs. (7–2.4) into the boundary conditions for the lateral surface, we see that the first two of Eqs. (7–1.4a) are satisfied identical. The third equation yields

$$\left(\frac{\partial \psi}{\partial x} - y\right)l + \left(\frac{\partial \psi}{\partial y} + x\right)m = 0$$

$$(7\text{-}2.6)$$

where (l, m) denote the components of the unit normal vector to the lateral surface S bounding the simply connected region R (Fig. 7–2.2). By Fig. 7–2.2 we find

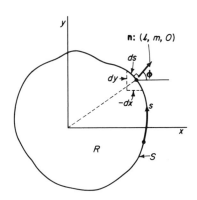

Figure 7-2.2

$$l = \cos\phi = \frac{dy}{ds}$$

$$(7\text{-}2.7)$$

$$m = \sin\phi = -\frac{dx}{ds}$$

Substitution of Eq. (7–2.7) into Eq. (7–2.6) yields

$$\frac{\partial \psi}{\partial x}\frac{dy}{ds} - \frac{\partial \psi}{\partial y}\frac{dx}{ds} = x\frac{dx}{ds} + y\frac{dy}{ds} = \frac{1}{2}\frac{d}{ds}(x^2 + y^2) \qquad (7\text{-}2.8)$$

Furthermore, by Fig. 7–2.2, we have

$$\frac{dy}{ds} = \frac{dx}{dn}, \qquad \frac{dx}{ds} = -\frac{dy}{dn} \tag{7–2.9}$$

Consequently, Eqs. (7–2.8) and (7–2.9) yield

$$\frac{d\psi}{dn} = \frac{\partial\psi}{\partial x}\frac{dx}{dn} + \frac{\partial\psi}{\partial y}\frac{dy}{dn} = \frac{1}{2}\frac{d}{ds}(x^2 + y^2) \tag{7–2.10}$$

For a circular cross section of radius a, $x^2 + y^2 = a^2 = \text{const}$. Then, Eq. (7–2.10) yields $d\psi/dn = 0$ on S. This result agrees with that obtained in Art. 4–13 (see also Prob. R-8 at the end of Chapter 4).

In general, we note that if the cross section is noncircular, Eqs. (7–2.6), (7–2.7), and (7–2.9) yield the result

$$\frac{d\psi}{dn} = yl - xm = f(s) \tag{7–2.11}$$

where $f(s)$ denotes a function of the parameter s on the bounding curve S (Fig. 7–2.2).

Finally, it may be shown (see problem end of this article) that

$$\Sigma\,F_x = \int_A \tau_{xz}\,dA = 0$$

$$\Sigma\,F_y = \int_A \tau_{yz}\,dA = 0 \tag{7–2.12}$$

$$\Sigma\,M_z = \int_A (x\tau_{yz} - y\tau_{xz})\,dA = M$$

Accordingly, we have obtained a solution of the torsion problem of a bar with simply connected cross section, provided $\psi(x, y)$ satisfies the equations

$$\nabla^2\psi = 0 \qquad\qquad \text{in } R$$

$$\frac{d\psi}{dn} = yl - xm = f(s) \qquad \text{on } S \tag{7–2.13}$$

Equations (7–2.13) define a well-known, extensively studied problem of potential theory:[1] the Neumann boundary-value problem. In other words, the torsion problem expressed in terms of the warping function $\psi(x, y)$ may be stated as follows:

Determine a function $\psi(x, y)$ which is harmonic ($\nabla^2\psi = 0$) in R, such that it is regular in R and continuous in $R + S$, and such that its normal derivative takes on prescribed values $f(s)$ on S.

Alternatively, Eqs. (7–2.13) may be reformulated by utilizing the complex

---

[1]O. D. Kellogg, *Foundations of Potential Theory* (New York: Dover Publications, Inc., 1953). A solution ϕ to the Neumann problem exists provided the integral of the normal derivative of the function ψ, calculated over the entire boundary S, vanishes. Then the solution ϕ is determined to within an arbitrary constant. For the torsion problem [Eqs. (7–2.13)], the solution ϕ exists (see the problem at the end of this article).

conjugate of $\psi(x, y)$, that is, by utilizing the function $\chi(x, y)$ related to $\psi(x, y)$ by the Cauchy-Riemann equations:[2]

$$\frac{\partial \psi}{\partial x} = \frac{\partial \chi}{\partial y}, \qquad \frac{\partial \psi}{\partial y} = -\frac{\partial \chi}{\partial x} \qquad (7\text{-}2.14)$$

Differentiating the first of Eqs. (7–2.14) by y, the second by x, and subtracting, we obtain $\nabla^2 \chi = 0$. Substitution of Eqs. (7–2.14) and (7–2.9) into the second of Eqs. (7–2.13) yields

$$\frac{d\chi}{ds} = yl - xm = \frac{1}{2}\frac{d}{ds}(x^2 + y^2) \quad \text{or} \quad \chi = \frac{1}{2}(x^2 + y^2) + \text{const.}$$

Accordingly, in terms of the complex conjugate χ of ψ, Eqs. (7–2.13) may be written

$$\nabla^2 \chi = 0 \qquad\qquad\qquad \text{in } R$$

$$\chi = \frac{1}{2}(x^2 + y^2) = g(s) \qquad \text{on } S \qquad (7\text{-}2.15)$$

where the constant in the second equation has been set equal to zero, since it does not affect the state of stress or displacement [see Eqs. (7–2.3), (7–2.4), and (7–2.14)].

In terms of χ, the strain and stress components are by Eqs. (7–2.3), (7–2.4), and (7–2.14)

$$\gamma_{xz} = \theta\left(\frac{\partial \chi}{\partial y} - y\right), \qquad \gamma_{yz} = -\theta\left(\frac{\partial \chi}{\partial x} - x\right) \qquad (7\text{-}2.16)$$

and

$$\tau_{xz} = G\theta\left(\frac{\partial \chi}{\partial y} - y\right), \qquad \tau_{yz} = -G\theta\left(\frac{\partial \chi}{\partial x} - x\right) \qquad (7\text{-}2.17)$$

The boundary-value problem defined by Eq. (7–2.15), namely, that of seeking a harmonic function χ in region R, whose values are prescribed on the boundary S of R, is known as the Dirichlet problem. The Dirichlet problem has been studied extensively.[3]

Problems. Verify the first two of Eqs. (7–2.12). Verify that a solution ψ to the Neumann problem exists for the torsion of a bar [see Eqs. (7–2.13)].

7-3 Prandtl Torsion Function

In the preceding article we have formulated the torsion problem of the bar with simply connected cross section in terms of two associated boundary-value problems [see Eqs. (7–2.13) and (7–2.15)]. In this article we consider an

---

[2]R. V. Churchill, *Introduction to Complex Variables and Applications* (New York: McGraw-Hill Book Company, 1948).

[3]Kellogg, *Foundations of Potential Theory*. See also R. Courant and D. Hilbert, *Methods of Mathematical Physics*, Vol. 2 (New York: Interscience Publishers, Inc., 1962).

alternate approach originally formulated by Prandtl.[4] Prandtl employed the semi-inverse procedure as follows:

Since in the classical torsion problem the lateral surface and the end planes of the bar are free from normal tractions, one might initially guess that the normal tractions are zero throughout the bar. Furthermore, since the end faces are subjected to shear stress components which produce a couple **M**, one might initially assume as a first guess that the shear component not associated with the couple **M** also vanishes. Then one has (with respect to x, y, z axes designated in Fig. 7–2.1)

$$\sigma_x = \sigma_y = \sigma_z = \tau_{xy} = 0 \qquad (7\text{–}3.1)$$

Next, since the left and right end planes are loaded identically it appears reasonable that the remaining two components of stress (τ_{xz}, τ_{yz}) are approximately independent of the axial coordinate z. Accordingly, assuming that τ_{xz}, τ_{yz} are functions of (x, y) only and substituting Eqs. (7–3.1) into Eqs. (7–1.1), we find

$$\frac{\partial \tau_{xz}}{\partial x} + \frac{\partial \tau_{yz}}{\partial y} = 0 \qquad (7\text{–}3.2)$$

Equations (7–3.2) represent the necessary and sufficient condition that there exists a function $\phi(x, y)$ such that (see Art. 1–13)

$$\tau_{xz} = \frac{\partial \phi}{\partial y}, \qquad \tau_{yz} = -\frac{\partial \phi}{\partial x} \qquad (7\text{–}3.3)$$

where here the function ϕ is called the *Prandtl torsion function*.

Equation (7–3.3) automatically satisfies the equation of equilibrium [Eq. (7–3.2)]. Substitution of Eqs. (7–3.1) and (7–3.3) into Eqs. (7–1.5) yields

$$\nabla^2 \phi = \frac{\partial^2 \phi}{\partial x^2} + \frac{\partial^2 \phi}{\partial y^2} = c = \text{const.} \qquad (7\text{–}3.4)$$

Accordingly, compatibility is satisfied provided $\nabla^2 \phi = c$. The constant c may be shown to have a physical significance in that it is related to the angle of twist. Before verifying this statement, we consider the boundary conditions on the lateral surface and on the end planes [Eqs. (7–1.4)]. The first two of Eqs. (7–1.4a) are satisfied automatically; the last of Eqs. (7–1.4a) with Eqs. (7–2.7) and (7–3.3) yield (see Fig. 7–2.2)

$$\frac{d\phi}{ds} = \frac{\partial \phi}{\partial x}\frac{dx}{ds} + \frac{\partial \phi}{\partial y}\frac{dy}{ds} = 0 \qquad \text{on } S$$

or

$$\phi = K = \text{const.} \qquad \text{on } S \qquad (7\text{–}3.5)$$

where K denotes an arbitrary constant. For the simply connected cross section we may set $K = 0$ (see Art. 7–6).

Finally, substitution of Eqs. (7–2.7) and (7–3.3) into Eqs. (7–1.4b) yields the following integrations over the end planes:

---

[4]L. Prandtl, *Physik. Zeit.*, Vol. 4 (1903), pp. 758–770. As we shall see, the results obtained by Prantl are related simply to those obtained by Saint-Venant.

$$\Sigma F_x = \int \int \sigma_{Px}\,dx\,dy = \int \int \tau_{xz}\,dx\,dy = \int dx \int \frac{\partial \phi}{\partial y}\,dy = \int \phi \Big|_{y_1}^{y_2} dx$$

$$\Sigma F_y = \int \int \sigma_{Py}\,dx\,dy = \int \int \tau_{yz}\,dx\,dy = -\int dy \int \frac{\partial \phi}{\partial x}\,dx = \int \phi \Big|_{x_1}^{x_2} dy$$

$$\Sigma M_z = M = \int \int (x\tau_{yz} - y\tau_{xz})\,dx\,dy = -\int \int \left(x\frac{\partial \phi}{\partial x} + y\frac{\partial \phi}{\partial y} \right) dx\,dy$$

$$= -\int x\phi \Big|_{x_1}^{x_2} dy - \int y\phi \Big|_{y_1}^{y_2} dx + 2 \int \int \phi\,dx\,dy$$

Since $\phi = $ const. on the lateral surface [we take $K = 0$ for the simply connected region; see Eq. (7–3.5)] and since x_1, x_2, y_1, y_2 denote points on the lateral surface, it follows that

$$\Sigma F_x = 0, \qquad \Sigma F_y = 0, \qquad \Sigma M_z = M = 2 \int \int \phi\,dx\,dy \qquad (7\text{–}3.6)$$

By the above discussion, we see that the torsion problem for a simply connected cross section R is solved precisely provided we obtain a function ϕ such that

$$\nabla^2 \phi = c = \text{const.} \qquad \text{in } R$$
$$\phi = 0 \qquad\qquad\quad \text{on } S \qquad\qquad (7\text{–}3.7)$$

and provided the shears τ_{xz}, τ_{yz} are distributed over the end planes in accordance with Eq. (7–3.3). The twisting moment M is then defined by Eq. (7–3.6). The constant c may be related to the angle of twist per unit length of the bar, as we now proceed to show.

Displacement components. Substitution of Eqs. (7–3.1) and (7–3.3) into the stress-strain relations [Eqs. (7–1.3)] yields with Eqs. (3–12.17)

$$\frac{\partial u}{\partial x} = \frac{\partial v}{\partial y} = \frac{\partial w}{\partial z} = 0, \qquad \gamma_{xy} = \frac{\partial u}{\partial y} + \frac{\partial v}{\partial x} = 0$$
$$\gamma_{xz} = \frac{\partial u}{\partial z} + \frac{\partial w}{\partial x} = \frac{1}{G}\tau_{xz}, \qquad \gamma_{yz} = \frac{\partial v}{\partial z} + \frac{\partial w}{\partial y} = \frac{1}{G}\tau_{yz} \qquad (7\text{–}3.8)$$

Integration of the first four of Eqs. (7–3.8) yields

$$u = -Az(y - b), \qquad v = Az(x - a) \qquad\qquad (7\text{–}3.9)$$

where A is a constant of integration and where $x = a, y = b$ defines the *center of twist*, that is, the z axis about which each cross section rotates as a rigid body (see Art. 4–13; there, $a = b = 0$ denotes the axis of twist). Substitution of Eqs. (7–3.9) into the last two of Eqs. (7–3.8) yields

$$\frac{\partial w}{\partial x} = \frac{1}{G}\tau_{xz} + A(y - b)$$
$$\frac{\partial w}{\partial y} = \frac{1}{G}\tau_{yz} - A(x - a) \qquad\qquad (7\text{–}3.10)$$

Integration of Eqs. (7–3.10) yields

$$w = w_0 - A(xb - ya) \qquad (7\text{–}3.11)$$

where $w_0 = w_0(x, y)$ represents the warping of the cross section. The terms involving the constants (a, b) in Eqs. (7–3.9) and (7–3.11) represent a rigid-body displacement relative to the center of twist.

To determine the angle of twist per unit length of the bar, we recall that the rotation ω_z of a volume element relative to the z axis is [see Eqs. (3–11.14)]

$$\omega_z = \frac{1}{2}\left(\frac{\partial v}{\partial x} - \frac{\partial u}{\partial y}\right) \qquad (7\text{–}3.12)$$

Substitution of Eqs. (7–3.9) into Eqs. (7–3.12) yields $\omega_z = Az$. Hence, the angle of twist θ per unit length of the bar is

$$\theta = \frac{\partial \omega_z}{\partial z} = A \qquad (7\text{–}3.13)$$

Therefore, the constant of integration A in Eqs. (7–3.9) is identical to the angle of twist per unit length of the bar. Furthermore, by the last two of Eqs. (7–3.8), we note that by differentiating γ_{xz} by y and γ_{yz} by x and subtracting, we obtain

$$2\theta = 2\frac{\partial \omega_z}{\partial z} = \frac{\partial}{\partial z}\left(\frac{\partial v}{\partial x} - \frac{\partial u}{\partial y}\right) = \frac{1}{G}\left(\frac{\partial \tau_{yz}}{\partial x} - \frac{\partial \tau_{xz}}{\partial y}\right) \qquad (7\text{–}3.14)$$

Hence, substitution of Eq. (7–3.3) into Eq. (7–3.14) yields [with Eq. (7–3.7)]

$$\nabla^2\phi = \frac{\partial^2\phi}{\partial x^2} + \frac{\partial^2\phi}{\partial y^2} = c = -2G\theta \qquad (7\text{–}3.15)$$

Accordingly, in terms of the Prandtl stress function ϕ, the torsion problem of a bar with simply connected cross section R bounded by S is defined by

$$\begin{aligned} \nabla^2\phi &= -2G\theta \qquad \text{in } R \\ \phi &= 0 \qquad\quad\ \text{on } S \end{aligned} \qquad (7\text{–}3.16)$$

For the case where $a = b = 0$, the warping displacement $w_0(x, y)$ is related to the warping function $\psi(x, y)$ by the equation [see Eqs. (7–2.2) and (7–3.11)]

$$w_0 = \theta\psi(x, y) \qquad (7\text{–}3.17)$$

Furthermore, the Prandtl stress function $\phi(x, y)$ is related to the warping function $\psi(x, y)$ by the equation [see Eqs. (7–2.4) and (7–3.3)]

$$\frac{\partial\phi}{\partial y} = G\theta\left(\frac{\partial\psi}{\partial x} - y\right), \qquad \frac{\partial\phi}{\partial x} = -G\theta\left(\frac{\partial\psi}{\partial y} + x\right) \qquad (7\text{–}3.18)$$

and to the complex conjugate χ of ψ by the relations [see Eqs. (7–2.14), (7–3.3), and (7–3.18)]

$$\frac{\partial\phi}{\partial y} = G\theta\left(\frac{\partial\chi}{\partial y} - y\right), \qquad \frac{\partial\phi}{\partial x} = G\theta\left(\frac{\partial\chi}{\partial x} - x\right) \qquad (7\text{–}3.19)$$

Integration of these relations yields

$$\phi = G\theta \left[\chi - \frac{1}{2}(x^2 + y^2) + b \right] \qquad (7\text{-}3.20)$$

where b denotes a constant. Thus, the Prandtl stress function ϕ may be simply related to the Saint-Venant warping function ψ [Eqs. (7–3.18)] or to the conjugate harmonic function χ of ψ [Eq. (7–3.20)].

Problem. Show that cylinders with circular cross sections are the only bodies whose lateral surface can be free from external load when the stress components are characterized by

$$\sigma_x = \sigma_y = \sigma_z = \tau_{xy} = 0, \qquad \tau_{xz} = -G\theta y, \qquad \tau_{yz} = G\theta x.$$

7-4 A Method of Solution of the Torsion Problem: Elliptic Cross Section

A direct approach to the solution of the torsion problem is difficult in most practical cases. However, in terms of Prandtl's stress function ϕ, the following indirect approach is sometimes useful, although it is not generally applicable.

Since $\phi = 0$ on the lateral boundary [Eq. (7–3.16)], we may seek stress functions ϕ_i such that $\phi_i = 0$ on the lateral boundary of the shaft, leaving sufficient arbitrariness in ϕ so that the equation $\nabla^2\phi = -2G\theta$ may be satisfied over the region R occupied by the cross section. For a certain class of cross sections with boundaries simply expressible in the form $f(x, y) = 0$, this procedure is sometimes fruitful.

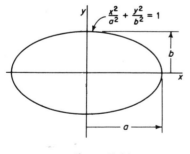

Figure 7-4.1

Example 7–4.1. Bar with elliptical cross section. The equation of the bounding curve C of a bar with elliptical cross section is (Fig. 7–4.1)

$$f(x, y) = \frac{x^2}{a^2} + \frac{y^2}{b^2} - 1 = 0 \qquad (7\text{-}4.1)$$

Hence, if we assume a stress function ϕ in the form

$$\phi = A\left(\frac{x^2}{a^2} + \frac{y^2}{b^2} - 1\right) \qquad (7\text{-}4.2)$$

where A is a constant, the boundary condition $\phi = 0$ on C is automatically satisfied. To yield a solution to the torsion problem the function ϕ must be chosen so that both of Eqs. (7–3.16) are satisfied. By Eq. (7–4.2) we find that

$$\nabla^2\phi = 2A\left(\frac{1}{a^2} + \frac{1}{b^2}\right)$$

Hence, in order that ϕ satisfy Eqs. (7–3.16) we must have

$$A = -\frac{a^2 b^2 G\theta}{a^2 + b^2} \tag{7–4.3}$$

Accordingly, if A is given by Eq. (7–4.3), Eq. (7–4.2) yields the solution of the torsion of a bar with elliptic cross section. With ϕ so determined, the theory of Art. 7–3 yields the stress components (τ_{zz}, τ_{yz}) and the moment M in terms of the dimensions a, b of the cross section, the shear modulus G, and the angle of twist θ per unit length of the bar.

Moment-angle of twist relation. The moment-stress function relation [Eq. (7–3.6)], with Eqs. (7–4.2) and (7–4.3), now yields

$$M = -\frac{2G\theta a^2 b^2}{a^2 + b^2} \left[\frac{1}{a^2} \int\int x^2\, dx\, dy + \frac{1}{b^2} \int\int y^2\, dx\, dy - \int\int dx\, dy \right] \tag{7–4.4}$$

Now, for the ellipse,

$$\int\int x^2\, dx\, dy = \int x^2\, dA = I_y = \frac{\pi a^3 b}{4}$$

$$\int\int y^2\, dx\, dy = \int y^2\, dA = I_x = \frac{\pi a b^3}{4} \tag{7–4.5}$$

$$\int\int dx\, dy = \int dA = \pi a b$$

where (I_x, I_y) denote the moment of inertia of the cross-sectional area with respect to the (x, y) axes, respectively. Consequently, Eqs. (7–4.4) and (7–4.5) yield

$$M = \frac{\pi G\theta a^3 b^3}{a^2 + b^2} = C\theta \tag{7–4.6}$$

where

$$C = \frac{\pi a^3 b^3 G}{a^2 + b^2} \tag{7–4.7}$$

is called the *torsional rigidity* of the bar. Equation (7–4.6) relates the twisting moment M to the angle of twist θ, the constant of proportionality being C, the torsional rigidity.

Also, by Eqs. (7–4.3) and (7–4.6), we find

$$A = -\frac{M}{\pi a b} \tag{7–4.8}$$

Therefore, we may write ϕ in the form

$$\phi = -\frac{M}{\pi a b} \left(\frac{x^2}{a^2} + \frac{y^2}{b^2} - 1 \right) \tag{7–4.9}$$

Stress components. By Eqs. (7–3.3) and (7–4.9) we obtain

$$\tau_{xz} = \frac{\partial \phi}{\partial y} = -\frac{2M}{\pi ab^3} y$$

$$\tau_{yz} = -\frac{\partial \phi}{\partial x} = \frac{2M}{\pi a^3 b} x$$

(7-4.10)

Hence, (τ_{xz}, τ_{yz}) vary linearly over the cross section with respect to (y, x), respectively. To determine the direction of the shearing stress vector $\boldsymbol{\tau} = \mathbf{i}\tau_{xz} + \mathbf{j}\tau_{yz}$ on the boundary of the shaft, we note that the tangent of the angle between the vector $\boldsymbol{\tau}$ and the positive x axis is given by [Eq. (7-4.10)]

$$\frac{\tau_{yz}}{\tau_{xz}} = -\frac{b^2 x}{a^2 y}$$

(7-4.11)

However, by the equation of the bounding curve C of the cross section [Eq. (7-4.1)], we see that the angle formed by the tangent to C and the positive x axis is

$$\frac{dy}{dx} = -\frac{b^2 x}{a^2 y}$$

(7-4.12)

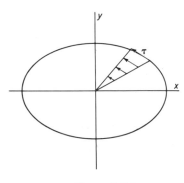

Figure 7-4.2

Equations (7-4.11) and (7-4.12) show that the shearing-stress vector $\boldsymbol{\tau}$ is tangent to the boundary C of the cross section. For $x = a$, $y = 0$, $\boldsymbol{\tau} = \mathbf{j}\tau_{yz}$; hence, $\boldsymbol{\tau}$ is directed perpendicular to the x axis. For $x = 0$, $y = b$, $\boldsymbol{\tau} = \mathbf{i}\tau_{xz}$; then $\boldsymbol{\tau}$ is directed perpendicular to the y axis (see Fig. 7-4.2). Also, the magnitude of $\boldsymbol{\tau}$ is

$$\tau = \sqrt{\tau_{xz}^2 + \tau_{yz}^2} = \frac{2M}{\pi ab} \sqrt{\frac{x^2}{a^4} + \frac{y^2}{b^4}}$$

(7-4.13)

Determining the maximum value of τ from Eq. (7-4.13), we find

$$\tau_{max} = \frac{2M}{\pi ab^2}, \qquad y = b, \qquad x = 0$$

(7-4.14)

For a circular shaft $a = b = r$; then $\pi_{max} = 2M/\pi r^3$, everywhere on the boundary C.

Problem. Derive Eq. (7-4.14).

Displacement components. With θ determined as a function of M and C [Eq. (7-4.6)], the displacement components (u, v) are known for all points in any cross section for a given moment and a given bar. They are $u = -\theta yz$, $v = \theta xz$ [Eq. (7-3.9), with $a = b = 0$]. To compute the displacement component w, we must compute $\psi(x, y)$, the warping function [Eqs. (7-2.2) or (7-3.17)], from its relation to the stress function $\phi(x, y)$ [Eq. (7-3.18)].

By Eqs. (7-3.18) and (7-4.9), we obtain

$$\frac{\partial \psi}{\partial x} = \frac{1}{G\theta} \frac{\partial \phi}{\partial y} + y = \left(1 - \frac{2M}{\pi a b^3 G\theta}\right) y$$

$$\frac{\partial \psi}{\partial y} = -\frac{1}{G\theta} \frac{\partial \phi}{\partial x} - x = \left(\frac{2M}{\pi a b^3 G\theta} - 1\right) x$$

(7-4.15)

Integration of Eqs. (7-4.15) yields

$$\psi = \frac{b^2 - a^2}{a^2 + b^2} xy + \text{const.}$$

(7-4.16)

If we set $w = 0$ for $x = y = 0$, the constant in Eq. (7-4.16) is zero. Consequently,

$$w = \theta \psi = \frac{\theta(b^2 - a^2)}{a^2 + b^2} xy$$

or

$$w = -Kxy$$

(7-4.17)

where

$$K = \frac{\theta(a^2 - b^2)}{a^2 + b^2} = \frac{M(a^2 - b^2)}{\pi a^3 b^3 G}$$

(7-4.18)

Equation (7-4.17) is the equation of a hyperbola. Accordingly, the contour map of w over the cross section of the bar is represented by a family of hyperbolas (Fig. 7-4.3), with the (x, y) axes representing lines of zero displacement. Since K is a positive constant, w is positive (in the direction of the positive z axis) in the second and fourth quadrants and negative in the first and third quadrants of the (x, y) plane.

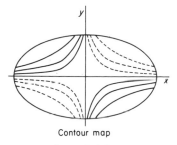

Contour map

Figure 7-4.3

Problem. Apply the method outlined in Art. 7-4 to the bar with circular cross section.

7-5 Remarks on Solutions of Laplace Equation, $\nabla^2 F = 0$

In the theory of complex variables[5] it is shown that the real and imaginary parts of an analytic function F of the complex variable $z = x + iy$ satisfy the Laplace equation $\nabla^2 F = 0$; that is, the real and imaginary parts of an analytic function are harmonic functions. Accordingly, by considering the real and the imaginary parts of analytic functions, F_n, one may proceed, inversely so to speak, to determine the equations of the boundaries of simply connected cross sections for which the real and imaginary parts of F_n represent solutions of the torsion problem. For example, we have previously noted that

[5]Churchill, *Introduction to Complex Variables and Applications.*

$f(z) = \psi + i\chi$ is an analytic function where χ is the conjugate harmonic of the warping function ψ, and that the torsion problem may be represented either in terms of ψ or χ (Art. 7–3).

One of the simplest sets of analytic functions of the complex variable $z = x + iy$ is the set $F_n = z^n = (x + iy)^n$. By letting $n = \pm 1, \pm 2, \pm 3, \ldots$, solutions of the torsion problem may be developed in the form of polynomials. For example, for $n = 2$, we obtain the solutions $x^2 - y^2$ and $2xy$. For $n = 3$, we find $x^3 - 3xy^2$ and $3x^2y - y^3$. For $n = 4$, we have $x^4 - 6x^2y^2 + y^4$ and $4x^3y - 4xy^3$, etc. Sums and differences of these polynomial solutions may also be employed, since the sums and the differences of harmonic functions yield other harmonic functions. A systematic application of this technique to the torsion problem has been employed by Weber and Günther.[6] Here we merely present a classical example of the method. Other examples are considered in the problems.

Example 7–5.1. Equilateral triangle. Consider the harmonic polynomial $\phi_1 = A(x^3 - 3xy^2)$ (obtained from z^n, with $n = 3$), where A is a constant. Since ϕ_1 is harmonic, by setting $\chi = \phi_1$, we may write Prandtl's stress function ϕ in the form [see Eq. (7–3.20)]

$$\phi = -G\theta \left[\frac{(x^2 + y^2)}{2} - \frac{(x^3 - 3xy^2)}{2a} - b \right] \qquad (7\text{–}5.1)$$

where a and b denote constants. If we assign the value $2a^2/27$ to the constant b, we may factor Eq. (7–5.1) into the form

$$\phi = \frac{G\theta}{2a} \left(x - \sqrt{3}\, y - \frac{2a}{3} \right) \left(x + \sqrt{3}\, y - \frac{2a}{3} \right) \left(x + \frac{a}{3} \right) \qquad (7\text{–}5.2)$$

Accordingly for $b = 2a^2/27$, the condition that ϕ vanish on the lateral boundary of a bar in torsion [Eqs. (7–3.16)] is satisfied identically by the three conditions

$$x - \sqrt{3}\, y - \frac{2a}{3} = 0$$

$$x + \sqrt{3}\, y - \frac{2a}{3} = 0 \qquad (7\text{–}5.3)$$

$$x + \frac{a}{3} = 0$$

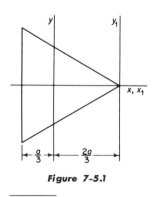

Figure 7-5.1

Equations (7–5.3) represent the equations of three straight lines in the (x, y) plane which form an equilateral triangle (Fig. 7–5.1). The region bounded by the three straight lines may be considered as the cross section of a bar in torsion.

[6]C. Weber and W. Günther, *Torsiontheorie* (Braunschweig: Friedr. Vieweg und Sohn, 1958).

Shear-stress components. By Eqs. (7–3.3) and (7–5.1) we find that the shear-stress components are

$$\tau_{xz} = -\frac{3G\theta y}{a}\left(x + \frac{a}{3}\right)$$

$$\tau_{yz} = G\theta\left(x - \frac{3x^2}{2a} + \frac{3y^2}{2a}\right) \tag{7-5.4}$$

Equations (7–5.4) show that $\tau_{xz} = 0$ for $y = 0$ and for $x = -a/3$ and that τ_{yz} is parabolically distributed along the y axis ($x = 0$).

Warping of cross section. Letting $\chi = (x^3 - 3xy^2)/2a$ and integrating Eqs. (7–2.14), we obtain the warping function

$$\psi = \frac{y}{2a}(y^2 - 3x^2) + C_0 \tag{7-5.5}$$

where C_0 is a constant. If we set $w = 0$ for $x = y = 0$, then Eq. (7–5.5) and the last of Eqs. (7–2.2) yield

$$w = \frac{\theta y}{2a}(y^2 - 3x^2) \tag{7-5.6}$$

By Eq. (7–5.6), we note that $w = 0$ for $y = 0$ and $y = \pm\sqrt{3}\,x$. In general, the w contour lines for which $w = $ const. are described by the equation

$$x^2 = \frac{y^2}{3} + \frac{K}{y} \tag{7-5.7}$$

where $K = $ const. If $K > 0$, $x \to \infty$ as $y \to 0$ and as $y \to \infty$. These conditions facilitate the visualization of the contour map for w (Prob. 7–5.1), where positive w is taken in the direction of positive z where (x, y, z) form a right-handed coordinate system. The sign of w changes upon crossing the lines $y = 0$ and $y = \pm\sqrt{3}\,x$. Consequently, the cross section warps into alternate convex ($+w$) and concave ($-w$) regions.

PROBLEM SET 7-5

1 Sketch the contour map for the warping of the triangular cross section under torsion [see Eq. (7–5.7) and Fig. 7–5.1)].

2 Derive Eqs. (7–5.2), (7–5.4), and (7–5.5).

3 Considering terms obtained from the analytic function $(x + iy)^4$, we can express a Prandtl stress function in the form

$$\phi = -G\theta\left[\frac{(x^2 + y^2)}{2} - \frac{a(x^4 - 6x^2 y^2 + y^4)}{2} + \frac{(a-1)}{2}\right]$$

Set $a = 0.2$; plot the cross section of the bar for which ϕ solves the torsion problem. Calculate the stress at the boundary point for which the radius vector forms an angle of $\beta = 45°$ with the positive x axis. Use $G = 12 \times 10^6$ lb/in.^{2}, $\theta = 0.001$ rad/in. Compare the result to that of a circle with radius equal to the radius vector of the plotted cross section at $\beta = 45°$. Repeat for $a = 0.5$. (In his investigations,

Saint-Venant found that the torsional rigidity of a given cross section may be approximated by replacing the given cross section with an elliptical cross section with the same area and the same polar moment of inertia.) Is the *circular* approximation noted above a good approximation?

4 Choosing axes (x_1, y_1) at the tip of the equilateral triangular cross section (Fig. 7–5.1), by means of Eqs. (7–3.6) and (7–5.2) show that

$$M = \frac{G\theta a^4}{15\sqrt{3}}$$

5 C. Weber proposed the following elementary method of examining the effects of a circular groove or slot in a circular bar (for other kinds of groove and bar combinations see the Weber reference footnoted on p. 176): Considering a pair of harmonic functions x and $x/(x^2 + y^2)$ obtained from z^n with $n = \pm 1$, Weber transformed the functions into polar coordinates (r, θ). Thus, $x = r \cos \theta$ and $x/(x^2 + y^2) = (\cos \theta)/r$. Hence, he took [see Eq. (7–3.20)] a Prandtl stress function in the form

$$\phi = \frac{G\theta}{2}\left[b^2 - r^2 + 2a(r^2 - b^2)\frac{\cos \theta}{r}\right] \qquad \text{(a)}$$

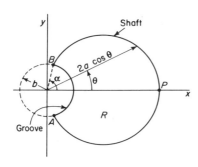

Figure P7-5.5

where θ is taken to denote the angle of twist per unit length. Setting $\phi = 0$ on the boundary, Weber obtained the equation of the boundary of the cross section as

$$(r^2 - b^2)\left(1 - \frac{2a}{r}\cos \theta\right) = 0 \qquad \text{(b)}$$

Equation (b) is satisfied identically by the conditions

$$\begin{aligned} r^2 - b^2 &= 0 \\ r - 2a \cos \theta &= 0 \end{aligned} \qquad \text{(c)}$$

Equations (c) may be considered to represent the cross section R of a circular shaft with a circular groove (Fig. P7–5.5). Hence, with Eq. (a), the stress components τ_{xz}, τ_{yz} may be computed by Eqs. (7–3.3). Derive the formulas for τ_{xz}, τ_{yz}.

6 Using the results derived in Prob. 5, derive formulas for the stress components τ_{xz}, τ_{yz} on the boundary of the shaft and on the boundary of the groove. Compute the maximum value of stress on the boundary of the shaft; on the groove.

7 Compute τ_{max} in terms of M and a for $\alpha = 60°$, for $\alpha = 45°$; for $\alpha = 30°$ (Fig. P7–5.5). Compute τ at the point P for these cases. Verify that $\tau_{xz} = \tau_{yz} = 0$ for corners A and B.

7-6 Torsion of Bars with Tubular Cavities

Consider a bar with cross section R, where R is the multiply connected region interior to C_0 and exterior to the longitudinal tubular cavities $C_1, C_2, \ldots, C_n$ (Fig. 7–6.1). As in the torsion problem of the simply connected cross section, the displacement components are taken in the form

$$u = -\theta z y$$

$$v = \theta z x \qquad (7\text{--}6.1)$$

$$w = \theta \psi(x, y)$$

where θ and ψ are a constant and a function of (x, y), respectively, that are to be determined.

The shearing-stress components in region R are given by the relations [see Eqs. (7–2.4)]

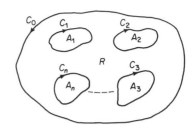

Figure 7-6.1

$$\tau_{xz} = \theta G \left(\frac{\partial \psi}{\partial x} - y \right), \qquad \tau_{yz} = \theta G \left(\frac{\partial \psi}{\partial y} + x \right) \qquad (7\text{--}6.2)$$

Since the boundaries $C_0, C_1, C_2, \ldots, C_n$ are free from external loads, the boundary conditions are

$$l\tau_{xz} + m\tau_{yz} = 0 \qquad \text{on } C_i, \qquad i = 0, 1, \ldots, n \qquad (7\text{--}6.3)$$

In terms of ψ, the boundary conditions may be written in the form

$$\frac{d\psi}{dn} = ly - mx \qquad \text{on } C_i, \qquad i = 0, 1, 2, \ldots, n \qquad (7\text{--}6.4)$$

Introducing the stress function ϕ, defined by Eqs. (7–3.3), we may write the boundary conditions in terms of the stress function ϕ in the form

$$l\frac{\partial \phi}{\partial y} - m\frac{\partial \phi}{\partial x} = \frac{d\phi}{ds} = 0 \qquad \text{on } C_i, \qquad i = 0, 1, \ldots, n \qquad (7\text{--}6.5)$$

or

$$\phi = K_i \qquad \text{on } C_i \qquad (i = 0, 1, 2, \ldots, n) \qquad (7\text{--}6.6)$$

where the K_i are constants.

In general, the function ϕ may be multiple-valued. However, the function ψ is determined by the boundary condition, Eq. (7–6.4), to within an arbitrary constant, and it follows by Eqs. (7–6.2) and (7–3.3) that the function ϕ is determined to within an arbitrary constant. Consequently, the stress function ϕ defined by Eqs. (7–3.3) must satisfy the conditions (7–6.6) where the value of only one of the constants K_i may be assigned arbitrarily. If the region R is simply connected (i.e., if there are no tubular cavities), $i = 0$, and $\phi = K_0$ on C_0. The constant K_0 may then be assigned an arbitrary value—for example, zero.

The remaining n constants must be chosen so that the displacement component w (and hence ψ, see Eq. 7–6.1) is a single-valued function, the constants K_i being related to the function ψ through Eqs. (7–3.18) and (7–6.6) or to the complex conjugate χ of ψ through Eqs. (7–3.20) and (7–6.6). For example, the values of K_i may be established so that the solution of the Dirichlet problem [with $b = 0$ in Eqs. (7–3.20)]

$$\nabla^2 \chi = 0 \quad \text{over } R$$

$$\chi = \tfrac{1}{2}(x^2 + y^2) + \bar{K}_i, \quad i = 1, \ldots, n \text{ on } C_i$$

$$G\theta\bar{K}_i = K_i$$

satisfies the conditions for the existence of a single-valued function in a multiply-connected region.[7]

Substituting Eqs. (7–3.3) into Eqs. (7–6.2), differentiating the first of Eqs. (7–6.2) by y and the second by x, and subtracting the resulting equations, we obtain the condition

$$\nabla^2 \phi = -2G\theta \quad \text{in the region } R \tag{7–6.7}$$

The twisting moment M that results from the shearing forces that act on the end plane of the bar is

$$M = \int\int_{\text{over } R} (x\tau_{yz} - y\tau_{xz}) \, dx \, dy \tag{7–6.8}$$

Substituting Eqs. (7–3.3) into Eq. (7–6.8), we obtain

$$M = -\int\int_{\text{over } R} \left(x\frac{\partial\phi}{\partial x} + y\frac{\partial\phi}{\partial y} \right) dx \, dy \tag{7–6.9}$$

Equation (7–6.9) may be written in the form

$$M = \int\int_{\text{over } R} 2\phi \, dx \, dy - \int\int_{\text{over } R} \left(\frac{\partial(x\phi)}{\partial x} + \frac{\partial(y\phi)}{\partial y} \right) dx \, dy \tag{7–6.10}$$

Transforming the second integral of Eq. (7–6.10) by Green's theorem for the plane, (Art. 1–10), we may write Eq. (7–6.10) in the form

$$M = 2\int\int_{\text{over } R} \phi \, dx \, dy - \sum_{i=0}^{n} \oint_{C_i} \phi(x \, dy - y \, dx) \tag{7–6.11}$$

Since we may assign the value of one of the K_i's in Eq. (7–6.6) arbitrarily, let K_0 on the boundary C_0 be zero; that is, let $\phi = 0$ on C_0. Then, substitution of Eq. (7–6.6) into Eq. (7–6.11) yields

$$M = 2\int\int_{\text{over } R} \phi \, dx \, dy + \sum_{i=1}^{n} K_i \oint_{C_i} (y \, dx - x \, dy)$$

Noting that $\oint_{C_i} (y \, dx - x \, dy) = 2\int\int_{\text{over } A_i} dx \, dy = 2A_i$, where A_i is the area bounded by the curve C_i, we obtain

$$M = 2\int\int_{\text{over } R} \phi \, dx \, dy + 2\sum_{i=1}^{n} K_i A_i \tag{7–6.12}$$

---

[7] See Eqs. (7–2.15) and the discussion at the end of Art. 5–4, particularly Eqs. (5–4.24) and (5–4.25). Here, $m = n$, and $G = \chi$.

Equation (7–6.12) is the moment-stress function relation for the torsion problem of bars with multiply connected cross sections.

Problem. For the hollow circular shaft of inner radius a and outer radius b, by the above theory, evaluate M using the stress function $\phi = A(r^2 - b^2)$.

7-7 Transfer of Axis of Twist

In the previous analysis of the torsion problem, it was assumed that any cross section of the beam was subjected to an infinitesimal rotation about a z axis. No assumption was made as to the location of the z axis relative to the cross section. In calculations, it may be convenient to choose a particular z axis. Hence, let us consider an axis z_1 that is parallel to the axis z, but that intersects the (x, y) plane at point (a, b). With respect to the z_1 axis, the displacement components are

$$u_1 = -\theta z(y - b), \qquad v_1 = \theta z(x - a), \qquad w_1 = \theta \psi_1(x, y) \qquad (7\text{-}7.1)$$

where ψ_1, not necessarily identical to ψ, is the warping function with respect to the z_1 axis.

In terms of the stress function ψ_1, the stress components are

$$\tau_{xz} = G\theta \left(\frac{\partial \psi_1}{\partial x} - y + b \right)$$

$$\tau_{yz} = G\theta \left(\frac{\partial \psi_1}{\partial y} + x - a \right) \qquad (7\text{-}7.2)$$

$$\sigma_x = \sigma_y = \sigma_z = \tau_{xy} = 0$$

Substitution of these stress components into the equilibrium equations [Eqs. (7–1.1)] yields the result

$$\nabla^2 \psi_1 = \frac{\partial^2 \psi_1}{\partial x^2} + \frac{\partial^2 \psi_1}{\partial y^2} = 0 \qquad (7\text{-}7.3)$$

Also, the boundary conditions [Eqs. (7–1.4)] reduce to the condition

$$\frac{d}{dn} (\psi_1 + bx - ay) = ly - mx \qquad (7\text{-}7.4)$$

Now the function $\psi_1 + bx - ay$ is harmonic, and it satisfies the same boundary conditions as the warping function ψ. Hence, by the uniqueness[8] of solution of the problem of Neumann, ψ and $\psi_1 + bx - ay$ can differ only by a constant; that is, $\psi_1 = \psi - bx + ay + c$, where c is a constant. Consequently, the displacement components measured with respect to axis z_1 are given by the formulas

---

[8] R. Courant and D. Hilbert, *Methods of Mathematical Physics*, Vol. 1 (New York: Interscience Publishers, Inc., 1953).

$$u_1 = -\theta z y + \theta z b$$
$$v_1 = \theta z x - \theta z a \qquad\qquad (7\text{-}7.5)$$
$$w_1 = \theta \psi + \theta y a - \theta x b + \theta c$$

These components differ by a rigid-body displacement from those with respect to the z axis [Eqs. (7–2.2)]. Consequently, the stress components are identical with those with respect to the z axis. Thus, the choice of the origin of coordinates is immaterial in the torsion problem of the bar, with regard to the stress components.

7-8 Shearing-stress Component in any Direction

Directional derivative. Let $P(x, y)$ be any point on a curve in the (x, y) plane. Let the scalar function $\phi(x, y)$ be defined on C with its partial derivatives $\partial\phi/\partial x$ and $\partial\phi/\partial y$; for example, ϕ may be the stress function in torsion. Let $Q: (x + \Delta x, y + \Delta y)$ be a point on C in the neighborhood of P (see Fig. 7–8.1). Let Δs be the length of arc PQ and $\Delta\phi$ be the change in ϕ due to

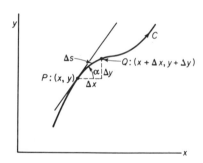

Figure 7-8.1

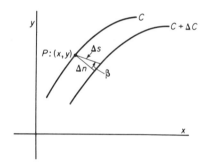

Figure 7-8.2

increments Δx and Δy. Then, the derivative

$$\frac{d\phi}{ds} = \lim_{\Delta s \to 0} \frac{\Delta\phi}{\Delta s}$$

determines the rate of change of ϕ along the curve C at the point $P: (x, y)$. Now the total differential of ϕ is

$$d\phi = \frac{\partial\phi}{\partial x} dx + \frac{\partial\phi}{\partial y} dy$$

and

$$\frac{d\phi}{ds} = \frac{\partial\phi}{\partial x}\frac{dx}{ds} + \frac{\partial\phi}{\partial y}\frac{dy}{ds}$$

Also,

$$\frac{dx}{ds} = \lim_{\Delta s \to 0} \frac{\Delta x}{\Delta s} = \cos\alpha$$

$$\frac{dy}{ds} = \lim_{\Delta s \to 0} \frac{\Delta y}{\Delta s} = \sin \alpha$$

Hence, $d\phi/ds = (\partial\phi/\partial x) \cos \alpha + (\partial\phi/\partial y) \sin \alpha$. By this equation, it is apparent that $d\phi/ds$ depends on the direction of s. For this reason, $d\phi/ds$ is called the *directional derivative*. It represents the rate of change of ϕ in the direction of the tangent to the particular curve chosen for point $P\colon (x, y)$. For example, if $\alpha = 0$,

$$\frac{d\phi}{ds} = \frac{\partial\phi}{\partial x}$$

is the rate of change of ϕ in the direction of the x axis.

Maximum value of the directional derivative: gradient. Consider two neighboring curves in the (x, y) plane; say C and $C + \Delta C$ (Fig. 7–8.2). Let the respective values of ϕ on these curves be ϕ and $\phi + \Delta\phi$. Then $\Delta\phi/\Delta s$ is the average rate of change of ϕ with respect to the distance Δs measured from curve C to the curve $C + \Delta C$. Now consider the ratio $\Delta n/\Delta s$, where Δn denotes the distance from C to $C + \Delta C$ measured along the normal to C at point $P\colon (x, y)$. The limiting value of this ratio is $\cos \beta$; that is,

$$\frac{dn}{ds} = \lim_{\Delta C \to 0} \frac{\Delta n}{\Delta s} = \cos \beta$$

Hence,

$$\frac{d\phi}{ds} = \frac{d\phi}{dn}\frac{dn}{ds} = \frac{d\phi}{dn} \cos \beta$$

Therefore, $d\phi/dn$, that is, the derivative of ϕ in the direction normal to C, is the maximum value that $d\phi/ds$ may take in any direction. Hence $(d\phi/ds)_{\max} = |d\phi/dn|$. The vector in the direction of the normal, of magnitude $|d\phi/dn|$, is called the gradient of ϕ; that is, $(\phi_x, \phi_y) = $ gradient $\phi = $ grad ϕ, where (x, y) subscripts on ϕ denote partial derivatives. Consequently, the maximum value of $d\phi/ds$ is equal to the magnitude of the gradient of ϕ, $|$ grad $\phi|$.

Stress component-directional derivative. Consider an arbitrary point $P\colon (x, y)$ in the cross section of a bar in torsion (Fig. 7–8.3). The stress component τ_θ in the direction θ is

$$\tau_\theta = \tau_{xz} \cos \theta + \tau_{yz} \sin \theta$$

In terms of the stress function ϕ, by Eqs. (7–3.3),

$$\tau_{xz} = \frac{\partial\phi}{\partial y}, \qquad \tau_{yz} = -\frac{\partial\phi}{\partial x}$$

Therefore,

$$\tau_\theta = \frac{\partial\phi}{\partial y} \cos \theta - \frac{\partial\phi}{\partial x} \sin \theta$$

$$= \phi_y \cos \theta - \phi_x \sin \theta$$

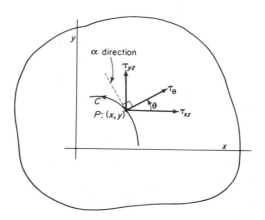

Figure 7-8.3

Now set $\alpha = \theta + \pi/2$. Then,

$$\tau_\theta = \phi_y \cos\left(\alpha - \frac{\pi}{2}\right) - \phi_x \sin\left(\alpha - \frac{\pi}{2}\right)$$

$$= \phi_x \cos\alpha + \phi_y \sin\alpha = \frac{d\phi}{ds}$$

Consequently, τ_θ is equal to the directional derivative of ϕ in a direction leading θ by $90°$. Note that if the direction α corresponds to a direction for which $\phi = $ constant, $d\phi/ds = 0$. Hence, the shearing stress perpendicular to the line $\phi = $ constant is zero. Therefore, lines $\phi = $ constant are shearing-stress trajectories, and the stress vector on lines $\phi = $ constant has magnitude

$$|\tau_\theta| = (\phi_x^2 + \phi_y^2)^{1/2} = \left(\frac{d\phi}{ds}\right)_{\max} = |\operatorname{grad}\phi|$$

The stress vector is tangent to lines $\phi = $ constant.

In polar coordinates (r, β) (see Fig. 7–8.4),

$$\tau_r = \frac{1}{r}\frac{\partial\phi}{\partial\beta}, \qquad \tau_\beta = -\frac{\partial\phi}{\partial r}$$

$$\tag{7-8.1}$$

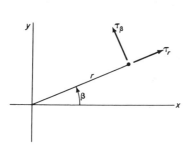

For example, in terms of polar coordinates (r, β), the Prandtl stress function of a circular shaft with circular groove is [see Eq. (a), Prob. 7–5.5]

$$\phi = \frac{G\theta}{2}\left[b^2 - r^2 + 2a(r^2 - b^2)\frac{\cos\beta}{r}\right]$$

$$\tag{7-8.2}$$

Figure 7-8.4

Consequently, Eqs. (7–8.1) and (7–8.2) yield

$$\tau_r = \tau_{rz} = \frac{1}{r}\frac{\partial \phi}{\partial \beta} = -\frac{G\theta a}{r^2}(r^2 - b^2)\sin\beta$$

$$\tau_\beta = \tau_{\beta z} = -\frac{\partial \phi}{\partial r} = G\theta\left[r - \frac{a}{r^2}(r^2 + b^2)\cos\beta\right]$$

(7–8.3)

Thus, for $\beta = 0$, $r = b$ (Fig. P7–5.5 and Prob. 7–5.5),

$$\tau_{rz} = 0, \qquad \tau_{\beta z} = -G\theta(2a - b)$$

and for $\beta = 0$, $r = 2a$ (point P in Fig. P7–5.5)

$$\tau_{rz} = 0, \qquad \tau_{\beta z} = \frac{G\theta}{4a}(4a^2 - b^2)$$

Problem. Plot out several shearing-stress trajectories for the cross section shown in Fig. P7–5.5

7-9 Solution of Torsion Problem by the Prandtl Membrane Analogy

In this article we consider an analogy method proposed by Prandtl[9] which lends itself to the obtaining of approximate solutions to the torsion problem. Although this method is of historical interest it is rarely used today to obtain quantitative results, and it is treated here primarily from the heuristic viewpoint.

The analogy is based upon the equivalence of the torsion equation

$$\nabla^2\phi = -2G\theta \qquad (7\text{–}9.1)$$

and the membrane equation

$$\nabla^2 z = -\frac{q}{S} \qquad (7\text{–}9.2)$$

where z denotes the lateral displacement of a membrane subjected to a lateral pressure q in terms of force per unit area and an initial (large) tension S (Fig. 7–9.1) in terms of force per unit length.

For example, if we consider an element $ABCD$ of dimensions dx, dy (Fig. 7–9.1), we see that the net vertical force due to the tension S acting along edge AD is

---

[9]L. Prandtl, "Zur Torsion von prismatischen Stäben," *Physikalische Zeitschrift*, Vol. 4 (1903), p. 758. Another analogy method, a hydrodynamic analogy, has been proposed by Pestel. See E. Pestel, "Eine neue hydrodynamische Analogie zur Torsion prismatischer Stäbe," *Ing.-Arch.*, Vol. XXIII (1955); "Ein neues Stromungsgleichnis der Torsion," *ZAMM*, Vol. 34 (1954); see also G. Grossmann, "Experimentalle Durchführung einer neuen hydrodynamischen Analogie für das torsion problem," *Ing.-Arch.*, Vol. XXV (1957). We shall discuss only the analogy proposed by Prandtl.

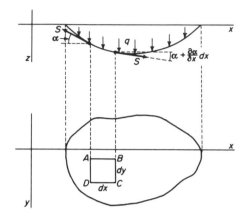

Figure 7-9.1

$$-S \, dy \tan \alpha = -S \, dy \frac{\partial z}{\partial x}$$

and the net vertical force due to the tension S (assumed to remain constant for sufficiently small values of q) acting along edge BC is

$$S \, dy \tan \left(\alpha + \frac{\partial \alpha}{\partial x} \, dx \right) = S \, dy \frac{\partial}{\partial x} \left(z + \frac{\partial z}{\partial x} \, dx \right)$$

Similarly for edges AB and DC we obtain

$$-S \, dx \frac{\partial z}{\partial y}, \qquad S \, dx \frac{\partial}{\partial y} \left(z + \frac{\partial z}{\partial y} \, dy \right)$$

Consequently, summation of force in the vertical direction yields for equilibrium of the membrane element $dx \, dy$

$$S \frac{\partial^2 z}{\partial x^2} \, dx \, dy + S \frac{\partial^2 z}{\partial y^2} \, dx \, dy + q \, dx \, dy = 0$$

or

$$\nabla^2 z = -\frac{q}{S}$$

Prandtl showed that the shearing-stress components in a straight elastic bar in torsion may be related to the slopes of a membrane (soap film) extended over a hole in a flat plate and subjected to a small pressure q, the hole having the shape of the cross section of the bar and the membrane being attached to the boundary of the hole.

By comparison of Eqs. (7–9.1) and (7–9.2), we arrive at the following analogous quantities:

$$z = c\phi, \qquad \frac{q}{S} = c \, 2G\theta \tag{7–9.3}$$

where c is a constant of proportionality. Hence,

$$\frac{z}{q/S} = \frac{\phi}{2G\theta}; \qquad \phi = \frac{2G\theta S}{q} z \tag{7-9.4}$$

Accordingly, the membrane displacement z is proportional to the Prandtl stress function ϕ, and since the shearing-stress components τ_{zz}, τ_{yz} are equal to the appropriate derivatives of ϕ with respect to x and y [see Eqs. (7–3.3)], it follows that the stress components are proportional to the derivatives of the membrane displacement z with respect to the coordinates (x, y) in the flat plate to which the membrane is attached (Fig. 7–9.1). In other words, the stress components at a point (x, y) of the bar are proportional to the slopes of the membrane at the corresponding point (x, y) of the membrane. Consequently, the distribution of shear-stress components in the cross section of the bar is easily visualized by forming a mental image of the slope of the corresponding membrane. Furthermore, for simply connected cross sections, since z is proportional to ϕ, by Eqs. (7–3.6) and (7–9.4) we note that the twisting moment M is proportional to the volume enclosed by the membrane and the (x, y) plane (Fig. 7–9.1).

For the multiply connected cross section additional conditions arise. For example, consider the cross section shown in Fig. 7–6.1. For this cross section, Eq. (7–6.12) shows that the twisting moment M is proportional to the integral of ϕ over R plus twice the sum of the products of area of the holes and the corresponding constant values of ϕ on the boundaries of the holes. With regard to the membrane analogy, one must then consider a membrane stretched over region R in such a manner that the membrane has a constant value on a boundary of a hole. Such an effect may be obtained if one stretches a membrane over a flat plate P_0 with a cutout corresponding to region R and with flat plates $P_1, P_2, \ldots, P_n$ placed over the holes $A_1, A_2, \ldots, A_n$, the plates $P_1, P_2, \ldots, P_n$ having appropriate heights $z_1, z_2, \ldots, z_n$ with respect to the holes $A_1, A_2, \ldots, A_n$. For example, for a cross section with a single tubular hole the equivalent membrane is shown in Fig. 7–9.2. This simple idea can be extended to n holes. On the basis of the directional derivative concept [see Art. 7–8 and particularly Eqs. (7–8.1)] and the membrane analogy, we see that for a curve C on the membrane defined by $z = $ const. (that is, for $\phi = $ const.) the shear-stress resultant τ is everywhere tangent to the curve (Fig. 7–9.3), where by Eq. (7–8.1),

$$\tau = -\frac{\partial \phi}{\partial n} = -\frac{d\psi}{dn} \qquad \text{on } C \tag{7-9.5}$$

Considering the equilibrium of the part of the membrane enclosed by C, we find

$$qA = \int S \sin \beta \, ds \tag{7-9.6}$$

where A denotes the plane area bounded by C (Fig. 7–9.4).

By Fig. 7 9.4 and Eqs. (7–9.4) and (7–9.5), we have

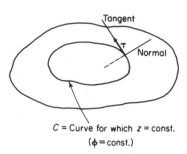

C = Curve for which z = const.
(ϕ = const.)

Figure 7-9.3

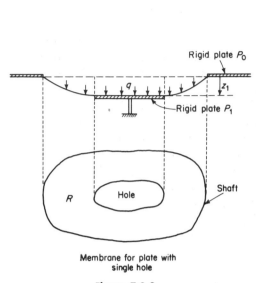

Membrane for plate with
single hole

Figure 7-9.2

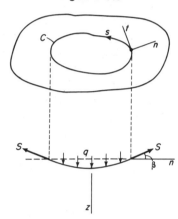

Figure 7-9.4

$$\sin \beta = -\frac{\partial z}{\partial n} = -\frac{d\phi}{dn}\frac{q}{2G\theta S} = \frac{\tau q}{2G\theta S} \tag{7-9.7}$$

Hence, Eqs. (7–9.6) and (7–9.7) yield

$$\int_c \tau \, ds = 2G\theta A \tag{7-9.8}$$

Accordingly, for multiply connected regions Eq. (7–9.8) becomes (see Figs. 7–6.1 and 7–9.2)

$$\int_{C_i} \tau \, ds = 2G\theta A_i \tag{7-9.9}$$

where C_i denotes the boundary of the plane area A_i.

Several cross sections and their associated membranes are shown schematically in Fig. 7–9.5.

Some useful conclusions may be drawn from consideration of Fig. 7–9.5. For example, noting that by Eqs. (7–4.6) and (7–6.12)

$$M = 2 \int\int_R \phi \, dx \, dy + 2 \sum_{i=1}^k K_i A_i = C\theta \tag{7-9.10}$$

Cross sections

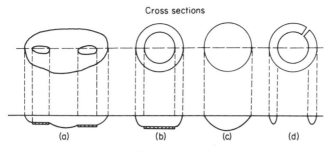

(a)   (b)   (c)   (d)

Associated membranes

Figure 7-9.5

it appears from Fig. 7–9.5 that for a bar with circular cross section and a given angle of twist (that is, for a given pressure q and tension S for the associated membrane) the required moment M is not changed as greatly by cutting a concentric circular hole in the shaft as it is by cutting a concentric circular hole *and* slit in the shaft [Figs. 7–9.5(b), (c), and (d)]. Calculations bear out this observation.

Certain kinds of approximations may also be suggested by examination of the membrane. For example, if the wall thickness of a circular tube is small [Fig. 7–9.5(b)], then by Eq. (7–9.10) we have, with $k = 1$,

$$M = 2 \int\int_R \phi\, dx\, dy + 2K_1 A_1 \approx 2K_1 A_1 \qquad (7\text{–}9.11)$$

where K_1 is the value of ϕ on the boundary of the hole and A_1 is the area of the hole. Other approximations of this type are often employed in practice.[10]

Example 7–9.1. Narrow rectangular cross section. Consider a bar subjected to torsion. Let the cross section of the bar be a solid rectangle with width $2a$ and depth $2b$, where $b \gg a$ (Fig. 7–9.6). The associated membrane is shown in Fig. 7–9.7.

Except for the region near $x = \pm b$, the membrane deflection is approximately independent of x. For a given x, the deflection with respect to y is assumed to be parabolic. Then,

$$z = z_0 \left[1 - \left(\frac{y}{a}\right)^2 \right] \qquad (a)$$

Hence,

$$\nabla^2 z = -\frac{2z_0}{a^2} \qquad (b)$$

By Eqs. (b), (7–9.2), and (7–9.3), we may write $\nabla^2 z = -2z_0/a^2 = -2cG\theta$ or

---

[10]Weber and Günther, *Torsiontheorie*. See also S. Timoshenko, *Strength of Materials*, Pt. II (Princeton, N.J.: D. Van Nostrand Company, Inc., 1941), Chap. 6.

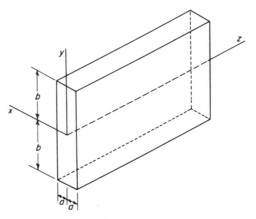

Figure 7-9.6

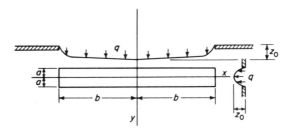

Figure 7-9.7

$$\phi = G\theta a^2 \left[1 - \left(\frac{y}{a}\right)^2\right] \tag{c}$$

Consequently, Eqs. (7–3.3) yield

$$\tau_{xz} = \frac{\partial \phi}{\partial y} = -2G\theta y, \qquad \tau_{yz} = 0 \tag{d}$$

and the last of Eqs. (7–3.6) yields

$$M = 2\int_{-b}^{b}\int_{-a}^{a} \phi \, dx \, dy = \frac{16}{3} G\theta a^3 b \tag{e}$$

By Eqs. (d), we note that the maximum value of $|\tau_{xz}|$ is $\tau_{\text{max}} = 2G\theta a$ for $y = \pm a$.

In summary, we note that the solution is approximate, and in particular the boundary conditions for $x = \pm b$ are not satisfied.

7-10 Solution by Method of Series. Rectangular Section

In Example 7–9.1 the torsion problem of a bar with narrow rectangular cross section was approximated by noting the deflection of the corresponding

membrane. In this article we again consider the
rectangular section $-a \leqq x \leqq a$, $-b \leqq y \leqq b$, but
we discard the restriction that $a \ll b$ (Fig. 7-10.1).

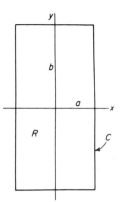

By visualizing the membrane corresponding to
the cross section of Fig. 7-10.1, we note that the
torsion stress function ϕ must be even in x and y.
Also, we recall that in terms of ϕ the torsion problem
is defined by the equations

$$\nabla^2 \phi = -2G\theta \qquad \text{over } R$$
$$\phi = 0 \qquad \text{on } C \tag{7-10.1}$$

By Example 7-9.1, we have seen that $G\theta(a^2 - x^2)$
is a particular integral of the first of Eqs. (7-10.1).
Accordingly, we take the stress function ϕ in the
form [see also Eq. (7-3.20)]

Figure 7-10.1

$$\phi = G\theta(a^2 - x^2) + V(x, y) \tag{7-10.2}$$

where $V(x, y)$ is an even function of (x, y). Substitution of Eq. (7-10.2) into
Eqs. (7-10.1) yields

$$\nabla^2 V = 0 \qquad \text{over } R$$
$$V = 0 \qquad \text{for } x = \pm a \tag{7-10.3}$$
$$V = G\theta(x^2 - a^2) \qquad \text{for } y = \pm b$$

Equations (7-10.3) represent a special case of the Dirichlet problem (Art.
7-2).

We seek solutions of Eqs. (7-10.3) by the method of separation of variables.
Thus, we take

$$V = f(x)g(y) \tag{7-10.4}$$

where $f(x)$ and $g(y)$ are functions of x and y, respectively. The first of Eqs.
(7-10.3) and (7-10.4) yield

$$\nabla^2 V = g f'' + g'' f = 0 \tag{7-10.5}$$

where primes denote derivatives with respect to x or y. In order that Eq.
(7-10.5) be satisfied, we must have

$$\frac{f''}{f} = -\frac{g''}{g} = -\lambda^2 \tag{7-10.6}$$

where λ^2 is a positive constant. Hence,

$$f'' + \lambda^2 f = 0, \qquad g'' - \lambda^2 g = 0 \tag{7-10.7}$$

The solutions of Eqs. (7-10.7) are

$$f = A \cos \lambda x + B \sin \lambda x$$
$$g = C \cosh \lambda y + D \sinh \lambda y \tag{7-10.8}$$

Since V must be even in x and y, it follows that $B = D = 0$. Consequently, the function V takes on the form [Eq. (7–10.4)]

$$V = A \cos \lambda x \cosh \lambda y \qquad (7\text{–}10.9)$$

where A denotes an arbitrary constant.

To satisfy the second of Eqs. (7–10.3), Eq. (7–10.9) yields the result

$$\lambda = \frac{n\pi}{2a}, \qquad n = 1, 3, 5, \ldots \qquad (7\text{–}10.10)$$

To satisfy the last of Eqs. (7–10.3) we employ the method of superposition ($\nabla^2 V = 0$ is a linear, homogeneous partial differential equation), and we write

$$V = \sum_{n=1,3,5\ldots}^{\infty} A_n \cos \frac{n\pi x}{2a} \cosh \frac{n\pi y}{2a} \qquad (7\text{–}10.11)$$

Equation (7–10.11) satisfies $\nabla^2 V = 0$ in R, provided the series converges and is termwise differentiable.[11] Equation (7–10.11) automatically satisfies the boundary condition for $x = \pm a$. The boundary condition for $y = \pm b$ yields the condition [Eqs. (7–10.3)]

$$\sum_{n=1,3,5,\ldots}^{\infty} C_n \cos \frac{n\pi x}{2a} = G\theta(x^2 - a^2) = f(x) \qquad (7\text{–}10.12)$$

where

$$C_n = A_n \cosh \frac{n\pi b}{2a} \qquad (7\text{–}10.13)$$

By the theory of Fourier series, we multiply both sides of Eq. (7–10.12) by $\cos(n\pi x/2a)$ and integrate between the limits $-a$ and $+a$ to obtain the coefficients C_n as follows:

$$C_n = \frac{1}{a} \int_{-a}^{a} f(x) \cos \frac{n\pi x}{2a}\, dx \qquad (7\text{–}10.14)$$

Since $f(x) \cos(n\pi x/2a) = G\theta(x^2 - a^2) \cos(n\pi x/2a)$ is symmetrical about $x = 0$, we may write

$$C_n = \frac{2G\theta}{a} \int_0^a (x^2 - a^2) \cos \frac{n\pi x}{2a}\, dx$$

or

$$C_n = \frac{2G\theta}{a} \int_0^a x^2 \cos \frac{n\pi x}{2a}\, dx - 2G\theta a \int_0^a \cos \frac{n\pi x}{2a}\, dx$$

Integration yields[12]

$$C_n = \frac{-32G\theta a^2 (-1)^{(n-1)/2}}{n^3 \pi^3} \qquad (7\text{–}10.15)$$

---

[11]R. V. Churchill, *Fourier Series and Boundary Value Problems* (New York: McGraw-Hill Book Company, 1941).

[12]B. O. Pierce and R. M. Foster, *A Short Table of Integrals*, 4th ed. (Boston: Ginn & Company, 1956), formula 350.

Hence, Eqs. (7–10.11), (7–10.13), and (7–10.15) yield

$$A_n = -\frac{32G\theta a^2 (-1)^{(n-1)/2}}{n^3 \pi^3 \cosh\dfrac{n\pi b}{2a}} \tag{7–10.16}$$

and

$$\phi = G\theta(a^2 - x^2) - \frac{32G\theta a^2}{\pi^3} \sum_{n=1,3,5,\ldots}^{\infty} \frac{(-1)^{(n-1)/2} \cos\dfrac{n\pi x}{2a} \cosh\dfrac{n\pi y}{2a}}{n^3 \cosh\dfrac{n\pi b}{2a}} \tag{7–10.17}$$

Note that since $\cosh x = 1 + x^2/2! + x^4/4! + \ldots$ the series in Eq. (7–10.17) goes to zero if $b/a \to \infty$ (that is, if the section is very narrow $b \gg a$). Then, Eq. (7–10.17) reduces to

$$\phi \approx G\theta(a^2 - x^2) \tag{7–10.18}$$

This result verifies the assumption employed in Example 7–9.1 for the slender rectangular cross section.

By Eqs. (7–3.3) and (7–10.17) we obtain

$$\tau_{xz} = \frac{\partial \phi}{\partial y} = -\frac{16G\theta a}{\pi^2} \sum_{n=1,3,5,\ldots}^{\infty} \frac{(-1)^{(n-1)/2} \cos\dfrac{n\pi x}{2a} \sinh\dfrac{n\pi y}{2a}}{n^2 \cosh\dfrac{n\pi b}{2a}} \tag{7–10.19}$$

$$\tau_{yz} = -\frac{\partial \phi}{\partial x} = 2G\theta x - \frac{16G\theta a}{\pi^2} \sum_{n=1,3,5,\ldots}^{\infty} \frac{(-1)^{(n-1)/2} \sin\dfrac{n\pi x}{2a} \cosh\dfrac{n\pi y}{2a}}{n^2 \cosh\dfrac{n\pi b}{2a}}$$

By Eqs. (7–3.6) and (7–10.17), the twisting moment is

$$M = 2 \int_{-b}^{b} \int_{-a}^{a} \phi \, dx \, dy = C\theta = GJ\theta \tag{7–10.20}$$

where J, a factor dependent on geometry of the cross section, is

$$J = 2 \int_{-b}^{b} \int_{-a}^{a} (a^2 - x^2) \, dx \, dy$$

$$- \frac{64a^2}{\pi^3} \sum_{n=1,3,5,\ldots}^{\infty} \frac{(-1)^{(n-1)/2}}{n^3 \cosh\dfrac{n\pi b}{2a}} \int_{-b}^{b} \int_{-a}^{a} \left(\cos\frac{n\pi x}{2a} \cosh\frac{n\pi y}{2a} \right) dx \, dy$$

Integration yields[13]

$$J = \frac{(2a)^3 (2b)}{3} \left[1 - \frac{192}{\pi^5} \left(\frac{a}{b}\right) \sum_{n=1,3,5,\ldots}^{\infty} \frac{1}{n^5} \tanh\frac{n\pi b}{2a} \right] \tag{7–10.21}$$

The factor outside the brackets on the right-hand side of Eq. (7–10.21) is an approximation for a thin rectangular cross section, since the series term goes to zero as b/a becomes large.

---

[13]Pierce and Foster, *A Short Table of Integrals*, formula 489.

In general, Eq. (7–10.21) may be written in the form

$$J = k_1(2a)^3(2b) \tag{7–10.22}$$

where

$$k_1 = \frac{1}{3}\left[1 - \frac{192}{\pi^5}\left(\frac{a}{b}\right)\sum_{n=1,3,5,\dots}^{\infty} \frac{1}{n^5}\tanh\frac{n\pi b}{2a}\right] \tag{7–10.23}$$

Equation (7–10.20) may then be written in the form

$$M = G\theta k_1(2a)^3(2b) \tag{7–10.24}$$

Values of k_1 for various ratios of b/a are given by Timoshenko and Goodier.[14]

PROBLEM SET 7-10

1 Verify Eq. (7–10.21).

2 With $b > a$, show that the maximum shear for the rectangular cross section (Fig. 7–10.1) occurs at $x = a$, $y = 0$. Hence, show that

$$\tau_{\max} = 2G\theta ak$$

where

$$k = 1 - \frac{8}{\pi^2}\sum_{n=1,3,5,\dots}^{\infty} \frac{1}{n^2\cosh\dfrac{n\pi b}{2a}}$$

3 Derive the warping function for the rectangular cross section. Consider the case $a = b$, and sketch in contour lines.

4 Calculate τ_{xz}, τ_{yz} at the indicated points in the cross section (Fig. P7–10.4). Calculate J [Eq. (7–10.21)].

5 Consider a shaft with a sector cross section with angle α and radius a (Fig. P7–10.5). Let (r, β) denote polar coordinates. Let the torsion stress function ϕ be given by $\phi = V - G\theta r^2/2$. By the method employed in Art. 7–10, show that

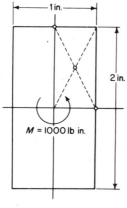

Figure P7-10.4

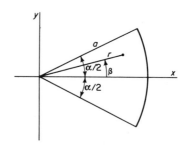

Figure P7-10.5

[14]S. Timoshenko and J. Goodier, *Theory of Elasticity*, 2nd ed. (New York: McGraw-Hill Book Company, 1951), p. 277.

$$\phi = \frac{G\theta}{2}\left[-r^2\left(1 - \frac{\cos 2\beta}{\cos \alpha}\right)\right.$$

$$\left. + \frac{16a^2\alpha^2}{\pi^3} \sum_{n=1,3,5,\ldots}^{\infty} (-1)^{(n+1)/2} \left(\frac{r}{a}\right)^{n\pi/\alpha} \frac{\cos \dfrac{n\pi\beta}{\alpha}}{n\left(n + \dfrac{2\alpha}{\pi}\right)\left(n - \dfrac{2\alpha}{\pi}\right)}\right]$$

6 Consider the torsion problem of a shaft whose cross section is shown in Fig. P7–10.6. Assume a stress function of the form $\phi = V - \frac{1}{2}G\theta r^2$, where V is a function of r alone, G denotes the shear modulus, θ denotes the angle of twist per unit length of the shaft, and r is the radial polar coordinate. For $h/a \ll 1$, derive an expression for V in terms of a, h, and r. Hence, derive an expression for the shearing stress τ. Discuss the validity of the solution in the vicinity of $\beta = \pi/2$.

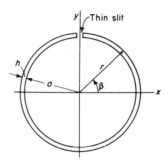

Figure P7-10.6

7-11 Bending of a Bar Subjected to Transverse End Force

Consider a prismatic elastic bar fixed[15] at the end $z = 0$ and subjected to a lateral force P at the end $z = L$ (Fig. 7–11.1). The cross section of the bar is contained in region R bounded by the surface S. We restrict our discussion to the case of simply connected regions R (see Arts. 7–2 and 7–6).

We let the origin of axes (x, y, z) be located arbitrarily in the cross section at $z = 0$. Furthermore, we take the x axis parallel to the line of action of force P. Then summation of forces on the end face $z = L$ yields

$$P_x = \int \int \tau_{zx}\, dx\, dy = P, \qquad P_y = P_z = M_x = M_y = M_z = 0 \qquad (7\text{-}11.1)$$

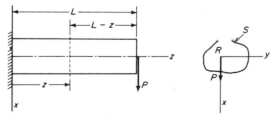

Figure 7-11.1

---

[15]For example, the conditions at $z = 0$ may be taken such that the displacement components $u = v = w = 0$ at $x = y = z = 0$ and the rotation $\omega = 0$ at $x = y = z = 0$.

Accordingly, over-all equilibrium of any portion of the beam (say between the sections $z = z$, $z = L$, Figs. 7–11.1 and 7–11.2) requires that

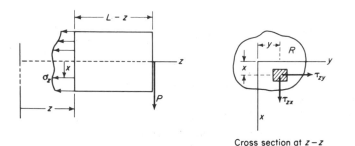

Cross section at $z-z$

Figure 7-11.2

$$\int\int \tau_{zx}\,dx\,dy = P, \qquad \int\int \sigma_z x\,dx\,dy = -P(L - z)$$

$$\int\int \tau_{zy}\,dx\,dy = \int\int \sigma_z\,dx\,dy = \int\int y\sigma_z\,dx\,dy = \int\int (x\tau_{zy} - y\tau_{zx})\,dx\,dy = 0$$

(7–11.2)

It follows from the first two of Eqs. (7–11.2) that τ_{zx} and σ_z are not zero. Also, in general, τ_{yz} is not zero by the last of Eqs. (7–11.2).

Following the semi-inverse method of Saint-Venant, we seek solutions such that σ_z, τ_{zx}, τ_{zy} are the only nonvanishing stress components; that is, we assume that

$$\sigma_x = \sigma_y = \tau_{xy} = 0 \tag{7–11.3}$$

Furthermore, we take the simplest linear dependence on (x, y) for the component σ_z; that is, we assume that σ_z is proportional to $Ax + By + C$, where A, B, C are constants. More explicitly, on the basis of the second of Eqs. (7–11.2) we assume

$$\sigma_z = P(Ax + By + C)(L - z) \tag{7–11.4}$$

Substitution of Eq. (7–11.4) into Eqs. (7–11.2) yields the result

$$AI_{yy} + BI_{xy} + CS_y = -1$$

$$AI_{xy} + BI_{xx} + CS_x = 0 \tag{7–11.5}$$

$$AS_y + BS_x + CS_0 = 0$$

where (I_{xx}, I_{yy}, I_{xy}) and (S_x, S_y) are the moments of inertia and the first moments, respectively, of the area of the cross section of the beam relative to axes (x, y) and S_0 is the area of the cross section of the rod.

Equations (7–11.5) are three linear algebraic equations in the unknowns A, B, C. Solving Eq. (7–11.5), we obtain

$$A = -\frac{I_{xx}S_0 - S_x^2}{\Delta}$$

$$B = \frac{I_{xy}S_0 - S_xS_y}{\Delta} \tag{7-11.6}$$

$$C = \frac{I_{xx}S_y - I_{xy}S_x}{\Delta} = -A\bar{x} - B\bar{y}$$

where

$$\Delta = \begin{vmatrix} I_{yy} & I_{xy} & S_y \\ I_{xy} & I_{xx} & S_x \\ S_y & S_x & S_0 \end{vmatrix} \tag{7-11.7}$$

and $\bar{x}$, $\bar{y}$ denote the coordinates of the center of gravity of the area of the cross section.

Problem. Derive Eqs. (7–11.6).

In the absence of body forces ($X = Y = Z = 0$), Eqs. (7–1.1), (7–11.3), and (7–11.4) yield

$$\frac{\partial \tau_{xz}}{\partial z} = \frac{\partial \tau_{yz}}{\partial z} = 0$$

$$\frac{\partial \tau_{xz}}{\partial x} + \frac{\partial \tau_{yz}}{\partial y} = P(Ax + By + C) \tag{7-11.8}$$

It follows by the first two of Eqs. (7–11.8) that τ_{xz}, τ_{yz} are independent of z. Furthermore, the last of Eqs. (7–11.8) may be written in the form

$$\frac{\partial}{\partial x}\left[\tau_{xz} - \frac{P}{2}(Ax^2 + Cx)\right] + \frac{\partial}{\partial y}\left[\tau_{yz} - \frac{P}{2}(By^2 + Cy)\right] = 0 \tag{7-11.9}$$

By the theory of Art. 1–13, Eq. (7–11.9) represents necessary and sufficient conditions that a function F exists such that

$$\tau_{xz} - \frac{P}{2}(Ax^2 + Cx) = \frac{P}{2}\frac{\partial F}{\partial y}$$

$$\tau_{yz} - \frac{P}{2}(By^2 + Cy) = -\frac{P}{2}\frac{\partial F}{\partial x}$$

or

$$\tau_{xz} = \frac{P}{2}\left[\frac{\partial F}{\partial y} + Ax^2 + Cx\right]$$

$$\tau_{yz} = \frac{P}{2}\left[-\frac{\partial F}{\partial x} + By^2 + Cy\right] \tag{7-11.10}$$

Hence, if τ_{xz}, τ_{yz} are expressed in the form of Eq. (7–11.10), the equations of equilibrium are satisfied. Furthermore, since τ_{xz}, τ_{yz} are independent of z, it follows that $F = F(x, y)$. The governing equations for F are the compati bility equations [Eqs. (7–1.5)] and the boundary conditions [Eqs. (7–1.4)]. Substitution of Eqs. (7–11.3), (7–11.4), and (7–11.10) into Eqs. (7–1.5) yields

$$\frac{\partial}{\partial y}(\nabla^2 F) = -\frac{2\nu A}{1+\nu}$$

$$\frac{\partial}{\partial x}(\nabla^2 F) = \frac{2\nu B}{1+\nu}$$

Integration yields

$$\nabla^2 F = \frac{2\nu}{1+\nu}(Bx - Ay) - 2C_o, \qquad \text{over } R \qquad (7\text{–}11.11)$$

where C_o is a constant of integration that may be interpreted physically [see Art. 7–12; see also Eq. (7–11.29)].

The boundary conditions [Eqs. (7–1.4a)] reduce to $l\tau_{xz} + m\tau_{yz} = 0$ or

$$\tau_{xz}\frac{dy}{ds} - \tau_{yz}\frac{dx}{ds} = 0 \qquad\qquad (7\text{–}11.12)$$

where [see Eq. (7–2.7) and Fig. 7–2.2]

$$l = \frac{dy}{ds}, \qquad m = -\frac{dx}{ds} \qquad\qquad (7\text{–}11.13)$$

Substitution of Eqs. (7–11.10) into Eq. (7–11.12) yields

$$\frac{\partial F}{\partial s} = (By^2 + Cy)\frac{dx}{ds} - (Ax^2 + Cx)\frac{dy}{ds}, \qquad \text{on } S \qquad (7\text{–}11.14)$$

Equations (7–11.11) which holds over region R and (7–11.14) which holds on the lateral surface S are the defining equations for F.

The above results may be simplified somewhat by noting the nature of Eqs. (7–11.11) and (7–11.14), and representing F in terms of two new functions. Thus, we set

$$F = \Gamma + C_o\phi \qquad\qquad (7\text{–}11.15)$$

Then Eqs. (7–11.11) and (7–11.14) yield

$$\left.\begin{aligned}\nabla^2\phi &= -2\\[4pt]\nabla^2\Gamma &= \frac{2\nu}{1+\nu}(Bx - Ay)\end{aligned}\right\} \qquad \text{over } R \qquad (7\text{–}11.16)$$

and

$$\left.\begin{aligned}\frac{\partial\phi}{\partial s} &= 0 \quad \text{or} \quad \phi = 0 \quad \text{(Art. 7–6)}\\[4pt]\frac{\partial\Gamma}{\partial s} &= (By^2 + Cy)\frac{dx}{ds} - (Ax^2 + Cx)\frac{dy}{ds}\end{aligned}\right\} \qquad \text{on } S \qquad (7\text{–}11.17)$$

By Eqs. (7–11.16) and (7–11.17), we see from the theory of Art. 7–3 that ϕ (except for the constant factor $G\theta$) is the Prandtl stress function. Accordingly, the problem of the bending of the cantilever beam subjected to transverse end load may be expressed in terms of the Prandtl stress function of torsion and an auxiliary function Γ which must satisfy the last of Eqs. (7–11.16) and (7–11.17). The function Γ is called the *flexural function* or the *bending function*.

If the x and y are axes of symmetry,

$$B = C = 0, \qquad A = -\frac{1}{I_{yy}} = -\frac{1}{I} \qquad (7\text{–}11.18)$$

Then, analogous to the principal-axes theories of stress ($\tau_{ij} = 0$, $i \neq j$) and strain ($\epsilon_{ij} = 0$, $i \neq j$), axes (x, y) are called principal axes of inertia ($I_{xy} = 0$). With x a principal axis of inertia, the equations for the flexural function [Eqs. (7–11.16) and (7–11.17)] reduce to

$$\nabla^2 \Gamma = \frac{2\nu}{1+\nu} \frac{y}{I} \qquad \text{over } R$$

$$\frac{\partial \Gamma}{\partial s} = \frac{x^2}{I} \frac{dy}{ds} \qquad \text{on } S \qquad (7\text{–}11.19)$$

For a certain class of problems it is convenient to redefine Γ in terms of two functions as follows:

$$\Gamma = \frac{1}{P} [\Psi(x, y) + h(y)] \qquad (7\text{–}11.20)$$

where Ψ is a function of both x and y, and h is a function of y only.[16] Then Eqs. (7–11.19) become

$$\nabla^2 \Psi = \frac{2\nu}{1+\nu} \frac{P}{I} y - \frac{df}{dy} \qquad \text{over } R$$

$$\frac{\partial \Psi}{\partial s} = \left(\frac{Px^2}{I} - f\right) \frac{dy}{ds} \qquad \text{on } S \qquad (7\text{–}11.21)$$

where $f = dh/dy = f(y)$. The objective of the substitution of Eq. (7–11.20) is to arrive at simpler boundary conditions. For example, if we can choose f such that

$$\left(\frac{Px^2}{I} - f\right) \frac{dy}{ds} = 0 \qquad \text{on } S \qquad (7\text{–}11.22)$$

then

$$\frac{\partial \Psi}{\partial s} = 0 \qquad \text{on } S \qquad (7\text{–}11.23)$$

and since R is a simply connected region it follows that we may take (see Art. 7–6)

$$\Psi = 0 \qquad \text{on } S \qquad (7\text{–}11.24)$$

We shall employ this technique below to obtain the solution of the flexure problem for the rectangular and the elliptic cross sections.

---

[16]This substitution was employed by S. Timoshenko to solve the problem of flexure of certain kinds of cross sections (see Arts. 7–14 and 7–15).

Alternatively, one may seek solutions of Eq. (7–11.11) by taking a particular integral in the form of a polynomial in x and y. For example, we may express F in the form

$$F = h(x, y) + \frac{v}{3(1 + v)}(Bx^3 - Ay^3) - \frac{1}{2}C_0(x^2 + y^2) \quad (7\text{–}11.25)$$

where $\nabla^2 h = 0$; that is, h is a harmonic function. Then, the problem of bending of a bar by transverse end force transforms into seeking a function such that [see Eqs. (7–11.10), (7–11.11), and (7–11.14)]

$$\nabla^2 h = 0 \qquad \text{over region } R$$

$$\frac{\partial h}{\partial s} = (By^2 + Cy)\frac{dx}{ds} - (Ax^2 + Cx)\frac{dy}{ds} \qquad (7\text{–}11.26)$$

$$+ \left(\frac{v}{1+v}Bx^2 - C_0 x\right)\frac{dx}{ds} + \left(\frac{v}{1+v}Ay^2 + C_0 y\right)\frac{dy}{ds} \qquad \text{on } S$$

where the stress components are given by

$$\tau_{xz} = \frac{P}{2}\left[\frac{\partial h}{\partial y} + A\left(x^2 - \frac{vy^2}{1+v}\right) + Cx - C_0 y\right]$$

$$\tau_{yz} = \frac{P}{2}\left[-\frac{\partial h}{\partial x} + B\left(y^2 - \frac{vx^2}{1+v}\right) + Cy + C_0 x\right] \qquad (7\text{–}11.27)$$

For principal axes, $B = C = C_0 = 0$, $A = -1/I$, and Eqs. (7–11.26) and (7–11.27) are simplified accordingly.

Determination of the constant of integration, C_0. The above formulation of the flexural problem of the bar (cantilever beam) subjected to end force P is complete except for the determination of the integration constant C_0 [Eq. (7–11.11)]. We find that if we substitute Eqs. (7–11.10) into Eqs. (7–11.2) all the equations are satisfied identically with the exception of the last equation, namely

$$M_z = \int\int (x\tau_{yz} - y\tau_{xz})\,dx\,dy = 0 \qquad (7\text{–}11.28)$$

The constant C_0 must be chosen to satisfy Eq. (7–11.28). Accordingly, if we employ the definitions of Eqs. (7–11.10) and Eq. (7–11.15), we obtain after some calculations

$$C_0 \int\int \phi\,dx\,dy = -\int\int \Gamma\,dx\,dy - \frac{1}{2}\int\int (By - Ax)\,xy\,dx\,dy$$

$$- \oint\left[(By^2 + Cy)\frac{dx}{ds} - (Ax^2 + Cx)\frac{dy}{ds}\right]R_s\,ds \qquad (7\text{–}11.29)$$

where the double integrals are evaluated over R, the line integral is taken over S, and

$$R_s = \frac{1}{2}\int_0^s (x\,dy - y\,dx) \qquad (7\text{–}11.30)$$

For principal axes, $B = C = 0$, $A = -1/I$, and Eq. (7-11.29) is simplified accordingly. With Eq. (7-11.29), the formulation of the problem of bending of a bar subjected to transverse end load is complete.

In general $C_0 \neq 0$. Hence, there is twisting of the bar (torsion) when a transverse end load is applied arbitrarily. It is for this reason that the Prandtl torsion function [Eqs. (7-11.15) through (7-11.17)] enters into the bending problem of bars.

Problem. Derive Eq. (7-11.29). Simplify the result for principal axes.

The constant C_0 may be related to the average rotation of a cross section of the bar with respect to the axis z. For example, for the state of stress defined above, we obtain by Eqs. (7-1.3)

$$\epsilon_x = \epsilon_y = -\frac{\nu\sigma_z}{E} = -\frac{\nu P}{E}(Ax + By + C)(L - z)$$

$$\epsilon_z = \frac{P}{E}(Ax + By + C)(L - z) \qquad (7\text{-}11.31)$$

$$\gamma_{xy} = 0, \qquad \gamma_{xz} = \frac{1}{G}\tau_{xz}, \qquad \gamma_{yz} = \frac{1}{G}\tau_{yz}$$

where

$$\epsilon_x = \frac{\partial u}{\partial x}, \qquad\qquad \epsilon_y = \frac{\partial v}{\partial y}, \qquad\qquad \epsilon_z = \frac{\partial w}{\partial z}$$

$$\gamma_{xy} = \frac{\partial u}{\partial y} + \frac{\partial v}{\partial x}, \qquad \gamma_{xz} = \frac{\partial u}{\partial z} + \frac{\partial w}{\partial x}, \qquad \gamma_{yz} = \frac{\partial v}{\partial z} + \frac{\partial w}{\partial y}$$

and where E is the modulus of elasticity and ν is Poisson's ratio of the material. With Eqs. (7-11.31), the three strain compatibility equations of the type (see Art. 3-14)

$$\frac{\partial^2 \epsilon_x}{\partial y^2} + \frac{\partial^2 \epsilon_y}{\partial x^2} = \frac{\partial^2 \gamma_{xy}}{\partial x \, \partial y}$$

are satisfied identically. Also, the equation

$$2\frac{\partial^2 \epsilon_z}{\partial x \, \partial y} = \frac{\partial}{\partial z}\left(\frac{\partial \gamma_{yz}}{\partial x} + \frac{\partial \gamma_{xz}}{\partial y} - \frac{\partial \gamma_{xy}}{\partial z}\right)$$

is satisfied. The remaining two equations of compatibility simplify to

$$\frac{\partial}{\partial x}\left(\frac{\partial \gamma_{yz}}{\partial x} - \frac{\partial \gamma_{xz}}{\partial y}\right) = -\frac{2\nu PB}{E}$$

$$\frac{\partial}{\partial y}\left(\frac{\partial \gamma_{yz}}{\partial x} - \frac{\partial \gamma_{xz}}{\partial y}\right) = \frac{2\nu PA}{E} \qquad (7\text{-}11.32)$$

Integration of Eqs. (7-11.32) leads to

$$\frac{\partial \gamma_{yz}}{\partial x} - \frac{\partial \gamma_{xz}}{\partial y} = \frac{2\nu P}{E}(-Bx + Ay) + 2K \qquad (7\text{-}11.33)$$

where K is a constant of integration.

Recalling the definition of γ_{yz}, γ_{zz}, and ω_z in terms of (u, v, w) [see Eqs. (3–11.4) and (3–11.5)], we note that Eq. (7–11.33) may be written as

$$\frac{\partial \omega_z}{\partial z} = \frac{vP}{E}(-Bx + Ay) + K$$

The term ω_z is the angle of rotation of an element of volume in the rod about the z axis. The term $\partial(\omega_z)/\partial z$ is hence the twist of fibers in the rod parallel to the z axis. Integration of the twist over the cross section R of the bar yields the result

$$\frac{\partial \bar{\omega}_z}{\partial z} = \frac{vP}{E}(-B\bar{x} + A\bar{y}) + K \qquad (7\text{--}11.34)$$

where

$$\bar{\omega}_z = \frac{1}{S_o} \int \int \omega_z \, dx \, dy$$

$$\bar{x} = \frac{1}{S_o} \int \int x \, dx \, dy \qquad (7\text{--}11.35)$$

$$\bar{y} = \frac{1}{S_o} \int \int y \, dx \, dy$$

denote, respectively, the average value of the angle of rotation ω_z, the x value of the centroid of the cross section, and the y value of the centroid, and S_o denotes the area of the cross section. Accordingly, by Eq. (7–11.34), the integration constant K may be related to the average angle of rotation of a cross section about the z axis. Furthermore, if the x axis is an axis of symmetry, $B = \bar{y} = 0$. Then $\partial(\bar{\omega}_z)/\partial z = K$. However, since x is an axis of symmetry (a principal axis), $\bar{\omega}_z = 0$. Hence, when x is a principal axis, $K = 0$.

Alternatively, the compatibility condition, Eq. (7–11.33), may be expressed in terms of τ_{xz} and τ_{yz} by means of the last two of Eqs. (7–11.31). Then, by Eqs. (7–11.10), the compatibility relation may be formulated in terms of the function F. This latter expression, with Eq. (7–11.11), yields the result

$$C_o = \frac{E}{(1 + v)P} K \qquad (7\text{--}11.36)$$

Accordingly, the above remarks made with regard to K hold also for the constant C_o. For example, the constant C_o defined by Eqs. (7–11.29) vanishes when x is a principal axis. In general, C_o is related to the mean rotation $\bar{\omega}_z$ by Eqs. (7–11.34) and (7–11.36). That is,

$$\frac{\partial \bar{\omega}_z}{\partial z} = \frac{(1 + v)P}{E}\left[\frac{v}{1 + v}(-B\bar{x} + A\bar{y}) + C_o\right] \qquad (7\text{--}11.37)$$

Remark on solution of $\nabla^2 \chi = F(x, y)$. The basic equation of the theories of torsion and of bending of bars is of the form

$$\nabla^2 \chi = F(x, y) \qquad (7\text{--}11.38)$$

where χ must satisfy certain requirements on the lateral surface of the bar [see, for example, Eqs. (7–2.5), (7–2.10), (7–2.13), (7–2.15), (7–3.10), (7–11.11), (7–11.14), (7–11.16), (7–11.17), (7–11.21), (7–11.26)]. In general, Eq. (7–11.38) is a linear nonhomogeneous partial differential equation of second order. Since it is linear, it may be transformed into an equivalent homogeneous equation. The following basic theorem holds for the equivalent homogeneous case[17] ($\nabla^2 \chi = 0$):

Theorem. *If* $\chi_1, \chi_2, \ldots, \chi_n$ *are n solutions of a homogeneous linear partial differential equation, then* $C_1 \chi_1 + C_2 \chi_2 + \cdots + C_n \chi_n$ *is also a solution, where* $C_1, C_2, \ldots, C_n$ *are arbitrary constants.*

Any function of x and y that satisfies Eq. (7–11.38) identically is called a *particular* integral. There are in general an infinite number of particular solutions to Eq. (7–11.38). Because of the linear character of Eq. (7–11.38), the sum of a complementary function ($\chi_1, \chi_2, \ldots, \chi_n$) and *any* particular integral will satisfy Eq. (7–11.38). In the torsion and bending problems of bars the solution of Eq. (7–11.38) must also satisfy the boundary conditions. In general, the boundary conditions are extremely complex. Particularly, we have seen that in general the bending problem of a bar entails both bending and twisting [see Eqs. (7–11.11), (7–11.15), (7–11.16), and (7–11.17)]. In Art. 7–13 we will examine explicitly the conditions under which a bar loaded by a transverse end force will bend without twisting of its end section about the z axis. By application of the conditions for which twisting of the end section is eliminated we obtain some simplification of the boundary conditions.

7-12 Displacement of a Cantilever Beam Subjected to Transverse End Force

In this article we derive formulas for the (x, y, z) displacement components (u, v, w) for the stress components defined in Art. 7–11. Hence, our task is to integrate Eqs. (7–11.31).

By the third of Eqs. (7–11.31) we have

$$\frac{\partial w}{\partial z} = \frac{P}{E}(Ax + By + C)(L - z)$$

Integration yields

$$w = \frac{PL}{E}(Ax + By + C)z - \frac{P}{2E}(Ax + By + C)z^2 + f(x, y) \qquad (7\text{-}12.1)$$

where $f(x, y)$ denotes a function of (x, y) only.

To obtain expressions for the displacement components (u, v), we consider

---

[17]Churchill, *Fourier Series and Boundary Value Problems.*

simultaneously certain of Eqs. (7–11.31) and Eq. (7–12.1). In the development of these expressions it is convenient to employ the following transformations. As noted by Eqs. (7–11.25) and (7–11.26), the bending problem of the bar may be defined in terms of a harmonic function h. Now, we introduce a function $g(x, y)$, the conjugate harmonic of $h(x, y)$, defined by the relations

$$\frac{\partial g}{\partial x} = \frac{\partial h}{\partial y}, \qquad \frac{\partial g}{\partial y} = -\frac{\partial h}{\partial x}, \qquad \nabla^2 g = 0 \qquad (7\text{–}12.2)$$

Then, with Eqs. (7–11.27) and (7–12.2) and the last two of Eqs. (7–11.31), we obtain

$$\gamma_{xz} = \frac{\partial u}{\partial z} + \frac{\partial w}{\partial x} = \frac{(1 + \nu)P}{E}\left[\frac{\partial g}{\partial x} + A\left(x^2 - \frac{\nu y^2}{1 + \nu}\right) + Cx - C_o y\right]$$

$$\gamma_{yz} = \frac{\partial v}{\partial z} + \frac{\partial w}{\partial y} = \frac{(1 + \nu)P}{E}\left[\frac{\partial g}{\partial y} + B\left(y^2 - \frac{\nu x^2}{1 + \nu}\right) + Cy + C_o x\right]$$

$$(7\text{–}12.3)$$

By the first of Eqs. (7–11.31) and (7–12.3) and Eq. (7–12.1), we find

$$\frac{\partial u}{\partial x} = -\frac{\nu P}{E}(Ax + By + C)(L - z)$$

$$\frac{\partial u}{\partial z} = \frac{(1 + \nu)P}{E}\left[\frac{\partial g}{\partial x} + A\left(x^2 - \frac{\nu y^2}{1 + \nu}\right) + Cx - C_o y\right] \qquad (7\text{–}12.4)$$

$$- \frac{PAL}{E}z + \frac{PA}{2E}z^2 - \frac{\partial f}{\partial x}$$

Equations (7–12.4) are compatible provided

$$\frac{\partial^2 (g - \bar{f})}{\partial x^2} = -\frac{(2 + \nu)A}{1 + \nu}x + \frac{\nu B}{1 + \nu}y - \frac{C}{1 + \nu} \qquad (7\text{–}12.5)$$

where

$$\bar{f} = \frac{Ef}{(1 + \nu)P} \qquad (7\text{–}12.6)$$

Similarly, we find

$$\frac{\partial v}{\partial y} = -\frac{\nu P}{E}(Ax + By + C)(L - z)$$

$$\frac{\partial v}{\partial z} = \frac{(1 + \nu)P}{E}\left[\frac{\partial g}{\partial y} + B\left(y^2 - \frac{\nu x^2}{1 + \nu}\right) + Cy + C_o x\right]$$

$$- \frac{PBL}{E}z + \frac{PB}{2E}z^2 - \frac{\partial f}{\partial y}$$

and

$$\frac{\partial^2 (g - \bar{f})}{\partial y^2} = \frac{\nu A}{1 + \nu}x - \frac{(2 + \nu)B}{1 + \nu}y - \frac{C}{1 + \nu} \qquad (7\text{–}12.7)$$

Finally, differentiation of the equation

$$\gamma_{xy} = \frac{\partial u}{\partial y} + \frac{\partial v}{\partial x} = 0$$

with respect to z yields

$$\frac{\partial^2(g - \bar{f})}{\partial x \, \partial y} = \frac{\nu}{1 + \nu} (Bx + Ay) \tag{7-12.8}$$

Equations (7–12.5), (7–12.7), and (7–12.8) require that [with Eq. (7–12.6)]

$$f = \frac{(1 + \nu)P}{E} g + \frac{PA}{2E} \left(\frac{2 + \nu}{3} x^3 - \nu x y^2 \right)$$

$$+ \frac{PB}{2E} \left(-\nu x^2 y + \frac{2 + \nu}{3} y^3 \right) + \frac{PC}{2E} (x^2 + y^2) - \beta x + \alpha y + \gamma_0 \tag{7-12.9}$$

where α, β, γ_0 are constants.

With Eqs. (7–12.1) and (7–12.9), the displacement component w is now determined in terms of the harmonic function g. Next, we substitute the expression for f into the equations for $\partial u / \partial z$ and $\partial v / \partial z$ to obtain [with Eq. (7–11.36)]

$$\frac{\partial u}{\partial z} = -Ky - \frac{P}{E} \left\{ A \left[Lz - \frac{z^2}{2} - \frac{\nu}{2} (x^2 - y^2) \right] - \nu Bxy - \nu Cx \right\} + \beta$$

$$\tag{7-12.10}$$

$$\frac{\partial v}{\partial z} = Kx - \frac{P}{E} \left\{ -\nu Axy + B \left[Lz - \frac{z^2}{2} + \frac{\nu}{2} (x^2 - y^2) \right] - \nu Cy \right\} - \alpha$$

From the equations for $\partial u / \partial x$ and $\partial u / \partial z$, we determine u in the form

$$u = -Kyz - \frac{P}{E} \left\{ A \left[\frac{Lz^2}{2} - \frac{z^3}{6} + \frac{\nu}{2} (L - z) x^2 + \frac{\nu}{2} y^2 z \right] \right.$$

$$\left. + \nu B(L - z)xy + \nu C(L - z)x \right\} + \beta z + F_1(y)$$

where $F_1(y)$ is an unknown function of y. Similarly, we find

$$v = Kxz - \frac{P}{E} \left\{ \nu A(L - z)xy + B \left[\frac{Lz^2}{2} - \frac{z^3}{6} + \frac{\nu}{2} (L - z) y^2 + \frac{\nu}{2} x^2 z \right] \right.$$

$$\left. + \nu C(L - z)y \right\} - \alpha z + F_2(x)$$

where $F_2(x)$ is an unknown function of x.

The functions $F_1(y)$ and $F_2(x)$ are determined by the condition

$$\frac{\partial u}{\partial y} + \frac{\partial v}{\partial x} = 0$$

Hence,

$$F_1(y) = \frac{\nu PAL}{2E} y^2 - \gamma y + \alpha_0$$

$$F_2(x) = \frac{\nu PBL}{2E} x^2 + \gamma x + \beta_0$$

where α_0, β_0, γ are constants.

In summary, by the analysis above we have determined the displacement components (u, v, w) in the form

$$u = -Kyz - \frac{P}{E}\left\{ A\left[\frac{Lz^2}{2} - \frac{z^3}{6} + \frac{v}{2}(L-z)(x^2 - y^2)\right]\right.$$

$$\left. + vB(L-z)xy + vC(L-z)x\right\} - \gamma y + \beta z + \alpha_0$$

$$v = Kxz - \frac{P}{E}\left\{ vA(L-z)xy + B\left[\frac{Lz^2}{2} - \frac{z^3}{6} - \frac{v}{2}(L-z)(x^2-y^2)\right]\right.$$

$$\left. + vC(L-z)y\right\} + \gamma x - \alpha z + \beta_0 \qquad (7\text{-}12.11)$$

$$w = \bar{g} + \frac{P}{E}\left\{ A\left[x\left(Lz - \frac{z^2}{2}\right) + \frac{2+v}{6}x^3 - \frac{v}{2}xy^2\right]\right.$$

$$+ B\left[y\left(Lz - \frac{z^2}{2}\right) - \frac{v}{2}x^2y + \frac{2+v}{6}y^3\right]$$

$$\left. + C\left[Lz + \frac{1}{2}(x^2 + y^2 - z^2)\right]\right\} - \beta x + \alpha y + \gamma_0$$

where $\alpha_0, \beta_0, \gamma_0, \alpha, \beta, \gamma$ are constants and

$$\bar{g} = \frac{(1+v)Pg}{E} \qquad (7\text{-}12.12)$$

In Eq. (7–12.11), the terms in $\alpha_0, \beta_0, \gamma_0, \alpha, \beta, \gamma$ represent a rigid-body displacement (see Art. 3–13 and the problem at the end of Art. 3–12). To evaluate the rigid-body displacement we may require that the displacement (u, v, w) and the rotation $(\omega_x, \omega_y, \omega_z)$ be prescribed at a point (x, y, z).

Problem. Discuss conditions that may be employed to evaluate $\alpha_0, \beta_0, \gamma_0, \alpha, \beta, \gamma$ of Eqs. (7–12.11).

7-13 Center of Shear

The condition for which there occurs no twisting of the end section of a bar loaded by transverse end force is obtained from Eq. (7–11.37) by setting the twist $\partial(\bar{\omega}z)/\partial z = 0$. Thus we obtain

$$C_0 = \frac{v}{1+v}(B\bar{x} - A\bar{y}) \qquad (7\text{-}13.1)$$

as the necessary and sufficient condition that the twist vanish. In general, if C_0 is defined by Eq. (7–13.1), the moment M_z does not vanish. For example, in general,

$$M_z = \int\int (x\tau_{yz} - y\tau_{xz})\, dx\, dy \qquad (7\text{-}13.2)$$

Accordingly, with Eqs. (7–11.10), (7–11.15), and (7–13.1), Eq. (7–13.2) yields

$$M_z = P \left\{ \frac{\nu}{1+\nu} (B\bar{x} - A\bar{y}) \int \int \phi \, dx \, dy + \int \int \Gamma \, dx \, dy \right.$$

$$+ \frac{1}{2} \int \int (By - Ax) \, xy \, dx \, dy \qquad \text{(7-13.3)}$$

$$\left. + \oint \left[(By^2 + Cy)\frac{dx}{ds} - (Ax^2 + Cx)\frac{dy}{ds} \right] R_s \, ds \right\}$$

Thus, Eq. (7–13.3) defines the moment that must be applied to the end of the bar, together with the force P directed along the x axis, to result in zero average twist of the end. By elementary statics and Saint-Venant's principle, we replace the moment M_z and the force P acting along the x axis by a force P_i, parallel to P and equal in magnitude to P, but located at a distance y_i from the x axis, where

$$y_i = -\frac{M_z}{P} = \frac{\nu}{1+\nu} (-B\bar{x} + A\bar{y}) \int \int \phi \, dx \, dy - \int \int \Gamma \, dx \, dy$$

$$- \frac{1}{2} \int \int (By - Ax) \, xy \, dx \, dy \qquad \text{(7-13.4)}$$

$$- \oint \left[(By^2 + Cy)\frac{dx}{ds} - (Ax^2 + Cx)\frac{dy}{ds} \right] R_s \, ds$$

The above theory defines bending of a bar without twisting when a force P is applied parallel to the x axis at a distance y_i from the x axis. Similarly, if the force P is applied parallel to the y axis, it must be located at a distance x_i from the y axis for bending of the rod without rotation of the end, where analogous to the computation for y_i [Eq. (7–13.4)], we find

$$x_i = \frac{\nu}{1+\nu} (b\bar{x} - a\bar{y}) \int \int \phi \, dx \, dy + \int \int \gamma \, dx \, dy$$

$$+ \frac{1}{2} \int \int (by - ax) \, xy \, dx \, dy \qquad \text{(7-13.5)}$$

$$+ \oint \left[(by^2 + cy)\frac{dx}{ds} - (ax^2 + cx)\frac{dy}{ds} \right] R_s \, ds$$

where over the cross section R

$$\nabla^2 \gamma = \frac{2\nu}{1+\nu} (bx - ay) \qquad \text{(7-13.6)}$$

and on the boundary S

$$\gamma = \oint \left[(by^2 + cy)\frac{dx}{ds} - (ax^2 + cx)\frac{dy}{ds} \right] ds \qquad \text{(7-13.7)}$$

and where

$$a = \frac{I_{xy}S_0 - S_x S_y}{\Delta}, \quad b = \frac{S_y^2 - S_0 I_{yy}}{\Delta}, \quad c = \frac{I_{yy}S_x - I_{xy}S_y}{\Delta} \qquad \text{(7-13.8)}$$

where Δ is defined by Eq. (7–11.7).

The intersection of the lines $x = x_i$, $y = y_i$ locates a point in the (x, y) plane. This point is called the *shear center*, since if a transverse force is applied at (x_i, y_i), it produces zero average twist of the end of the rod.

It may be shown that the location of the shear center may be determined provided the solution of the torsion problem is known; that is, in general, it is not necessary to know the solution to the bending problem to compute (x_i, y_i) (see Probs. 1–4 below). In strength of materials definitions of shear center, Poisson's ratio is usually discarded.

PROBLEM SET 7-13

1 With the fact that (Green's theorem)

$$\int\int (F\,\nabla^2 G - G\,\nabla^2 F)\,dx\,dy = \oint \left(F\frac{\partial G}{\partial n} - G\frac{\partial F}{\partial n}\right) ds \qquad \text{(a)}$$

where F, G are functions of (x, y), let $F = \phi$, $G = \Gamma$, take into consideration Eqs. (7–11.16) and (7–11.17), and show that

$$\frac{2\nu}{1+\nu}\int\int \phi(Bx - Ay)\,dx\,dy + 2\int\int \Gamma\,dx\,dy = -\oint \Gamma\frac{\partial\phi}{\partial n}\,ds \qquad \text{(b)}$$

2 Noting by Eqs. (7–2.4) and (7–3.3) that

$$\frac{\partial\phi}{\partial y} = \frac{\partial\psi}{\partial x} - y, \qquad \frac{\partial\phi}{\partial y} = -\frac{\partial\psi}{\partial y} - x \qquad \text{(a)}$$

where the factor $G\theta$ has been absorbed in ϕ, show that [with Eqs. (7–2.7), (7–2.9), and (7–11.30)]

$$\frac{\partial\phi}{\partial n} = \frac{\partial\phi}{\partial x}\frac{dx}{dn} + \frac{\partial\phi}{\partial y}\frac{dy}{dn} = -\frac{\partial\psi}{\partial s} - 2\frac{dR_s}{ds} \qquad \text{(b)}$$

Hence, show that

$$\oint \Gamma\frac{\partial\phi}{\partial s}\,ds = -\oint \Gamma\left(\frac{\partial\psi}{\partial s} + 2\frac{dR_s}{ds}\right) ds$$

$$= \oint (\psi + 2R_s)\frac{\partial\Gamma}{\partial s}\,ds \qquad \text{(c)}$$

$$= \oint (\psi + 2R_s)\left[(By^2 + Cy)\frac{dx}{ds} - (Ax^2 + Cx)\frac{dy}{ds}\right] ds$$

3 With Eqs. (7–2.7) and Eq. (a) of Prob. 1 show that

$$I = \oint \psi\left[(By^2 + Cy)\frac{dx}{ds} - (Ax^2 + Cx)\frac{dy}{ds}\right] ds$$

$$= -\int\int \left\{\frac{\partial}{\partial y}[(By^2 + Cy)\psi] + \frac{\partial}{\partial x}[(Ax^2 + Cx)\psi]\right\} dx\,dy$$

$$= -2\int\int (Ax + By + C)\psi\,dx\,dy$$

$$- \int\int \left[(By^2 + Cy)\frac{\partial\psi}{\partial y} + (Ax^2 + Cx)\frac{\partial\psi}{\partial x}\right] dx\,dy$$

Hence, with Eq. (a) of Prob. 2, with Eq. (a) of Prob. 1, and with the fact that $\phi = 0$ on S for a simply connected region R [see Eq. (7–11.17)] show that

$$I = -2 \int \int (Ax + By + C)\psi \, dx \, dy + \int \int (By - Ax) \, xy \, dx \, dy$$

4 With the results of Probs. 1, 2, and 3 above, show that

$$\int \int \Gamma \, dx \, dy = -\frac{\nu}{1+\nu} \int \int \phi(Bx - Ay) \, dx \, dy$$

$$- \oint \left[(By^2 + Cy)\frac{dx}{ds} - (Ax^2 + Cx)\frac{dy}{ds} \right] R_s \, ds$$

$$+ \int \int (Ax + By + C)\psi \, dx \, dy - \frac{1}{2} \int \int (By - Ax) \, xy \, dx \, dy.$$

Hence, show that [see Eqs. (7–13.4) and (7–13.5)]

$$y_i = - \int \int (Ax + By + C)\psi \, dx \, dy + \frac{\nu}{1+\nu} \int \int [B(x - \bar{x}) - A(y - \bar{y})]\phi \, dx \, dy$$

$$x_i = \int \int (ax + by + c)\psi \, dx \, dy + \frac{\nu}{1+\nu} \int \int [b(x - \bar{x}) - a(y - \bar{y})]\phi \, dx \, dy$$

$$(7–13.9)$$

Equation (7–13.9) shows that if the solution to the torsion problem for region R is known, that is, if either ϕ or ψ is known [see Eq. (a) of Prob. 2], the coordinates (x_i, y_i) of the shear center may be calculated. In other words, (x_i, y_i) may be determined even though the solution of the bending problem ($F = \Gamma + C_0\phi$) is not known.

5 Show that when the cross section of a bar has one axis of symmetry the shear center will lie on this axis. Show that when the cross section of a bar has two axes of symmetry the shear center coincides with the intersection of these two axes.

6 Show by calculations and examples that the shear center of a cross section of a bar does not necessarily lie in the region R occupied by the cross section.

7-14 Bending of a Bar with Elliptic Cross Section

In this article, we consider a technique introduced by Timoshenko[18] for solving the bending problem of bars for certain types of cross section. The motivation of the method lies in seeking to represent the boundary conditions [taken in the form of the second of Eqs (7–11.21)] in the simplest possible form. For example, for a simply connected cross section we may choose $f(y)$ to make the right-hand side of the second of Eqs. (7–11.21) equal to zero. Then, $\partial\Psi/\partial s = 0$ on S. Since the cross section is simply connected, it follows that Ψ may be taken equal to zero on S (see Art. 7–6). We illustrate the method for a bar with elliptic cross section.

---

[18]S. Timoshenko, *Bull. Inst. Engineers of Ways of Communications*, St. Petersburg, 1913, and *Proc. London Math. Soc.*, Ser. 2, Vol. 20 (1922), p. 398.

For an elliptic cross section, the lateral surface of the cross section is defined by the equation

$$\frac{x^2}{a^2} + \frac{y^2}{b^2} = 1 \tag{7–14.1}$$

where (a, b) denote the major and minor semi-axes of the ellipse. Accordingly, the right-hand side of the second of Eqs. (7–11.21) vanishes identically provided we set

$$f(y) = -\frac{Pa^2}{Ib^2}(y^2 - b^2) \tag{7–14.2}$$

Substitution of Eq. (7–14.2) into the first of Eqs. (7–11.21) yields

$$\nabla^2 \Psi = \frac{2Py}{I}\left(\frac{a^2}{b^2} + \frac{\nu}{1+\nu}\right) \tag{7–14.3}$$

The boundary condition $\Psi = 0$ on S [see Eq. (7–11.24)] will be satisfied if we take Ψ in the form

$$\Psi(x, y) = D\left(\frac{x^2}{a^2} + \frac{y^2}{b^2} - 1\right)y \tag{7–14.4}$$

where $D = $ const. Substitution of Eq. (7–14.4) into Eq. (7–14.3) yields

$$D = \frac{P}{I}\left(\frac{a^2 b^2}{3a^2 + b^2}\right)\left(\frac{a^2}{b^2} + \frac{\nu}{1+\nu}\right) \tag{7–14.5}$$

With the cross section defined by Eq. (7–14.1), the axes (x, y) are axes of symmetry. Hence, with the resultant force P directed along the x axis, $C_0 = 0$ (see Art. 7–11). Then Eqs. (7–11.10), (7–11.15), (7–11.20), and (7–11.21) yield the following expressions for the stress components τ_{xz}, τ_{yz}:

$$\tau_{xz} = \frac{1}{2}\left[\frac{\partial \Psi}{\partial y} + f - \frac{Px^2}{I}\right]$$
$$\tau_{yz} = -\frac{1}{2}\frac{\partial \Psi}{\partial x} \tag{7–14.6}$$

Substitution of Eqs. (7–14.2), (7–14.4), and (7–14.5) into Eqs. (7–14.6) yields

$$\tau_{xz} = \frac{Pa^2}{2I}\left[\frac{(1+\nu)a^2 + \nu b^2}{(1+\nu)(3a^2 + b^2)}\left(\frac{x^2}{a^2} + \frac{3y^2}{b^2} - 1\right) - \left(\frac{x^2}{a^2} + \frac{y^2}{b^2} - 1\right)\right]$$
$$\tau_{yz} = -\frac{(1+\nu)a^2 + \nu b^2}{(1+\nu)(3a^2 + b^2)}\frac{Pxy}{I} \tag{7–14.7}$$

The normal stress component σ_z for this case $(A = -1/I, B = C = 0)$ is found from Eq. (7–11.4) to be

$$\sigma_z = -\frac{Px}{I}(L - z) \tag{7–14.8}$$

Equation (7–14.8) agrees precisely with elementary beam theory. However, the shearing-stress components differ from results predicted by elementary beam theory. Elementary beam theory predicts that τ_{yz} vanishes everywhere and that τ_{xz} is a function of x only.

If $b \ll a$, Eqs. (7–14.7) may be approximated by the equations

$$\tau_{xz} = \frac{P}{3I}(a^2 - x^2), \qquad \tau_{yz} = -\frac{Pxy}{3I} \qquad (7\text{–}14.9)$$

Then, τ_{xz} agrees with the stress component computed by elementary theory. However, again τ_{yz} is in disagreement with elementary theory although it is very small (since y is small; it is at most equal to b). The maximum value of τ_{xz} predicted by Eq. (7–14.9) is (for $x = 0$)

$$(\tau_{xz})_{\text{max}} = \frac{Pa^2}{3I} = \frac{4P}{3A} \qquad (7\text{–}14.10)$$

where $I = Aa^2/4$, where A = cross-sectional area of the ellipse.

By Eqs. (7–14.7), the maximum value of τ_{xz} is (for $x = y = 0$)

$$(\tau_{xz})_{\text{max}} = \frac{Pa^2}{2I}\left[1 - \frac{(1+\nu)a^2 + \nu b^2}{(1+\nu)(3a^2 + b^2)}\right] \qquad (7\text{–}14.11)$$

Again, for $b \ll a$, Eq. (7–14.11) yields the result given by Eq. (7–14.10).

Bar with circular cross section. If in the above analysis we let $a = b$, the cross section of the bar becomes circular. Thus, for the circular bar we obtain from Eqs. (7–14.7)

$$\tau_{xz} = \frac{P}{2I}\left[\frac{1 + 2\nu}{4(1 + \nu)}(x^2 + 3y^2 - a^2) - (x^2 + y^2 - a^2)\right]$$

$$\tau_{yz} = -\frac{1 + 2\nu}{4(1 + \nu)}\frac{Pxy}{I} \qquad (7\text{–}14.12)$$

and hence,

$$(\tau_{xz})_{\text{max}} = \frac{3 + 2\nu}{8(1 + \nu)}\frac{Pa^2}{I} \qquad (7\text{–}14.13)$$

7-15 Bending of a Bar with Rectangular Cross Section

Consider a cantilever beam with rectangular cross section R and with lateral surface S. Let end load P be applied to the end of the beam and directed along the vertical centroidal axis (x axis, Fig. 7–15.1). The cross section is defined by the equation

$$(x^2 - a^2)(y^2 - b^2) = 0 \qquad (7\text{–}15.1)$$

By the theory of Art. 7–11, the beam undergoes bending with no twisting of the end plane ($A = -1/I$, $B = C = C_0 = 0$).

Since the net load P is equivalent to shear-stress components τ_{xz}, τ_{yz} distributed over the end of the bar, we may employ the semi-inverse method by assuming simple distributions for τ_{xz}, τ_{yz}, and then attempt to satisfy the

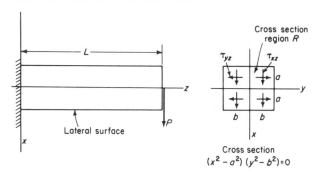

Figure 7-15.1

elasticity equations. For example, since $\Sigma F_x = P$, $\Sigma F_y = 0$, it appears reasonable to assume τ_{yz} to be odd in y and τ_{zz} to be even in x and y (see Fig. 7–15.1). Furthermore, we employ the technique demonstrated in Art. 7–14 for the elliptic cross section. Hence, taking $f = Pa^2/I$ and noting the nature of the dependency of (τ_{zz}, τ_{yz}) on x and y, we find by Eqs. (7–14.6) that Ψ is even in x and odd in y. Also by choosing $f = Pa^2/I$ and noting that $dy/ds = 0$ for $y = \pm b$, by eqs. (7–11.21), we obtain

$$\nabla^2 \Psi = \frac{2v}{1+v} \frac{Py}{I} \qquad \text{over } R$$

$$\Psi = 0 \qquad \text{on } S \tag{7-15.2}$$

By inspection, a particular solution of the first of Eqs. (7–15.2) is

$$\Psi_1 = Ay^3 + By \tag{7-15.3}$$

Substitution of Eq. (7–15.3) into Eq. (7–15.2) yields

$$A = \frac{vP}{3(1+v)I} \tag{7-15.4}$$

with B arbitrary.

By the discussion at the end of Art. 7–11, we choose Ψ in the form

$$\Psi = \Omega + \frac{vP}{3(1+v)I} y^3 + By \tag{7-15.5}$$

where by Eqs. (7–15.2) and (7–15.5)

$$\nabla^2 \Omega = 0 \qquad \text{on } R$$

$$\Omega = -\frac{vP}{3(1+v)I} y^3 - By \qquad \text{on } S \tag{7-15.6}$$

Let us choose[19] B so that $\Omega = 0$ for $y = \pm b$. Then, Eq. (7–15.6) yields

$$B = -\frac{vPb^2}{3(1+v)I} \tag{7-15.7}$$

---

[19]Note that we could assume a particular solution of Eq. (7–15.2) in the form $Ay^3 + B$. Then we could choose B so that $\Omega = 0$ for $y = b$, but Ω would not be zero on the line $y = -b$. Hence, our choice of Ψ_1 [Eq. (7–15.3)] leads to a simpler boundary condition for Ω.

Thus, by Eqs. (7–15.5) and (7–15.6), we arrive at the stress function

$$\Psi = \Omega + \frac{\nu P}{3(1+\nu)I}(y^3 - b^2 y) \qquad (7\text{–}15.8)$$

where

$$\nabla^2 \Omega = 0 \qquad\qquad \text{on } R \qquad (7\text{–}15.9)$$

and

$$\Omega = 0 \qquad\qquad \text{for } y = \pm b$$

$$\Omega = \frac{\nu P}{3(1+\nu)I}(b^2 y - y^3), \qquad \text{for } x = \pm a \qquad (7\text{–}15.10)$$

Since Ψ is even in x and odd in y, Ω is even in x and odd in y.

Consider solutions of Eq. (7–15.9) of the form

$$\Omega = f(x)g(y) \qquad (7\text{–}15.11)$$

where $f(x)$, $g(y)$ are functions of x and y, respectively. Substitution of Eq. (7–15.11) into Eq. (7–15.9) with the requirement that Ω be even in x and odd in y yields solutions of the form

$$\Omega = A \cosh kx \sin ky \qquad (7\text{–}15.12)$$

where A and k are constants.

Substitution of Eq. (7–15.12) into the first of Eqs. (7–15.10) yields $A \cosh Kx \sin Kb = 0$, or $K = n\pi/b$, $n = 1, 2, 3, \ldots$. Hence, superposition of solutions of the type given by Eq. (7–15.12) yields

$$\Omega = \sum_{n=1}^{\infty} A_n \cosh \frac{n\pi x}{b} \sin \frac{n\pi y}{b} \qquad (7\text{–}15.13)$$

Let $A_n \cosh (n\pi a/b) = a_n$. Then, by Eq. (7–15.13) and the second of Eqs. (7–15.10), we must require that

$$\sum_{n=1}^{\infty} a_n \sin \frac{n\pi y}{b} = \frac{\nu P}{3(1+\nu)I}(by - y^3) \qquad (7\text{–}15.14)$$

Multiplying Eq. (7–15.14) by $\sin (m\pi y/b)$ and integrating from $-b$ to b, we obtain

$$\sum_{n=1}^{\infty} a_n \int_{-b}^{b} \sin \frac{n\pi y}{b} \sin \frac{m\pi y}{b}\, dy = \frac{\nu P}{3(1+\nu)I} \int_{-b}^{b} (b^2 y - y^3) \sin \frac{m\pi y}{b}\, dy$$

$$(7\ 15.15)$$

Observing that

$$\int_{-b}^{b} \sin \frac{m\pi y}{b} \sin \frac{n\pi y}{b}\, dy = \begin{cases} 0, & m \neq n \\ b, & m = n \end{cases}$$

$$\int_{-b}^{b} y \sin \frac{m\pi y}{b}\, dy = -\frac{2(-1)^m b^2}{m\pi}$$

$$\int_{-b}^{b} y^3 \sin \frac{m\pi y}{b}\, dy = -\frac{2(-1)^m b^4}{m^3 \pi^3}(m^2 \pi^2 - 6)$$

We obtain after integration of Eq. (7–15.15)

$$a_n = -\frac{4\nu P b^3}{(1+\nu)I}\frac{(-1)^n}{n^3\pi^3}$$

Hence, the constant A_n in Eq. (7–15.13) is determined, and the stress function Ψ is given by the formula

$$\Psi = \frac{\nu P}{3(1+\nu)I}\left[y^3 - b^2 y - \frac{12b^3}{\pi^3}\sum_{n=1}^{\infty}\frac{(-1)^n}{n^3}\frac{\cosh\dfrac{n\pi x}{b}\sin\dfrac{n\pi y}{b}}{\cosh\dfrac{n\pi a}{b}}\right] \quad (7\text{–}15.16)$$

Then, since $f = Pa^2/I$, substitution of Eq. (7–15.16) into Eqs. (7–14.6) yields

$$\tau_{xz} = \frac{P}{2I}(a^2 - x^2) + \frac{\nu P}{6(1+\nu)I}$$

$$\times\left[3y^2 - b^2 - \frac{12b^2}{\pi^2}\sum_{n=1}^{\infty}\frac{(-1)^n}{n^2}\frac{\cosh\dfrac{n\pi x}{b}\cos\dfrac{n\pi y}{b}}{\cosh\dfrac{n\pi a}{a}}\right] \quad (7\text{–}15.17)$$

$$\tau_{yz} = \frac{2\nu P b^2}{\pi^2(1+\nu)I}\sum_{n=1}^{\infty}\frac{(-1)^n}{n^2}\frac{\sinh\dfrac{n\pi x}{b}\sin\dfrac{n\pi y}{b}}{\cosh\dfrac{n\pi a}{b}}$$

Equations (7–15.17) express the solution to the bending of a cantilever beam with rectangular cross section and with load P directed along the vertical centroidal axis in the end plane $x = L$.

Examination of τ_{xz}. On the horizontal line $x = 0$, Eqs. (7–15.17) yield

$$\tau_{xz} = \frac{Pa^2}{2I}\left\{1 + \frac{\nu}{1+\nu}\left[\frac{y^2}{a^2} - \frac{b^2}{3a^2} - \frac{4b^2}{\pi^2 a^2}\sum_{n=1}^{\infty}\frac{(-1)^n}{n^2}\frac{\cos\dfrac{n\pi y}{b}}{\cosh\dfrac{n\pi a}{b}}\right]\right\} \quad (7\text{–}15.18)$$

$$\tau_{yz} = 0$$

Elementary theory of beams yields the result (for $x = 0$) $\tau_{xz} = Pa^2/(2I)$. Hence, the quantity in braces in Eq. (7–15.18) represents a correction factor K to elementary beam theory; that is, the result of elementary beam theory must be multiplied by the factor

$$K = 1 + \frac{\nu}{1+\nu}\left[\frac{y^2}{a^2} - \frac{b^2}{3a^2} - \frac{4b^2}{\pi^2 a^2}\sum_{n=1}^{\infty}\frac{(-1)^n}{n^2}\frac{\cos\dfrac{n\pi y}{b}}{\cosh\dfrac{n\pi a}{b}}\right] \quad (7\text{–}15.19)$$

If $\nu = 0$, the correction factor is 1. Also, if $b \ll a$, the correction factor is approximately 1. That is elementary theory is approximately correct (at $x = 0$) for beams of narrow cross section (Fig. 7–15.1, with $b \ll a$). The fact that the correction factor approaches 1 as b/a approaches zero is apparent from Eq. (7–15.19) since $\cos(n\pi y/b)$ is never larger than 1 and $\cosh(n\pi a/b)$ becomes very large as $b/a \to 0$.

It may also be shown that $K \to 1$ as b/a becomes very large. For example, consider the point $x = y = 0$. Then, Eq. (7–15.19) yields

$$K = 1 - \frac{\nu}{1+\nu}\left[\frac{b^2}{3a^2} + \frac{4b^2}{\pi^2 a^2}\sum_{n=1}^{\infty}\frac{(-1)^n}{n^2}\operatorname{sech}\frac{n\pi a}{b}\right]$$

Note that as $b/a \to \infty$, $\operatorname{sech}(n\pi a/b) \to 1$. To evaluate the series $\sum_{n=1}^{\infty}(-1)^n/n^2$, we first observe that by Fourier series, we may express θ^2 in series form as follows:

$$\theta^2 = \frac{C^2}{3} - \frac{4C^2}{\pi^2}\left(\cos\frac{\pi\theta}{C} - \frac{1}{2^2}\cos\frac{2\pi\theta}{C} + \frac{1}{3^2}\cos\frac{3\pi\theta}{C} - \frac{1}{4^2}\cos\frac{4\pi\theta}{C} + \cdots\right)$$

where C is a constant. Letting $\theta = 0$ and $C = \frac{1}{2}$, we obtain

$$0 = \frac{1}{12} - \frac{1}{\pi^2}\left(1 - \frac{1}{2^2} + \frac{1}{3^2} - \frac{1}{4^2} + \cdots\right)$$

or

$$\frac{\pi^2}{12} = 1 - \frac{1}{2^2} + \frac{1}{3^2} - \frac{1}{4^2} + \cdots = \sum_{n=1}^{\infty}\frac{(-1)^n}{n^2}$$

Accordingly, for $b/a \to \infty$, $\tau_{zz} \to Pa^2/(2I)$ at $x = y = 0$. That is, the elementary theory of beams also gives the correct result for a very wide beam (Fig. 7–15.1 for $b \gg a$).

Problem. Let $b/a = 6$ and $\nu = 0.3$. For the horizontal line $x = 0$, evaluate the correction factor K [Eq. (7–15.19)] for $y/b = 0, 0.2, 0.4, 0.6, 0.8$, and 1.0.

Review Problems

R-1 Let the resultant vector of the forces acting on the end $z = L$ of a bar be directed along the z axis. Let the resultant moment be zero. Consider the simplest stress distribution which is statically equivalent to the resultant vector and the resultant moment. Hence, by the semi-inverse method solve the problem of the cylindrical bar subjected to a longitudinal end force.

R-2 Let the forces that act on the end of a rod at $z = L$ be statically equivalent to a couple of moment $M_y = M$, where M_y denotes the moment relative to the y axis in the end plane at $z = L$. Compute a statically equivalent system for the end plane $z = 0$. Assume the simplest stress distribution that is statically equivalent to M_y. Hence, solve the problem of bending of a bar subjected to end couple M. Express the stress components, the strain components, and the displacement components in terms of M and material and geometrical properties of the bar.

R-3 Figure R7-3 represents the cross section of a cantilever beam subjected to transverse end load P directed along the x axis. Derive a formula for $f(y)$ to make Ψ vanish on the lateral boundary [see Eq. (7–11.22)]. Discuss the application of the method demonstrated in Arts. 7–14 and 7–15 for this problem.

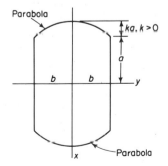

Figure R7-3

8
THERMAL STRESS

8-1 Introduction

The classical study of thermal stress is concerned with the distribution of stress (or strain) in a solid subjected to a nonuniform temperature distribution $T(x, y, z)$—that is, a temperature distribution that is not linear in (x, y, z)—or in a solid that is physically or geometrically constrained and that is then subjected to a uniform or nonuniform temperature change.

The subject was initially formulated by Duhamel,[1] when he derived equations for the distribution of strain in an elastic medium containing temperature gradients. Duhamel's results were subsequently reformulated by a number of authors. Finally, Neumann[2] presented the theory of thermal stress in the following way:

Consider an *isotropic* elastic solid in an arbitrary state of stress. Let a small element of the solid be detached from its surroundings. Let the element be subjected to a temperature change T. The additional straining in the element is given by the components $\epsilon'_{ij} = kT\delta_{ij}$, where k is the the coefficient of linear thermal expansion for the solid and δ_{ij} is the Kronecker delta (see Art. 1–20). Consequently, if the net strain in the body is denoted by the components of the strain tensor ϵ_{ij}, then the portion of the strain produced by the stress is characterized by the components $\epsilon_{ij} - kT\delta_{ij}$. To arrive at a

---

[1]J. M. C. Duhamel, "Second memoire sur les phenomenes thermo-mecaniques," *J. de l'Ecole Polytechnique*, Vol. 15, book 25 (1837), pp. 1–57, and "Memoire sur le calcul des actions moleculaires developpees par les changements de temperature dans les corps solides," *Memoires . . . par divers savans*, Vol. 5 (1838), pp. 440–498.

[2]F. E. Neumann, *Vorlesungen über die Theorie der Elastizität der festen Körper* (Leipzig: 1885).

stress-strain-temperature relation, one then replaces the components ϵ_{ij} by the components $\epsilon_{ij} - kT\delta_{ij}$ in the generalized Hooke's law. In Art. 8–4 we shall see that by modifying the stress-strain relations in this manner and expressing the equilibrium conditions in terms of displacement components, one obtains the result that the usual displacement equilibrium equations are modified by a body force $Ek\,\nabla T/(1-2\nu)$ per unit volume where E is Young's modulus of elasticity and ν is Poisson's ratio. Furthermore, one must super-impose on the load stress a "hydrostatic stress" equal to $-EkT/(1-2\nu)$, and finally, one must superimpose a surface traction with (x, y, z) components $EkTl/(1-2\nu)$, $EkTm/(1-2\nu)$, $EkTn/(1-2\nu)$, where l, m, n denote the (x, y, z) components of the unit normal vector to the surface. In other words, if T is a known function (found by solving the heat-conduction equation; see Art. 8–2), the thermoelasticity problem reduces to determination of the displacement field from a determinate set of equations.

Duhamel applied the basic theory outlined above to a number of specific problems. Later Neumann and others used the theory to study the double refracting property of nonuniformly heated glass plates. In these investigations a number of techniques were developed for the solution of thermoelasticity boundary-value problems. Although for a long time these methods appeared to be more or less academic, recently the study of thermal stress has been stimulated by practical problems, and it has become an increasingly important factor in the design of components of modern structures that undergo heating.

As implied in the foregoing, the classical Duhamel-Neumann theory of thermal stress assumes that although the state of strain of an elastic solid is affected by a nonuniform temperature distribution, the heat conduction process is unaffected by a deformation. This assumption is true if the system is in mechanical and thermal equilibrium. However, it is an approximation in the time-dependent thermal problem, since then the acceleration terms cannot vanish identically as implied by the Duhamel-Neumann theory. Ordinarily, the thermal acceleration effects are small. Nevertheless, application of the Duhamel-Neumann theory to the transient thermal problem leads to inconsistencies that cannot be resolved within the scope of this theory, since elastic and thermal constants which appear in the Duhamel-Neumann formulation are defined under conditions which are not met in the transient case.

An extensive discussion of the dynamical theory of thermoelasticity has been given by Chadwick.[3] The theory has been generalized to encompass the transient problem by Biot,[4] through application and further development of

---

[3]P. Chadwick, *Thermoelasticity; The Dynamical Theory*, Vol. 1, *Progress in Solid Mechanics* (Amsterdam: North-Holland Publishing Co., 1960), Chap. 4.

[4]M. A. Biot, "Thermoelasticity and Irreversible Thermodynamics," *J. Appl. Phys.*, Vol. 27, No. 3 (March, 1956), pp. 240–254.

the methods of irreversible thermodynamics. A survey of mathematical methods and techniques of treating thermoelastic problems has been presented by Parkus.[5]

In the following articles we restrict ourselves to classical thermoelasticity theory as developed by Duhamel and Neumann. Comprehensive treatises on thermoelasticity have been written recently by Boley and Weiner[6] and by Nowacki.[7]

8-2 The Differential Equation of Heat Conduction

For a large class of problems, temperature distribution in a solid may be calculated by solving the heat-conduction equation, subject to the geometrical and temperature boundary conditions.[8] In general, the temperature distribution T will depend on time t. However, unless the inertia effects that arise due to a suddenly applied temperature change are significant, time t enters the thermal-stress problem only as a passive parameter. The problem may then be treated as a quasi-static one since the temperature distribution enters into the thermal-stress calculation as an integral load function. Accordingly, for a large class of problems, the temperature distribution may be expressed functionally as follows:

$$T = T(x, y, z; t)$$

where (x, y, z) denote rectangular cartesian coordinates and t denotes time. For a given time $t = t_1$, the above equation defines the temperature distribution as a function of coordinates (x, y, z).

By the theory of heat, the temperature $T(x, y, z; t)$ that exists at a point (x, y, z) of a thermally isotropic homogeneous body referred to rectangular cartesian coordinates is determined by the partial differential equation

$$\frac{\partial T}{\partial t} = \kappa \, \nabla^2 T + \frac{Q}{c\rho} \tag{8-2.1}$$

where ∇^2 denotes the Laplacian operator

$$\frac{\partial^2}{\partial x^2} + \frac{\partial^2}{\partial y^2} + \frac{\partial^2}{\partial z^2} \tag{8-2.2}$$

In Eq. (8–2.1), ρ denotes the mass density; c denotes the specific heat, that is,

---

[5]H. Parkus, "Methods of Solution of Thermoelastic Boundary Value Problems," *Proceedings of Third Symposium on Naval Structures* (New York: Columbia University Press, 1963).

[6]B. A. Boley and J. H. Weiner, *Theory of Thermal Stresses* (New York: John Wiley & Sons, Inc., 1960).

[7]W. Nowacki, *Thermoelasticity* (Reading, Mass.: Addison-Wesley Publishing Co., Inc., 1963).

[8]H. S. Carslaw and J. C. Jaeger, *Conduction of Heat in Solids*, 2nd ed. (London: Oxford University Press, 1959).

the quantity of heat that is necessary to raise the temperature of a unit mass
$1°$ C. The term κ is the *temperature diffusivity*. It is defined by the ratio

$$\kappa = \frac{\alpha}{c\rho} \tag{8-2.3}$$

where α is the *thermal conductivity*. In turn, α is related to the quantity of
heat dq that flows through a surface element ΔS with normal n during the
time dt by the relation

$$dq = -\alpha \frac{dT}{dn} \Delta S \, dt \tag{8-2.4}$$

In the following, we consider mainly thermally isotropic and homogeneous
bodies. Hence, ordinarily α depends neither on direction nor on location in
the body. Additionally, if it is assumed that α and c do not depend on
temperature or stress level, they remain constant. If the temperature gradient
is not too great, this last assumption is permissible. However, if large
temperature gradients occur, it may be necessary to consider variations of
α and c with temperature.

The term Q in Eq. (8-2.1) represents the quantity of heat per unit time and
unit volume that is produced by heat sources that lie in the interior of the
volume element. A unit volume dV produces accordingly the quantity of
heat $Q \, dV \, dt$ during time dt.

If the temperature distribution is independent of time, we speak of a
stationary or *steady-state temperature distribution*. Equation (8-2.1) then
reduces to the Poisson equation of potential theory, namely,

$$\nabla^2 T + \frac{Q}{\alpha} = 0 \tag{8-2.5}$$

In the absence of heat sources in the body, $Q = 0$. Hence, for steady-state
heat flow in the absence of heat sources, the temperature distribution in the
body must satisfy the equation

$$\nabla^2 T = 0 \tag{8-2.6}$$

Equation (8-2.6) is subject to the temperature conditions on the surface of the
body.

The temperature distribution is not determined completely by Eqs. (8-2.1)
to (8-2.6). For nonsteady heat flow, an initial temperature distribution
(at $t = 0$) must be specified. This initial temperature distribution may be
a continuous or a discontinuous function of the coordinates; that is, $T(x,
y, z; 0) = f(x, y, z)$.

The boundary conditions of the problem depend on the effect which the
environment of the body exerts on its surface. The equations describing this
effect must be known at each point on the surface. The boundary conditions
are in their simplest form when the temperature T_0 on the surface is given as
a function of position and time. However, they can also be specified in terms

of heat flow, that is, in terms of the quantity of heat that flows through the surface as a function of time [Eq. (8–2.4)]. Finally, as is common, but also mathematically more difficult, the boundary conditions may be represented in terms of the temperature θ of the environment by the law of heat exchange between the surface of the body and its environment. To formulate the problem mathematically, an approximation due to Newton is often used:

$$\frac{\partial T}{\partial n_0} = \frac{e}{\alpha}(\theta - T_0) \qquad (8\text{–}2.7)$$

Equation (8–2.7) relates the temperature gradient on the surface of the body to the temperature difference between the surface of the body and its environment. The ratio e/α is called the *relative emissivity* and e is called the *emissivity* of the surface.

8-3 Elementary Approach to Thermal-stress Problem in One And Two Variables

Consider an infinitesimal element dx of a solid body. Initially, let the temperature of the element be T_0. The temperature T_0 is considered to be that temperature for which the length of the element is dx. For simplicity, let us take $T_0 = 0$, since the elongation of the element depends on differences between existing temperature in the element and temperature T_0. Let the element be subjected to temperature T. Then, the element will undergo an infinitesimal elongation de (provided T is positive; for negative T, a contraction occurs). By the theory of heat, the elongation de is related to the temperature T by the equation

$$de = kT\,dx \qquad (a)$$

where k is the coefficient of thermal expansion for the material of the element. In general k is a function of temperature T. For example, for crystals, the following relation between k and T is often used:

$$k = a + bT + cT^2 \qquad (b)$$

where T is temperature in °C, and where a, b, c are constants with magnitudes of the order 10^{-6}, 10^{-8}, 10^{-11}, respectively. Theoretically, the coefficient of thermal expansion for a material is defined by the relation

$$k = \frac{1}{L_T}\frac{dL}{dT} \qquad (c)$$

where L_T denotes the length of the element for temperature T. Usually, k is determined experimentally by employing the relation

$$\bar{k} = \frac{1}{L_0}\frac{\Delta L}{\Delta T} \qquad (d)$$

where $\bar{k}$ denotes an average value of k, ΔL denotes the finite change in length of the element for the finite change in temperature ΔT, and L_0 denotes the length of the element at some temperature, say, room temperature. Accordingly, the constants a, b, c of Eq. (b) are not generally well defined, although average values for certain materials are often employed in practice. Furthermore, in the development of the theory of thermoelasticity, we will find that k enters into the equations only in the product form kT. Consequently, we may account for variations of k with T by setting $\bar{T} = kT$ and considering $\bar{T}$ as a pseudotemperature parameter for the body; that is, the variation of k with T may be accounted for by replacing the product kT by the parameter $\bar{T}$.

By Eq. (a), the strain in the fiber due to T is

$$\epsilon = \frac{de}{dx} = kT \tag{e}$$

In general, a temperature change in the element will not produce stress in the element unless either the element is physically prevented by forces from expanding or, if physically free to expand, it is unable to expand in a manner compatible with the temperature distribution in the element. For example, if the element is restrained so that its length is unchanged under a temperature increase of T, forces P must act at its ends (Fig. 8–3.1). Figuratively speaking, we imagine that first the element is allowed to elongate a distance de. Then by application of forces P the element is returned to its initial length dx. Hence, to compute the stress induced in the element by the temperature change T when its ends are restrained from moving, we compute the stress σ induced in the element by forces P under compression de. Hence,

$$\sigma = P/A = -E\epsilon \tag{f}$$

where A is the cross-sectional area of the element and E is the modulus of elasticity of the material.

By Eqs. (e) and (f) we obtain

$$\sigma = -EkT \tag{g}$$

where the minus sign denotes compression.

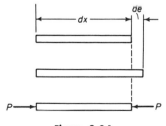

Figure 8-3.1

Thermal-stress problems in beams. The above argument may be applied to elementary beam (strip) problems. For example, consider a rectangular strip in the (x, y) plane (Fig. 8–3.2). Let the strip be subjected to a temperature distribution $T = T(x, y)$, even in x and y. Then the resulting elongation of the strip is symmetrical with respect to axes (x, y). Now on each infinitesimal longitudinal element dx of the strip, we imagine that the stress

$$\sigma'_x = -EkT \qquad \text{(h)}$$

acts. If the strip is prevented from elongating, Eq. (h) determines the normal stress component in the x direction. In elementary beam theory, the stress components $\sigma_y, \sigma_z, \tau_{xz}, \tau_{yz}$ are neglected. Furthermore, if the weight of the beam is neglected and no other loads act, there is no shear stress τ_{xy}. Hence, the stress of elementary beam theory is given completely in this case by Eq. (h).

If the beam is free to expand, that is, if it is free of forces at its ends, the stress σ_x must vanish on the ends. For a beam with free ends, the end stress due to σ'_x (Eq. h) is $\sigma_x = -EkT$, where T is evaluated at the ends. Accordingly, to eliminate the boundary forces, we need to add a distributed stress EkT over the ends of the beam. It follows by Saint-Venant's principle (see Art. 4–10) that the stress σ''_x at some distance from the ends (a distance several times the depth $2c$ of the strip) due to the distributed load EkT is (Fig. 8–3.3)

$$\sigma''_x = \frac{1}{2c} \int_{-c}^{c} EkT \, d\zeta \qquad \text{(i)}$$

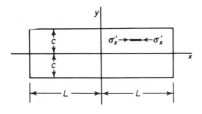

Figure 8-3.2

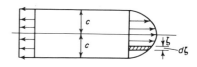

Figure 8-3.3

Hence, except near the ends, the stress σ_x in the beam is obtained by super-position of σ'_x and σ''_x; that is,

$$\sigma_x = \sigma'_x + \sigma''_x = \frac{1}{2c} \int_{-c}^{c} EkT \, d\zeta - EkT \qquad \text{(j)}$$

Equation (j) is valid for variable k and E; that is, k and E may be functions of temperature T or coordinate x. If EkT is a constant, Eq. (j) yields $\sigma_x = 0$.

Hence, if the free strip is subjected to a constant temperature change and if E and k are constant, no stress is induced. The beam simply elongates with no stress.

If the temperature distribution is nonsymmetrical with respect to the longitudinal axis of the beam, $T = T(x, y)$ is an odd function of y. Accordingly, the end forces EkT give rise to a resultant moment M which alters the stress σ_x in the beam.

By theory of moments (Fig. 8–3.3)

$$M = \int_{-c}^{c} EkT\zeta \, d\zeta \qquad (k)$$

The moment M produces stress σ_x''' in the beam. If we assume that this stress varies linearly with respect to y, as is done in elementary beam theory, we may write

$$\sigma_x''' = \sigma y/c \qquad (l)$$

where σ denotes the values of σ_x''' at $y = c$. The moment M may also be expressed in terms of σ_x''' as follows:

$$M = \int_{-c}^{c} \sigma_x''' \zeta \, d\zeta \qquad (m)$$

Equations (k), (l), and (m) yield

$$\sigma_x''' = \frac{y}{I} \int_{-c}^{c} EkT\zeta \, d\zeta \qquad (n)$$

where $I = 2c^3/3$ denotes the moment of inertia of the area of the cross section of the beam with respect to the z axis. Equation (n) is restricted to a linear distribution of stress across the cross section of the beam (the beam has unit thickness).

The net stress in the beam may be obtained by superposition of the stresses $\sigma_x', \sigma_x'', \sigma_x'''$. Thus, for a beam with free ends and with rectangular cross section, the stress due to a temperature distribution $T(x, y)$ is given by the relation

$$\sigma_x = -EkT + \frac{1}{2c} \int_{-c}^{c} EkT \, d\zeta + \frac{3y}{2c^3} \int_{-c}^{c} EkT\zeta \, d\zeta \qquad (o)$$

Equation (o) holds for the plane-stress problem ($\sigma_z = 0$) of rectangular strips. For plane-strain problems ($\epsilon_z = 0$), it may be shown that

$$\sigma_x = \frac{-EkT}{(1-v)} + \frac{1}{2c} \int_{-c}^{c} \frac{EkT}{(1-v)} \, d\zeta + \frac{3y}{2c^3} \int_{-c}^{c} \frac{EkT}{(1-v)} \zeta \, d\zeta \qquad (p)$$

where v denotes Poisson's ratio for the material.

Problem. Derive Eq. (p).

8-4 Transformation of the Equations of Thermal Stress to Equivalent Displacement Problem

The equilibrium equations and the strain-displacement relations remain valid in thermal-stress problems since they are independent of material properties. However, the stress-strain relations are altered by temperature.

If a body is subjected to a temperature change T, and if the body is allowed to expand freely, a line element of length ds in the body is elongated to a length $(1 + kT)\, ds$, where k is the coefficient of thermal expansion. For thermal isotropic bodies, k is independent of the direction of ds. Additionally, for a number of structural materials, k remains fairly constant for a wide range of temperature (see Art. 8–3). Hence, unless large temperature gradients occur, k may be taken as a constant.

Recently it has been observed that k also depends on the stress level.[9] Although this effect is not included in the subsequent discussion, it may be of considerable importance, since the experiments of Rosenfield and Averbach show that k for steel may increase as much as 10 per cent in the elastic range for a tensile-stress change of 40,000 lb/in.[2] They also observed that the coefficient of thermal expansion of Invar in the elastic range *decreased* with increasing tensile stress. Accordingly, for certain temperature ranges the variation of k with stress may be more significant than variations of material properties with temperature. Further study of the dependency of k on stress level is needed.

Under the above assumptions, for a thermally isotropic body the angles of an infinitesimal rectangular parallelepiped remain unchanged. Hence the strains in perpendicular directions are equal, and the shearing strains are zero. Consequently the strain-temperature relations for a body subjected to temperature $T = T(x, y, z; t)$ measured above an arbitrary zero are

$$\epsilon_x' = \epsilon_y' = \epsilon_z' = kT, \qquad \gamma_{xy}' = \gamma_{yz}' = \gamma_{xz}' = 0 \qquad \text{(a)}$$

If a body is geometrically or physically constrained, heating will induce stress in it. Then the strains $(\epsilon_x'', \epsilon_y'', \epsilon_z'', \gamma_{xy}'', \ldots)$ due to the induced stress components $(\sigma_x, \sigma_y, \ldots, \tau_{yz})$ are given by the relations

$$\epsilon_x'' = \epsilon_x - \epsilon_x' = \epsilon_x - kT = \frac{1}{E}\left[\sigma_x - \nu(\sigma_y + \sigma_z)\right]$$

$$\epsilon_y'' = \epsilon_y - \epsilon_y' = \epsilon_y - kT = \frac{1}{E}\left[\sigma_y - \nu(\sigma_x + \sigma_z)\right]$$

$$\epsilon_z'' = \epsilon_z - \epsilon_z' = \epsilon_z - kT = \frac{1}{E}\left[\sigma_z - \nu(\sigma_x + \sigma_y)\right] \qquad \text{(b)}$$

$$\gamma_{xy}'' = \gamma_{xy} = \frac{1}{G}\,\tau_{xy}, \qquad \gamma_{xz}'' = \gamma_{xz} = \frac{1}{G}\,\tau_{xz}, \qquad \gamma_{yz}'' = \gamma_{yz} = \frac{1}{G}\,\tau_{yz}$$

---

[9] H. R. Rosenfield and B. L. Averbach, "Effect of Stress on the Expansion Coefficient," *J. Appl. Phys. (U.S.)*, Vol. 27, No. 2 (Feb., 1956), pp. 154–156.

where $\epsilon_x, \epsilon_y, \epsilon_z, \frac{1}{2}\gamma_{xy}, \ldots$ are the components of the total strain tensor. Hence, the strain-stress-temperature relations are

$$
\begin{aligned}
\epsilon_x &= E^{-1}[\sigma_x - v(\sigma_y + \sigma_z)] + kT \\
\epsilon_y &= E^{-1}[\sigma_y - v(\sigma_x + \sigma_z)] + kT \\
\epsilon_z &= E^{-1}[\sigma_z - v(\sigma_x + \sigma_y)] + kT \\
\gamma_{xy} &= G^{-1}\tau_{xy}, \quad \ldots, \quad \ldots
\end{aligned}
\tag{8-4.1}
$$

Introducing the notations $I_1 = \sigma_x + \sigma_y + \sigma_z$, $E = 2(1 + v)\,G$, we may write Eqs. (8–4.1) in the form

$$
\begin{aligned}
\epsilon_x &= \frac{1}{2G}\left(\sigma_x - \frac{v}{1+v}I_1\right) + kT \\
\epsilon_y &= \frac{1}{2G}\left(\sigma_y - \frac{v}{1+v}I_1\right) + kT \\
\epsilon_z &= \frac{1}{2G}\left(\sigma_z - \frac{v}{1+v}I_1\right) + kT \\
\gamma_{xy} &= \frac{1}{G}\tau_{xy}, \quad \ldots, \quad \ldots
\end{aligned}
\tag{8-4.2}
$$

or briefly, in index notation (see the appendices to Chapters 2 and 3),

$$
\epsilon_{\alpha\beta} = \frac{1}{2G}\left(\sigma_{\alpha\beta} - \frac{v\delta_{\alpha\beta}}{1+v}I_1\right) + kT\delta_{\alpha\beta}, \qquad \alpha, \beta = 1, 2, 3
$$
$$
\delta_{\alpha\beta} = \begin{cases} 1 & \alpha = \beta \\ 0 & \alpha \neq \beta \end{cases}
\tag{8-4.3}
$$

Adding the first three of Eqs. (8–4.2), we obtain

$$
e = \frac{1-2v}{1+v}\frac{I_1}{2G} + 3kT = \frac{1-2v}{E}I_1 + 3kT
\tag{8-4.4}
$$

where $e = \epsilon_x + \epsilon_y + \epsilon_z$ is the volume dilation (or the strain invariant J_1).

The temperature-displacement relations may be determined as follows: Solving Eqs. (8–4.2) for stresses and utilizing Eq. (8–4.4), we obtain the stress-strain-temperature relations:

$$
\sigma_x = \lambda e + 2G\epsilon_x - \frac{kET}{1-2v}, \quad \ldots, \quad \ldots
$$
$$
\tau_{xy} = G\gamma_{xy}, \quad \ldots, \quad \ldots
\tag{8-4.5}
$$

where the ellipses denote similar equations in (σ_y, σ_z) and in (τ_{xz}, τ_{yz}) and

$$
\lambda = \frac{vE}{(1+v)(1-2v)}
$$

Substituting Eqs. (8–4.5) into the equilibrium equations, namely,

$$\frac{\partial \sigma_x}{\partial x} + \frac{\partial \tau_{xy}}{\partial y} + \frac{\partial \tau_{xz}}{\partial z} + X = 0, \qquad \cdots, \qquad \cdots \qquad (c)$$

we obtain

$$(\lambda + G)\frac{\partial e}{\partial x} + G\nabla^2 u + \left(X - \frac{E}{1 - 2\nu}\frac{\partial kT}{\partial x}\right) = 0$$

$$(\lambda + G)\frac{\partial e}{\partial y} + G\nabla^2 v + \left(Y - \frac{E}{1 - 2\nu}\frac{\partial kT}{\partial y}\right) = 0 \qquad (8\text{–}4.6)$$

$$(\lambda + G)\frac{\partial e}{\partial z} + G\nabla^2 w + \left(Z - \frac{E}{1 - 2\nu}\frac{\partial kT}{\partial z}\right) = 0$$

Equations (8–4.6) are the displacement-temperature equilibrium relations. They reduce to the usual displacement-equilibrium relations if $T = \text{const.}$

Boundary conditions. The boundary conditions in terms of stress components are

$$\sigma_{Px} = \sigma_x l + \tau_{xy} m + \tau_{xz} n$$

$$\sigma_{Py} = \tau_{xy} l + \sigma_y m + \tau_{yz} n \qquad (8\text{–}4.7)$$

$$\sigma_{Pz} = \tau_{xz} l + \tau_{yz} m + \sigma_z n$$

Substituting Eqs. (8–4.5) into Eq. (8–4.7), we obtain

$$\sigma_{Px} + \frac{kET}{1 - 2\nu} l = el + G\left(\frac{\partial u}{\partial x} l + \frac{\partial u}{\partial y} m + \frac{\partial u}{\partial z} n\right)$$

$$+ G\left(\frac{\partial u}{\partial x} l + \frac{\partial v}{\partial x} m + \frac{\partial w}{\partial x} n\right), \qquad \cdots, \qquad \cdots \qquad (8\text{–}4.8)$$

where the ellipses denote similar equations in σ_{Py} and σ_{Pz}. Equations (8–4.8) reduce to the usual displacement boundary conditions if the terms in T are discarded. Consequently, by the above equations, the problem of thermal stress is reduced to the problem of determining displacement components (u, v, w) which satisfy the temperature-displacement relations [Eq. (8–4.6)] and the boundary conditions [Eq. (8–4.8)]. With (u, v, w) known, the strain components may be computed by the strain-displacement relations. Then by Eq. (8–4.5) the stress components may be determined. Compatibility is automatically satisfied.

A physical interpretation of the thermal-stress problem. Referring to Eq. (8–4.5), we note that the stress components consist of two parts: (a) a part related directly to the strain components in the usual manner, and (b) a part proportional to the temperature at each point. The latter part may be imagined to be due to a "hydrostatic" pressure equal in magnitude to $kET/(1 - 2\nu)$.

Referring to Eqs. (8–4.6) and (8–4.8), we note that the body forces (X, Y, Z) and the surface stresses $(\sigma_{Px}, \sigma_{Py}, \sigma_{Pz})$ are modified by the terms

$$\left(-\frac{E}{1-2\nu}\frac{\partial kT}{\partial x}, \ -\frac{E}{1-2\nu}\frac{\partial kT}{\partial y}, \ -\frac{E}{1-2\nu}\frac{\partial kT}{\partial z}\right) \qquad (8\text{–}4.9)$$

and

$$\left(\frac{kET}{1-2\nu}l, \ \frac{kET}{1-2\nu}m, \ \frac{kET}{1-2\nu}n\right) \qquad (8\text{–}4.10)$$

respectively. Equation (8–4.10) represents a normal tension on the surface equal to $kET/(1-2\nu)$. Hence, the total stress produced in a body subjected to temperature distribution $T(x, y, z; t)$ is obtained by superimposing on the load stress the "hydrostatic stress" $-kET/(1-2\nu)$, the stress produced by the equivalent body forces [Eq. (8–4.9)], and the stress produced by the equivalent surface stresses [Eq. (8–4.10)]. When the thermal-stress problem is formulated in terms of stress components, the solution must satisfy the compatibility equations [Eqs. (4–9.2)] as well as the equations of equilibrium [Eqs. (c)] and the boundary conditions [Eqs. (8–4.7)].

Problem. Derive the most general temperature distribution $T(x, y, z)$ for which an unrestrained isotropic homogeneous elastic body may undergo stress-free thermal expansion, that is, for which the stresses ($\sigma_x, \sigma_y, \sigma_z, \tau_{xy}, \tau_{xz}, \tau_{yz}$) are zero.

8-5 Spherically Symmetrical Stress Distribution (The Sphere)

Let a sphere be subjected to a temperature T which is a function only of the radial coordinate R. Then the displacement of each point in the sphere is radial. Hence, the displacement vector is $U = U(R)$; that is, the deformation is symmetrical with respect to the center of the sphere. Consequently the equations of equilibrium reduce to the single equation [see Eq. (A-2.4)]

$$\frac{d\sigma_R}{dR} + \frac{2}{R}(\sigma_R - \sigma_T) = 0 \qquad (8\text{–}5.1)$$

where the radial component of the stress vector is σ_R and the tangential components of the stress vector are equal to σ_T. The components (σ_R, σ_T) are functions of R only. The stress-strain-temperature relations [see Eqs. (8–4.5)] reduce to

$$\sigma_R = \lambda e + 2G\epsilon_R - \frac{EkT}{1-2\nu}$$

$$\sigma_T = \lambda e + 2G\epsilon_T - \frac{EkT}{1-2\nu} \qquad (8\text{–}5.2)$$

where

$$e = \epsilon_R + 2\epsilon_T \qquad (8\text{–}5.3)$$

The strain-displacement relations are

$$\epsilon_R = \frac{dU}{dR}, \qquad \epsilon_T = \frac{U}{R} \tag{8-5.4}$$

Substitution of Eqs. (8–5.4) into Eqs. (8–5.3) and (8–5.2) yields

$$\sigma_R = (\lambda + 2G)\frac{dU}{dR} + 2\lambda\frac{U}{R} - \frac{EkT}{1 - 2\nu}$$

$$\sigma_T = 2(\lambda + G)\frac{U}{R} + \lambda\frac{dU}{dR} - \frac{EkT}{1 - 2\nu} \tag{8-5.5}$$

Substituting Eqs. (8–5.5) into Eqs. (8–5.1), we obtain

$$\frac{d^2U}{dR^2} + \frac{2}{R}\frac{dU}{dR} - \frac{2U}{R^2} = \frac{1 + \nu}{1 - \nu}\frac{d(kT)}{dR} \tag{8-5.6}$$

Rewriting Eq. (8–5.6), we obtain

$$\frac{d}{dR}\left[\frac{1}{R^2}\frac{d}{dR}(R^2U)\right] = \frac{1 + \nu}{1 - \nu}\frac{d(kT)}{dR} \tag{8-5.7}$$

Integration of Eq. (8–5.7) yields

$$U = \frac{1 + \nu}{1 - \nu}\frac{1}{R^2}\int_a^R \rho^2 kT\, d\rho + AR + \frac{B}{R^2} \tag{8-5.8}$$

In Eq. (8–5.8) the coefficient of thermal expansion k may vary with temperature; that is, it may vary with ρ. The constants A and B are determined by boundary conditions.

Substitution of Eq. (8–5.8) into Eq. (8–5.5) yields the following expressions for the stress components:

$$\sigma_R = -\frac{2E}{1 - \nu}\frac{1}{R^3}\int_a^R \rho^2 kT\, d\rho + \frac{EA}{1 - 2\nu} - \frac{2EB}{1 + \nu}\frac{1}{R^3}$$

$$\sigma_T = \frac{E}{1 - \nu}\frac{1}{R^3}\int_a^R \rho^2 kT\, d\rho + \frac{EA}{1 - 2\nu} + \frac{EB}{1 + \nu}\frac{1}{R^3} - \frac{kTE}{1 - \nu} \tag{8-5.9}$$

Equations (8–5.9) are the general formulas for the stress components in a sphere subjected to temperature symmetrically distributed with respect to the center of the sphere. For the special cases of the solid sphere and the thick-walled spherical shell subjected to a temperature distribution $T = T(R; t)$, the constants of integration are determined from the following boundary conditions:

Solid sphere: $\qquad \sigma_R = 0$ on outer surface; $U = 0$ at $R = 0$

Hollow sphere: $\qquad \sigma_R = 0$ on outer and inner surfaces $\tag{8-5.10}$

PROBLEM SET 8-5

1 Evaluate the constants A, B of Eq. (8–5.9) for the solid sphere using the conditions of Eq. (8–5.10); repeat for the hollow sphere.

2 Let $kT = CR^2$, where C is a constant. For this temperature distribution, express (in terms of E, v, C, R) the stress components σ_R, σ_T for a hollow sphere with inner radius r_i and outer radius r_o. Repeat for a solid sphere.

8-6 Plane Theory of Thermoelasticity

The plane theory of thermoelasticity is based upon assumptions equivalent to those of plane-elasticity theory. Consequently, plane thermoelasticity consists of two cases: plane strain and plane stress (or, more generally, "generalized plane stress").

Plane strain. We recall that a body is in a state of plane strain parallel to the (x, y) plane if the z-displacement component w is const. and if (u, v), the (x, y) components of displacement, are functions of (x, y) only. Consequently, the strain-displacement relations in (x, y) coordinates reduce to

$$\epsilon_x = \frac{\partial u}{\partial x}, \qquad \epsilon_y = \frac{\partial v}{\partial y}, \qquad \epsilon_z = 0$$

$$\gamma_{xy} = \frac{\partial u}{\partial y} + \frac{\partial v}{\partial x}, \qquad \gamma_{xz} = \gamma_{yz} = 0$$

(8-6.1)

Substituting Eqs. (8–6.1) into the equations of thermoelasticity (see Art. 8–4), we obtain relations for the plane-strain theory of thermoelasticity.

In cylindrical coordinates (r, θ, z) the plane-strain condition is expressed by the relations

$$u = u(r, \theta), \qquad v = v(r, \theta), \qquad w = \text{const.}$$

Hence, the strain-displacement relations in cylindrical coordinates are [see Eqs. (A-3.9)]

$$\epsilon_r = \frac{\partial u}{\partial r}, \qquad \epsilon = \frac{u}{r} + \frac{1}{r}\frac{\partial v}{\partial \theta}, \qquad \epsilon_z = 0$$

$$\gamma_{r\theta} = \frac{1}{r}\frac{\partial u}{\partial \theta} + \frac{\partial v}{\partial r} - \frac{v}{r}, \qquad \gamma_{rz} = \gamma_{\theta z} = 0$$

(8-6.2)

The stress-strain-temperature relations in cylindrical coordinates are [see Eqs. (8–4.1) and Appendix A]

$$\epsilon_r = E^{-1}[\sigma_r - v(\sigma_\theta + \sigma_z)] + kT, \qquad \gamma_{r\theta} = G^{-1}\tau_{r\theta}$$

$$\epsilon_\theta = E^{-1}[\sigma_\theta - v(\sigma_r + \sigma_z)] + kT, \qquad \gamma_{rz} = \gamma_{\theta z} = 0 \qquad (8-6.3)$$

$$\epsilon_z = E^{-1}[\sigma_z - v(\sigma_r + \sigma_\theta)] + kT,$$

For plane strain $\epsilon_z = 0$; hence, the last of Eqs. (8–6.3) yields

$$\sigma_z = v(\sigma_r + \sigma_\theta) - EkT \qquad (8-6.4)$$

Substitution of Eq. (8–6.4) into Eq. (8–6.3) yields the stress-strain-temperature relations for plane strain:

$$\epsilon_r = E^{-1}[(1 - v^2)\sigma_r - v(1 + v)\sigma_\theta] + (1 + v)kT$$

$$\epsilon_\theta = E^{-1}[(1 - v^2)\sigma_\theta - v(1 + v)\sigma_r] + (1 + v)kT \qquad (8\text{–}6.5)$$

$$\gamma_{r\theta} = G^{-1}\tau_{r\theta}$$

For axial-symmetry problems $v = 0$ and $\partial/\partial\theta = 0$, and Eqs. (8–6.2) are modified accordingly. Consequently, u and T are functions of r only.

For axially symmetric plane strain in the absence of body forces the equilibrium equations reduce to the single equation [see Eqs. (A-2.8) and (A-3.9) and let $(\partial/\partial\theta) = v = 0$]

$$\frac{d\sigma_r}{dr} + \frac{\sigma_r - \sigma_\theta}{r} = 0 \qquad (8\text{–}6.6)$$

Substituting Eqs. (8–6.2) into Eqs. (8–6.5), solving Eqs. (8–6.5) for $(\sigma_r, \sigma_\theta)$, and substituting the resulting equations into the equilibrium equation [Eq. (8–6.6)], we obtain

$$\frac{d^2u}{dr^2} + \frac{1}{r}\frac{du}{dr} - \frac{u}{r^2} = \frac{1 + v}{1 - v}\frac{d(kT)}{dr}$$

Rewriting this equation, we obtain

$$\frac{d}{dr}\left[\frac{1}{r}\frac{d(ru)}{dr}\right] = \frac{1 + v}{1 - v}\frac{d(kT)}{dr} \qquad (8\text{–}6.7)$$

Integration of Eq. (8–6.7) yields

$$u = \frac{1 + v}{1 - v}\frac{1}{r}\int_a^r \rho kT\, d\rho + Ar + \frac{B}{r} \qquad (8\text{–}6.8)$$

Equations (8–6.1) to (8–6.8) and corresponding modifications of the equations of Art. 8–4 summarize the plane-strain theory of thermoelasticity.

Plane stress. A body is in a state of plane stress in the (x, y) plane if $\sigma_z = \tau_{xz} = \tau_{yz} = 0$. Substitution of these conditions into the general thermo-elasticity theory of Art. 8–4 yields the corresponding equations of plane-stress thermoelasticity.

In cylindrical coordinates, the stress-strain-temperature relations for plane stress are [see Eqs. (8–6.3)]

$$\epsilon_r = E^{-1}(\sigma_r - v\sigma_\theta) + kT$$

$$\epsilon_\theta = E^{-1}(\sigma_\theta - v\sigma_r) + kT \qquad (8\text{–}6.9)$$

$$\epsilon_z = -\frac{v}{E}(\sigma_r + \sigma_\theta) + kT$$

Inverting the first two of Eq. (8–6.9), we obtain

$$\sigma_r = \frac{E}{1 - v^2}(\epsilon_r + v\epsilon_\theta) - \frac{EkT}{1 - v}$$

$$\sigma_\theta = \frac{E}{1 - v^2}(\epsilon_\theta + v\epsilon_r) - \frac{EkT}{1 - v} \qquad (8\text{–}6.10)$$

Substitution of Eqs. (8–6.10) into the last of Eqs. (8–6.9) yields

$$\epsilon_z = \frac{-\nu}{1-\nu}(\epsilon_r + \epsilon_\theta) + \frac{1+\nu}{1-\nu}kT \tag{8–6.11}$$

Equation (8–6.6) is the equilibrium condition for axially symmetric plane-stress thermoelasticity since $\sigma_z = \tau_{rz} = \tau_{\theta z} = 0$. Also, since $v = (\partial/\partial\theta) = 0$ for axial symmetry, the strain-displacement relations [Eqs. (8–6.2)] reduce to

$$\epsilon_r = \frac{du}{dr}, \qquad \epsilon_\theta = \frac{u}{r} \tag{8–6.12}$$

where u is the displacement in the r direction.

Substitution of Eqs. (8–6.12) and (8–6.10) into Eqs. (8–6.6) yields

$$\frac{d^2u}{dr^2} + \frac{1}{r}\frac{du}{dr} - \frac{u}{r^2} = (1+\nu)\frac{d(kT)}{dr} \tag{8–6.13}$$

Integration of Eq. (8–6.13) yields

$$u = (1+\nu)\frac{1}{r}\int_a^r kT\rho\,d\rho + Ar + \frac{B}{r} \tag{8–6.14}$$

Equations (8–6.9) to (8–6.14) and corresponding modifications of the equations of Art. 8–4 summarize the theory of plane-stress thermoelasticity. Plane-stress thermoelasticity problems of radial heating of a thin circular disk and axial heating of beams and strips are important in practice.

PROBLEM SET 8-6

1 Modify the equations of Art. 8–4 for plane strain. Repeat for plane stress.

2 Consider the problem of small-displacement plane thermoelasticity for which

$$\epsilon_z = \gamma_{xz} = \gamma_{yz} = 0$$

(a) Derive an expression for σ_z in terms of stress components σ_x and σ_y, material properties k (thermal coefficient of linear expansion) and E (modulus of elasticity), and temperature change T measured from an arbitrary zero.

(b) Assume the additional conditions that stress components $\sigma_x = \sigma_y = \tau_{xy} = 0$. Hence, derive expressions for the strain components ϵ_x, ϵ_y, and γ_{xy}.

(c) Show that under the combined conditions of parts (a) and (b) the compatibility conditions reduce to $\nabla^2 T = 0$ for constant E and k

(d) Using the results of part (b), show that the rotation of a volume element in the xy plane is

$$\omega_z = \frac{\partial v}{\partial x} = -\frac{\partial u}{\partial y}$$

Hence show that

$$\frac{\partial\epsilon'}{\partial x} = \frac{\partial\omega_z}{\partial y}, \qquad \frac{\partial\epsilon'}{\partial y} = -\frac{\partial\omega_z}{\partial x}$$

where $\epsilon' = (1+\nu)kT$. That is, show that ϵ' and ω_z satisfy the Cauchy-Riemann

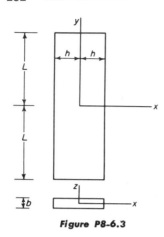

Figure P8-6.3

equations. (Consequently, the theory associated with the Cauchy-Riemann equations may be applied to ϵ' and ω_z.)

3 Consider a plane element of rectangular plan form (Fig. P8–6.3) ($b \ll L$, $b \ll h$, and $h \ll L$). A known temperature variation (measured from an arbitrary zero) $T = T(x)$ through the depth ($2h$) of the element exists. Since the flat element is thin (b small), it is reasonable to assume that a state of *plane stress* ($\sigma_z = \tau_{zx} = \tau_{yz} = 0$) exists. Assume also that $\sigma_x = \tau_{xy} = 0$ and that $\sigma_y = \sigma_y(x)$.

(a) Show that in the absence of body forces and acceleration, the equations of motion are satisfied.

(b) Determine the equations of compatibility for this case. Hence, solve these equations to obtain the most general expression for $\sigma_y(x)$.

(c) To evaluate arbitrary constants in σ_y, employ the boundary conditions that the resultant force and the resultant moment at $y = \pm L$ vanishes; that is, for $y = \pm L$

$$\Sigma F_y = \int_{-h}^{h} \sigma_y \, dx = 0, \qquad \Sigma M_z = \int_{-h}^{h} x\sigma_y \, dx = 0$$

Hence, express σ_y as a known function of x.

4 For an axisymmetrical plane problem of elasticity including thermal effects, show that the compatibility equation in polar coordinates is

$$\frac{1}{r} \frac{d}{dr} \left(r \frac{dF}{dr} \right) = -EkT + C$$

where C is an unknown constant of integration (to be determined by boundary conditions).

5 A thin solid circular disk of radius a is subjected to a temperature distribution

$$T = A \left(1 - \frac{r}{a} \right)$$

where A is a known constant. The disk is unrestrained. Determine the change in diameter of the disk due to the applied temperature T.

8-7 Concept of Displacement Potential. Plane Theory of Thermoelasticity

For the plane problem of elasticity relative to (x, y) axes (Art. 5–3), the compatibility equations reduce to

$$\frac{\partial^2 \epsilon_x}{\partial y^2} + \frac{\partial^2 \epsilon_y}{\partial x^2} = \frac{\partial^2 \gamma_{xy}}{\partial x \, \partial y} \qquad (8\text{–}7.1)$$

In terms of the Airy stress function F (Art. 5–4), the stress components may be represented by the relations

$$\sigma_x = \frac{\partial^2 F}{\partial y^2}, \qquad \sigma_y = \frac{\partial^2 F}{\partial x^2}, \qquad \tau_{xy} = -\frac{\partial^2 F}{\partial x \partial y} \tag{8-7.2}$$

Hence, for the plane-strain theory of thermoelasticity ($\epsilon_z = \gamma_{xz} = \gamma_{yz} = 0$), expressing $\epsilon_x, \epsilon_y, \gamma_{xy}$ in terms of $\sigma_x, \sigma_y, \tau_{xy}$ by means of Eqs. (8–4.1) and (8–6.1), employing Eq. (8–7.2), and eliminating $\epsilon_x, \epsilon_y, \gamma_{xy}$ from Eq. (8–7.1), we find in the absence of body force

$$\nabla^2 \nabla^2 F = -\frac{1}{1-\nu} E \nabla^2 (kT)$$

where

$$\nabla^2 = \frac{\partial^2}{\partial x^2} + \frac{\partial^2}{\partial y^2}$$

This equation represents the compatibility relation for plane-strain thermoelasticity in terms of the Airy stress function F and temperature T. Similarly for plane-stress thermoelasticity ($\sigma_z = \tau_{xz} = \tau_{yz} = 0$),

$$\nabla^2 \nabla^2 F = -E \nabla^2 (kT)$$

Accordingly, in the absence of body forces the plane theory of thermoelasticity may be reduced to the problem of determining a stress function F such that

$$\nabla^2 \nabla^2 F = CE \nabla^2 (kT) \tag{8-7.3}$$

where $C = -1$ for the plane-stress state and $C = -1/(1-\nu)$ for the plane-strain state. In addition to Eq. (8–7.3), the stress function F must satisfy appropriate boundary conditions (see Art. 5–4). In general, the solution of Eq. (8–7.3) subject to specific boundary conditions is a difficult mathematical problem, although in certain special cases simple solutions may be obtained. A general solution of Eq. (8–7.3) may be obtained by adding a particular solution, for which the right-hand side of Eq. (8–7.3) is satisfied identically, to the solution (complementary solution) of $\nabla^2 \nabla^2 F = 0$. A method of obtaining a particular integral of Eq. (8–7.3) has been outlined by Goodier.[10] The method is frequently referred to as the method of displacement potential, since displacement representations and certain concepts from potential theory are employed.

Following Goodier, we represent the plane theory of thermoelasticity in terms of displacement components. Initially, we consider the case of plane stress, the results for plane strain being obtained by a simple transformation of material constants.

Let (x, y) denote rectangular cartesian coordinates. Let (u, v) denote

[10]J. N. Goodier, "On the Integration of the Thermo-Elastic Equations," *Phil. Mag.*, Ser. 7, Vol. 23, No. 157 (May, 1937), pp. 1017–1032.

displacement components in the (x, y) directions, respectively. In terms of (u, v), the stress components for plane stress are (see Arts. 8–4 and 8–6)

$$\sigma_x = \frac{E}{1 - \nu^2}\left[\frac{\partial u}{\partial x} + \nu\frac{\partial v}{\partial y} - (1 + \nu)kT\right]$$

$$\sigma_y = \frac{E}{1 - \nu^2}\left[\frac{\partial v}{\partial y} + \nu\frac{\partial u}{\partial x} - (1 + \nu)kT\right] \tag{8–7.4}$$

$$\tau_{xz} = \frac{E}{2(1 + \nu)}\left(\frac{\partial u}{\partial y} + \frac{\partial v}{\partial x}\right) = G\left(\frac{\partial u}{\partial y} + \frac{\partial v}{\partial x}\right)$$

Substitution of Eqs. (8–7.4) into the equilibrium equations for plane stress yields, in the absence of body force (see Arts. 5–2 and 8–4),

$$\frac{\partial e}{\partial x} + \frac{1 - \nu}{1 + \nu}\nabla^2 u = 2k\frac{\partial T}{\partial x}$$

$$\frac{\partial e}{\partial y} + \frac{1 - \nu}{1 + \nu}\nabla^2 v = 2k\frac{\partial T}{\partial y} \tag{8–7.5}$$

$$e = \frac{\partial u}{\partial x} + \frac{\partial v}{\partial y}$$

Let

$$u = \frac{\partial \psi}{\partial x}, \qquad v = \frac{\partial \psi}{\partial y} \tag{8–7.6}$$

where $\psi = \psi(x, y)$ is called the displacement potential function. Substitution of Eqs. (8–7.6) into Eqs. (8–7.5) yields

$$\frac{\partial}{\partial x}\left[\frac{1}{1 + \nu}\nabla^2\psi - kT\right] = 0$$

$$\frac{\partial}{\partial y}\left[\frac{1}{1 + \nu}\nabla^2\psi - kT\right] = 0$$

These equations are satisfied identically if

$$\nabla^2\psi = (1 + \nu)kT \tag{8–7.7}$$

Accordingly, the solution of Eq. (8–7.7) represents a particular solution of Eqs. (8–7.5). To obtain a general solution of Eqs. (8–7.5), we must add to the solution of Eq. (8–7.7) the complementary solution of Eqs. (8–7.5); that is, we must add the solution of Eqs. (8–7.5) for the case $T = 0$. This general solution must then be made to satisfy the boundary conditions of the problem.

By Eqs. (8–7.4), (8–7.6), and (8–7.7), the stress components corresponding to the particular solution ψ are

$$\sigma_x' = -2G\frac{\partial^2\psi}{\partial y^2}$$

$$\sigma_y' = -2G\frac{\partial^2\psi}{\partial x^2} \tag{8–7.8}$$

$$\tau_{xy}' = 2G\frac{\partial^2\psi}{\partial x\partial y}$$

In the absence of temperature T, the complementary solution of the plane problem is expressed in terms of the Airy stress function F [Eqs. (8–7.2)]. Accordingly, the stress components for a general solution of the plane-stress thermoelastic problem are, by Eqs. (8–7.2) and (8–7.8),

$$\sigma_x = \frac{\partial^2}{\partial y^2} (F - 2G\psi)$$

$$\sigma_y = \frac{\partial^2}{\partial x^2} (F - 2G\psi) \tag{8–7.9}$$

$$\tau_{xy} = -\frac{\partial^2}{\partial x \partial y} (F - 2G\psi)$$

Similarly, for the case of plane strain, we have
Stress-displacement relations:

$$\sigma_x = \lambda e + 2G \frac{\partial u}{\partial x} - \frac{EkT}{1 - 2v}$$

$$\sigma_y = \lambda e + 2G \frac{\partial v}{\partial y} - \frac{EkT}{1 - 2v}$$

$$\sigma_z = v(\sigma_x + \sigma_y) - EkT = \lambda e - \frac{EkT}{1 - 2v} \tag{8–7.10}$$

$$\tau_{xy} = G \left(\frac{\partial u}{\partial y} + \frac{\partial v}{\partial x} \right)$$

$$\lambda = \frac{vE}{(1 + v)(1 - 2v)}, \qquad G = \frac{E}{2(1 + v)}, \qquad e = \frac{\partial u}{\partial x} + \frac{\partial v}{\partial y}$$

Equilibrium equations in terms of displacement:

$$\frac{\partial e}{\partial x} + (1 - 2v) \nabla^2 u = 2(1 + v) \frac{\partial (kT)}{\partial x}$$

$$\frac{\partial e}{\partial y} + (1 - 2v) \nabla^2 v = 2(1 + v) \frac{\partial (kT)}{\partial y} \tag{8–7.11}$$

Displacement potential-temperature relation:

$$\nabla^2 \psi = \frac{1 + v}{1 - v} kT \tag{8–7.12}$$

With the displacement potential function ψ defined[11] by Eq. (8–7.12), the

---

[11]Equation (8–7.7) [or Eq. (8–7.12)] is of the same form as Poisson's equation of potential theory [see O. D. Kellog, *Foundations of Potential Theory* (New York: Dover Publications, Inc., 1953)]. For the plane, its solution is expressible in terms of the logarithmic integral; that is,

$$\psi = \frac{c}{2\pi} \int\!\!\int kT(\xi, \eta) \log r \, d\xi \, d\eta$$

where $r^2 = (x - \xi)^2 + (y - \eta)^2$, $c = (1 + v)$ for plane stress, $c = (1 + v)/(1 - v)$ for plane strain, and the integration extends over the (ξ, η) plane. Alternatively, for many cases, Eqs. (8–7.7) or (8–7.12) may be integrated by other well-known methods—for example, by the method of separation of variables.

stress components $(\sigma_x, \sigma_y, \tau_{xy})$ are again given by Eqs. (8–7.9). Then σ_z is determined by Eq. (8–7.10).

In the preceding method of integration of the stress equations we have used a stress function or a displacement potential. In a certain class of problems the thermal-stress equations may be integrated more directly by other methods.[12]

PROBLEM SET 8-7

1 Let $T = T(r, \theta)$ for a plane thermoelasticity problem in polar coordinates (r, θ). Determine an explicit expression for $T(r, \theta)$ for the steady-state case in absence of heat source, expressing $T(r, \theta)$ in the form $T = T_1(r) + T_2(r, \theta)$ where $T_1(r)$ is the part of $T(r, \theta)$ dependent upon r alone. That is, show that $T_1(r) = A_0 + B_0 \log r$

$$T_2(r, \theta) = \sum_{n=1}^{\infty} [(A_n r^n + B_n r^{-n}) \cos n\theta + (C_n r^n + D_n r^{-n}) \sin n\theta]$$

where A_n, B_n, C_n, D_n are constants.

2 In Prob. 1, set all constants except B_1 and D_1 equal to zero. For the resulting temperature field determine the stress produced in a hollow circular cylinder defined by cylindrical coordinates (r, θ, z), the z axis coinciding with the longitudinal axis of the cylinder. Assume that axial displacement of the cylinder is prevented.

3 A nuclear fuel element in the form of a solid right-circular cylinder is free to expand laterally, but not axially. It is subjected to a radiation heat source in the form of the Gaussian distribution

$$Q = Ae^{-\alpha^2 r^2}$$

where α^2 is a constant and r is the radial coordinate. Generally, $\alpha^2 \ll 1$. Compute the temperature distribution T. What reasonable approximation may be used for T? Determine the stress distribution in the cylinder. What practical restriction must be imposed on A?

8-8 Thermoelastic Equations for Axially Symmetrical Stress Distribution

In cylindrical coordinates, the axially symmetric state of stress is characterized by the conditions $\tau_{r\theta} = \tau_{z\theta} = 0$, $\partial/\partial\theta = 0$. Then the general equations of equilibrium reduce to the form (see Appendix A)

---

[12] B. Sen, "Direct Determination of Stresses from the Stress Equations in Some Two-Dimensional Problems of Elasticity. Part II. Thermal Stresses," *Phil. Mag.*, Ser. 7, Vol. 27, No. 183 (1939), pp. 437–44. See also B. Sharma, "Thermal Stresses in Infinite Elastic Disks," *J. Appl. Mech.*, Vol. 23, No. 4 (1956), pp. 527–531; E. L. McDowell and E. Sternberg, "Axisymmetric Thermal Stresses in a Spherical Shell of Arbitrary Thickness," *J. Appl. Mech.*, Vol. 24, No. 3 (1957), pp. 376–380.

$$\frac{\partial \sigma_r}{\partial r} + \frac{\partial \tau_{rz}}{\partial z} + \frac{\sigma_r - \sigma_\theta}{r} = 0$$

$$\frac{\partial \tau_{rz}}{\partial r} + \frac{\partial \sigma_z}{\partial z} + \frac{\tau_{rz}}{r} = 0$$

(8–8.1)

Body forces are not included in Eq. (8–8.1). The strain-displacement relations are (since $v = 0$ and $\partial/\partial\theta = 0$; see Appendix A):

$$\epsilon_r = \frac{\partial u}{\partial r}, \qquad \epsilon_\theta = \frac{u}{r}, \qquad \epsilon_z = \frac{\partial w}{\partial z}$$

$$\gamma_{rz} = \frac{\partial u}{\partial z} + \frac{\partial w}{\partial r}$$

(8–8.2)

The stress-strain-temperature relations are

$$\epsilon_r = E^{-1}[\sigma_r - v(\sigma_\theta + \sigma_z)] + kT$$

$$\epsilon_\theta = E^{-1}[\sigma_\theta - v(\sigma_r + \sigma_z)] + kT$$

$$\epsilon_z = E^{-1}[\sigma_z - v(\sigma_\theta + \sigma_r)] + kT$$

$$\gamma_{rz} = G^{-1}\tau_{rz}$$

(8–8.3)

where k is the coefficient of thermal expansion and $T = T(r, z)$ is the temperature. Solving Eq. (8–8.3) for the stresses, we obtain

$$\sigma_r = \lambda e + 2G\epsilon_r - \frac{EkT}{1 - 2v}$$

$$\sigma_\theta = \lambda e + 2G\epsilon_\theta - \frac{EkT}{1 - 2v}$$

$$\sigma_z = \lambda e + 2G\epsilon_z - \frac{EkT}{1 - 2v}$$

$$\tau_{rz} = G\gamma_{rz}$$

(8–8.4)

where

$$\lambda = \frac{vE}{(1 + v)(1 - 2v)} \qquad \text{and} \qquad G = \frac{E}{2(1 + v)}$$

(8–8.5)

Substitution of Eq. (8–8.2) into Eq. (8–8.4) and substitution of the results into Eqs. (8–8.1) yields

$$\nabla^2 u - \frac{u}{r^2} + \frac{1}{1 - 2v}\frac{\partial e}{\partial r} - \frac{2(1 + v)}{1 - 2v}\frac{\partial(kT)}{\partial r} = 0$$

$$\nabla^2 w + \frac{1}{1 - 2v}\frac{\partial e}{\partial z} - \frac{2(1 + v)}{1 - 2v}\frac{\partial(kT)}{\partial z} = 0$$

(8–8.6)

where

$$\nabla^2 = \frac{\partial^2}{\partial r^2} + \frac{1}{r}\frac{\partial}{\partial r} + \frac{\partial^2}{\partial z^2}$$

(8–8.7)

A particular solution of Eq. (8–8.6) may be obtained through the concept of the displacement potential. Accordingly, we let

$$u = \frac{\partial \psi}{\partial r}, \qquad w = \frac{\partial \psi}{\partial z}, \qquad e = \nabla^2 \psi \tag{8–8.8}$$

where $\psi = \psi(r, z)$ is the displacement-potential function.

Noting that

$$\nabla^2 \left(\frac{\partial \psi}{\partial r} \right) = \frac{\partial}{\partial r} (\nabla^2 \psi) + \frac{1}{r^2} \frac{\partial \psi}{\partial r}$$

$$\nabla^2 \left(\frac{\partial \psi}{\partial z} \right) = \frac{\partial}{\partial z} (\nabla^2 \psi) \tag{8–8.9}$$

by Eqs. (8–8.6) and (8–8.8), we obtain

$$\frac{\partial}{\partial r} [(1 - \nu) \nabla^2 \psi - (1 + \nu) kT] = 0$$

$$\frac{\partial}{\partial z} [(1 - \nu) \nabla^2 \psi - (1 + \nu) kT] = 0 \tag{8–8.10}$$

Accordingly, a particular integral of Eq. (8–8.10) is

$$\nabla^2 \psi = \frac{1 + \nu}{1 - \nu} kT \tag{8–8.11}$$

For a prescribed temperature T, Eq. (8–8.11) defines the displacement-potential function ψ.

By Eqs. (8–8.3), (8–8.4), and (8–8.8), we find the stress components associated with the particular solution ψ:

$$\sigma_r' = 2G \left(\frac{\partial^2 \psi}{\partial r^2} - \nabla^2 \psi \right), \qquad \sigma_\theta' = 2G \left(\frac{1}{r} \frac{\partial \psi}{\partial r} - \nabla^2 \psi \right)$$

$$\sigma_z' = 2G \left(\frac{\partial^2 \psi}{\partial z^2} - \nabla^2 \psi \right), \qquad \tau_{rz}' = 2G \left(\frac{\partial^2 \psi}{\partial r \partial z} \right) \tag{8–8.12}$$

The complementary solution of Eqs. (8–8.1) or (8–8.6) expressed in terms of a stress function is[13]

$$\sigma_r'' = \frac{\partial}{\partial z} \left[\nu \nabla^2 F - \frac{\partial^2 F}{\partial r^2} \right]$$

$$\sigma_\theta'' = \frac{\partial}{\partial z} \left[\nu \nabla^2 F - \frac{1}{r} \frac{\partial F}{\partial r} \right]$$

$$\sigma_z'' = \frac{\partial}{\partial z} \left[(2 - \nu) \nabla^2 F - \frac{\partial^2 F}{\partial z^2} \right] \tag{8–8.13}$$

$$\tau_{rz}'' = \frac{\partial}{\partial r} \left[(1 - \nu) \nabla^2 F - \frac{\partial^2 F}{\partial z^2} \right]$$

[13]See S. Timoshenko and J. N. Goodier, *Theory of Elasticity*, 2nd ed. (New York: McGraw-Hill Book Company, 1951), Chap. 13.

provided that the stress function F satisfies the relation $\nabla^2 \nabla^2 F = 0$, where ∇^2 is defined by Eq. (8–8.7). A general solution of the axially symmetric thermal-stress problem is given by the sum of Eqs. (8–8.12) and (8–8.13).

PROBLEM SET 8-8

1 Consider a hollow right-circular cylinder subjected to the temperature distribution $kT = (Ar^2 + B)e^{-\beta z}$, where A, B, and β are constants, and r denotes the radial coordinate of the cylinder. Consider a particular solution of the form $\psi = f(r)e^{-\beta z}$, where $f(r)$ is a function of r. Derive the explicit form of ψ. Derive the stress components associated with the particular solution.

2 A right-circular hollow cylinder of inner radius a and outer radius b is free to expand laterally, but it is constrained at its ends to prevent axial displacements. It is subjected to a steady-state heat source Q specified by the relation $Q = Az$ where A is a constant and z is the axial coordinate measured from one end of the cylinder. Discuss the temperature distribution in the cylinder, specifying required quantities where needed. Discuss the stress distribution in the cylinder. Perform appropriate analyses to aid your discussion.

EQUATIONS OF EQUILIBRIUM
AND STRAIN-DISPLACEMENT
RELATIONS IN ORTHOGONAL
CURVILINEAR COORDINATES

A-1 Geometrical Preliminaries

In Arts. 1–14, 1–15, and 1–16 certain properties of orthogonal curvilinear coordinate systems in three-dimensional space are discussed. In this article we develop some additional properties prerequisite to the derivation of stress-equilibrium relations and strain-displacement relations in orthogonal curvilinear coordinate systems. For convenience, we employ notation that differs somewhat from that used in Chapter 1.

We let three independent scalar functions (X, Y, Z) be defined in terms of three independent variables (x, y, z) as follows:

$$X = X(x, y, z), \qquad Y = Y(x, y, z), \qquad Z = Z(x, y, z) \qquad \text{(A-1.1)}$$

If (X, Y, Z) denote rectangular cartesian coordinates, then for any set of (X, Y, Z) the variables (x, y, z) are space coordinates (see Art. 1–14). By independent functions, we mean that Eq. (A-1.1) may be solved uniquely (in a region of regularity) for (x, y, z); that is,

$$x = x(X, Y, Z), \qquad y = y(X, Y, Z), \qquad z = z(X, Y, Z) \qquad \text{(A-1.2)}$$

If (x, y, z) are assigned constant values (x_0, y_0, z_0), Eq. (A-1.2) yields

$$x(X, Y, Z) = x_0, \qquad y(X, Y, Z) = y_0, \qquad z(X, Y, Z) = z_0 \qquad \text{(A-1.3)}$$

The equation $x = x_0$ defines a surface, called a *coordinate surface*. Hence, corresponding to various values of x_0 there exists a family of coordinate surfaces, one surface for each value of x_0. Similarly, the equations $y = y_0$, $z = z_0$ yield two other families of coordinate surfaces. As noted in Art. 1–14, the intersection of two coordinate surfaces defines a *coordinate line*. For example, the intersection of the surface $y = y_0$ with the surface $z = z_0$ defines a coordinate line along which only x varies; it is called the x-coordinate line. Similarly, intersection of the surfaces $x = x_0$ and $z = z_0$ defines a y-coordinate line; intersection of the surfaces $x = x_0$ and $y = y_0$ defines a z-coordinate line. In general, the coordinate lines are curved. Hence, the variables (x, y, z) are called *curvilinear* coordinates.

Three coordinate surfaces in general intersect at a point in space. Hence, a point in space is associated with a triplet (x_i, y_i, z_i). If the curvilinear coordinate lines through any point (x, y, z) are mutually perpendicular, they are said to be *orthogonal*. Then, the curvilinear coordinates (x, y, z) are called *orthogonal curvilinear coordinates*. For example, cylindrical coordinates (r, θ, z) and spherical coordinates (r, θ, ϕ) are systems of orthogonal curvilinear coordinates.

Relative to rectangular cartesian axes (X, Y, Z), the position vector $\mathbf{r}$ of a point (x, y, z) may be written $\mathbf{r} = \mathbf{i}X + \mathbf{j}Y + \mathbf{k}Z$, where $\mathbf{i}, \mathbf{j}, \mathbf{k}$ denote unit vectors in the X, Y, Z directions, respectively. Hence, a system of curvilinear coordinates (x, y, z) may be defined by the single vector equation $\mathbf{r} = \mathbf{r}(x, y, z)$. Furthermore, $\mathbf{r}_x, \mathbf{r}_y, \mathbf{r}_z$ are tangent vectors to the (x, y, z) coordinate lines, respectively, where (x, y, z) subscripts on $\mathbf{r}$ denote partial derivatives relative to (x, y, z). This statement follows from the fact that $d\mathbf{r} = \mathbf{r}_x\, dx + \mathbf{r}_y\, dy + \mathbf{r}_z\, dz$, and from the fact that $d\mathbf{r} = \mathbf{r}_x\, dx$ for $dy = dz = 0$, $d\mathbf{r} = \mathbf{r}_y\, dy$ for $dx = dz = 0$ and $d\mathbf{r} = \mathbf{r}_z\, dz$ for $dx = dy = 0$. Accordingly, for an orthogonal curvilinear coordinate system

$$\mathbf{r}_x \cdot \mathbf{r}_y = \mathbf{r}_x \cdot \mathbf{r}_z = \mathbf{r}_y \cdot \mathbf{r}_z = 0 \tag{A–1.4}$$

Noting that the distance ds between two neighboring points is defined by $ds^2 = d\mathbf{r} \cdot d\mathbf{r}$, we find with Eq. (A-1.4)

$$ds^2 = \alpha^2\, dx^2 + \beta^2\, dy^2 + \gamma^2\, dz^2 \tag{A–1.5}$$

where

$$\alpha^2 = \mathbf{r}_x \cdot \mathbf{r}_x, \qquad \beta^2 = \mathbf{r}_y \cdot \mathbf{r}_y, \qquad \gamma^2 = \mathbf{r}_z \cdot \mathbf{r}_z \tag{A–1.6}$$

Accordingly, since $\mathbf{r}_x, \mathbf{r}_y, \mathbf{r}_z$ are tangent vectors to (x, y, z) coordinate lines, unit tangent vectors with respect to (x, y, z) coordinate lines are defined by

$$\mathbf{e}_1 = \frac{\mathbf{r}_x}{\alpha}, \qquad \mathbf{e}_2 = \frac{\mathbf{r}_y}{\beta}, \qquad \mathbf{e}_3 = \frac{\mathbf{r}_z}{\gamma} \tag{A–1.7}$$

Since $\mathbf{r}_x, \mathbf{r}_y, \mathbf{r}_z$ (and hence $\mathbf{e}_1, \mathbf{e}_2, \mathbf{e}_3$) are orthogonal vectors relative to (x, y, z) coordinate lines, any other vector may be expressed linearly in terms of them. For example, the second derivative of $\mathbf{r}$ with respect to x may be expressed in the form

$$\mathbf{r}_{xx} = a\mathbf{e}_1 + b\mathbf{e}_2 + c\mathbf{e}_3$$

To compute the coefficients (a, b, c), we form the scalar products of $\mathbf{r}_{xx}$ with $\mathbf{e}_1, \mathbf{e}_2, \mathbf{e}_3$. Thus, we find

$$\mathbf{e}_1 \cdot \mathbf{r}_{xx} = a, \qquad \mathbf{e}_2 \cdot \mathbf{r}_{xx} = b, \qquad \mathbf{e}_3 \cdot \mathbf{r}_{xx} = c \qquad \text{(A–1.8)}$$

To evaluate the scalar products $\mathbf{e}_1 \cdot \mathbf{r}_{xx}$, etc., we differentiate Eqs. (A-1.4) and (A-1.6) with respect to (x, y, z) and take into account Eqs. (A-1.7). A few typical results of these differentiations are

$$\mathbf{r}_x \cdot \mathbf{r}_{xx} = \alpha \alpha_x, \qquad \mathbf{r}_x \cdot \mathbf{r}_{xy} = \alpha \alpha_y, \qquad \mathbf{r}_x \cdot \mathbf{r}_{xz} = \alpha \alpha_z$$
$$\mathbf{r}_z \cdot \mathbf{r}_{xx} + \mathbf{r}_x \cdot \mathbf{r}_{xz} = 0, \qquad \mathbf{r}_x \cdot \mathbf{r}_{xy} + \mathbf{r}_y \cdot \mathbf{r}_{xx} = 0 \qquad \text{(A–1.9)}$$

Equations (A-1.7), (A-1.8), and (A-1.9) yield $a = \alpha_x, b = -\alpha\alpha_y/\beta,$ $c = -\alpha\alpha_z/\gamma$. Similarly, the other second derivatives of $\mathbf{r}$ may be expressed as linear combinations of $\mathbf{e}_1, \mathbf{e}_2, \mathbf{e}_3$. The complete set of relations is

$$\mathbf{r}_{xx} = \alpha\left(\frac{\alpha_x}{\alpha}\mathbf{e}_1 - \frac{\alpha_y}{\beta}\mathbf{e}_2 - \frac{\alpha_z}{\gamma}\mathbf{e}_3\right)$$

$$\mathbf{r}_{yy} = \beta\left(-\frac{\beta_x}{\alpha}\mathbf{e}_1 + \frac{\beta_y}{\beta}\mathbf{e}_2 - \frac{\beta_z}{\gamma}\mathbf{e}_3\right)$$

$$\mathbf{r}_{zz} = \gamma\left(-\frac{\gamma_x}{\alpha}\mathbf{e}_1 - \frac{\gamma_y}{\beta}\mathbf{e}_2 + \frac{\gamma_z}{\gamma}\mathbf{e}_3\right) \qquad \text{(A–1.10)}$$

$$\mathbf{r}_{xy} = \alpha_y\mathbf{e}_1 + \beta_x\mathbf{e}_2$$

$$\mathbf{r}_{xz} = \alpha_z\mathbf{e}_1 + \gamma_x\mathbf{e}_3$$

$$\mathbf{r}_{yz} = \beta_z\mathbf{e}_2 + \gamma_y\mathbf{e}_3$$

The preceding equations[1] are employed in the following article.

A-2 Equations of Equilibrium

Let S be a closed surface within a deformed medium, and let V denote the volume enclosed by S (Fig. 2–8.1). Let (l, m, n) be the direction cosines of the outwardly directed unit normal to S with respect to orthogonal curvilinear coordinates (x, y, z) in the deformed region.

As noted in Chapter 2 the stress vector is defined, by the equilibrium conditions, in terms of the stress components $(\sigma_x, \sigma_y, \sigma_z, \tau_{xy}, \tau_{xz}, \tau_{yz})$ defined relative to (x, y, z) axes. Defining the coordinate system by a vector function $\mathbf{r} = \mathbf{r}(x, y, z)$ and noting that unit vectors relative to (x, y, z) coordinate lines are defined by Eq. (A-1.7), we express the stress vector on surface S as

$$(l\sigma_x + m\tau_{xy} + n\tau_{xz})\frac{\mathbf{r}_x}{\alpha} + (l\tau_{xy} + m\sigma_y + n\tau_{yz})\frac{\mathbf{r}_y}{\beta}$$

$$+ (l\tau_{xz} + m\tau_{yz} + n\sigma_z)\frac{\mathbf{r}_z}{\gamma} \qquad \text{(a)}$$

---

[1] This development and the derivations in the following articles follow closely the treatment given by H. L. Langhaar, *Theory of Shells* (class notes).

The body forces acting on the body (see Arts. 2–8 and A2–4) may be written

$$\rho\left(B_x\frac{\mathbf{r}_x}{\alpha} + B_y\frac{\mathbf{r}_y}{\beta} + B_z\frac{\mathbf{r}_z}{\gamma}\right)\alpha\beta\gamma\,dx\,dy\,dz \tag{b}$$

where (B_x, B_y, B_z) denotes the body force per unit mass, ρ denotes mass density, and $\alpha\beta\gamma\,dx\,dy\,dz$ represents the volume in curvilinear coordinates (x, y, z). (In Art. 2–8 we employed the notation $X = \rho B_x$, etc.)

With Eqs. (a) and (b), the equilibrium of forces acting on the material in V requires

$$\iint_S \left[(l\sigma_x + m\tau_{xy} + n\tau_{xz})\frac{\mathbf{r}_x}{\alpha} + (l\tau_{xy} + m\sigma_y + n\tau_{yz})\frac{\mathbf{r}_y}{\beta}\right.$$
$$\left. + (l\tau_{xz} + m\tau_{yz} + n\sigma_z)\frac{\mathbf{r}_z}{\gamma}\right) dS$$
$$+ \iiint_V \rho\left(B_x\frac{\mathbf{r}_x}{\alpha} + B_y\frac{\mathbf{r}_y}{\beta} + B_z\frac{\mathbf{r}_z}{\gamma}\right)\alpha\beta\gamma\,dx\,dy\,dz = 0 \tag{c}$$

Transforming the surface integral in Eq. (c) into a volume integral by means of the divergence theorem [Eqs. (1–16.8) and (1–16.12)], we find

$$\iiint_V \left\{\frac{\partial}{\partial x}\left[\beta\gamma\left(\sigma_x\frac{\mathbf{r}_x}{\alpha} + \tau_{xy}\frac{\mathbf{r}_y}{\beta} + \tau_{xz}\frac{\mathbf{r}_z}{\gamma}\right)\right]\right.$$
$$+ \frac{\partial}{\partial y}\left[\gamma\alpha\left(\tau_{xy}\frac{\mathbf{r}_x}{\alpha} + \sigma_y\frac{\mathbf{r}_y}{\beta} + \tau_{yz}\frac{\mathbf{r}_z}{\gamma}\right)\right]$$
$$+ \frac{\partial}{\partial z}\left[\alpha\beta\left(\tau_{xz}\frac{\mathbf{r}_x}{\alpha} + \tau_{yz}\frac{\mathbf{r}_y}{\beta} + \sigma_z\frac{\mathbf{r}_z}{\gamma}\right)\right]$$
$$\left. + \rho(\beta\gamma B_x\mathbf{r}_x + \gamma\alpha B_y\mathbf{r}_y + \alpha\beta B_z\mathbf{r}_z)\right\} dx\,dy\,dz = 0 \tag{d}$$

Equation (d) must hold for arbitrary volume element; hence the integrand must vanish identically. Accordingly, setting the integrand equal to zero and performing the indicated differentiations of products, we obtain the vector equilibrium equation

$$\left[\frac{\partial}{\partial x}\left(\frac{\beta\gamma}{\alpha}\sigma_x\right) + \frac{\partial}{\partial y}(\gamma\tau_{xy}) + \frac{\partial}{\partial z}(\beta\tau_{xz}) + \rho\beta\gamma B_x\right]\mathbf{r}_x$$
$$+ \left[\frac{\partial}{\partial x}(\gamma\tau_{xy}) + \frac{\partial}{\partial y}\left(\frac{\gamma\alpha}{\beta}\sigma_y\right) + \frac{\partial}{\partial z}(\alpha\tau_{yz}) + \rho\gamma\alpha B_y\right]\mathbf{r}_y$$
$$+ \left[\frac{\partial}{\partial x}(\beta\tau_{xz}) + \frac{\partial}{\partial y}(\alpha\tau_{yz}) + \frac{\partial}{\partial z}\left(\frac{\alpha\beta}{\gamma}\sigma_z\right) + \rho\alpha\beta B_z\right]\mathbf{r}_z$$
$$+ \frac{\beta\gamma}{\alpha}\sigma_x\mathbf{r}_{xx} + \frac{\gamma\alpha}{\beta}\sigma_y\mathbf{r}_{yy} + \frac{\alpha\beta}{\gamma}\sigma_z\mathbf{r}_{zz}$$
$$+ 2\alpha\tau_{yz}\mathbf{r}_{yz} + 2\beta\tau_{xz}\mathbf{r}_{xz} + 2\gamma\tau_{xy}\mathbf{r}_{xy} = 0 \tag{e}$$

The three scalar equations of equilibrium with respect to axes (x, y, z) are obtained by taking the scalar products of Eq. (e) with $\mathbf{r}_x$, $\mathbf{r}_y$, $\mathbf{r}_z$, respectively.

Expressing the scalar products $\mathbf{r}_x \cdot \mathbf{r}_x, \mathbf{r}_x \cdot \mathbf{r}_y, \ldots, \mathbf{r}_x \cdot \mathbf{r}_{xy}$, etc., in terms of α, β, γ by means of Eqs. (A-1.4), (A-1.6), and (A-1.10), we obtain the three scalar equations

$$\frac{\partial}{\partial x}(\beta\gamma\sigma_x) + \frac{\partial}{\partial y}(\gamma\alpha\tau_{xy}) + \frac{\partial}{\partial z}(\alpha\beta\tau_{xz}) + \gamma\alpha_y\tau_{xy}$$

$$+ \beta\alpha_z\tau_{xz} - \gamma\beta_x\sigma_y - \beta\gamma_x\sigma_z + \rho\alpha\beta\gamma B_x = 0$$

$$\frac{\partial}{\partial x}(\beta\gamma\tau_{xy}) + \frac{\partial}{\partial y}(\gamma\alpha\sigma_y) + \frac{\partial}{\partial z}(\alpha\beta\tau_{yz}) + \alpha\beta_z\tau_{yz}$$

$$+ \gamma\beta_x\tau_{xy} - \alpha\gamma_y\sigma_z - \gamma\alpha_y\sigma_x + \rho\alpha\beta\gamma B_y = 0 \tag{A-2.1}$$

$$\frac{\partial}{\partial x}(\beta\gamma\tau_{xz}) + \frac{\partial}{\partial y}(\gamma\alpha\tau_{yz}) + \frac{\partial}{\partial z}(\alpha\beta\sigma_z) + \beta\gamma_x\tau_{xz}$$

$$+ \alpha\gamma_y\tau_{yz} - \beta\alpha_z\sigma_x - \alpha\beta_z\sigma_y + \rho\alpha\beta\gamma B_z = 0$$

Equations (A-2.1) represent the three scalar equilibrium equations relative to orthogonal curvilinear coordinates (x, y, z). Since they are purely statical in nature, they apply to all continuous-media materials. They may be extended to include dynamical problems, provided the body-force (B_x, B_y, B_z) is considered to include inertial forces. Love[2] has derived Eq. (A-2.1) without employing vector algebra.

Specialization of Eqs. (A-2.1). Commonly employed orthogonal curvilinear coordinate systems in three-dimensional problems are the cylindrical coordinate system (r, θ, z) and the spherical coordinate system (r, θ, ϕ); in plane problems the plane coordinate system (r, θ) is frequently used. Specialization of Eqs. (A-2.1) for these systems follows:

(a) *Cylindrical coordinate system* (r, θ, z). In Eqs. (A-2.1) we let $x = r$, $y = \theta, z = z$. Then the differential length ds is defined by the relation

$$ds^2 = dr^2 + r^2\,d\theta^2 + dz^2 \tag{A-2.2}$$

Comparison of Eqs. (A-1.5) and (A-2.2) yields

$$\alpha = 1, \qquad \beta = r, \qquad \gamma = 1 \tag{A-2.3}$$

Substituting Eq. (A-2.3) into Eqs. (A-2.1) we obtain the equilibrium equations

$$\frac{\partial\sigma_r}{\partial r} + \frac{1}{r}\frac{\partial\tau_{r\theta}}{\partial\theta} + \frac{\partial\tau_{rz}}{\partial z} + \frac{\sigma_r - \sigma_\theta}{r} + \rho B_r = 0$$

$$\frac{\partial\tau_{r\theta}}{\partial r} + \frac{1}{r}\frac{\partial\sigma_\theta}{\partial\theta} + \frac{\partial\tau_{\theta z}}{\partial z} + \frac{2\tau_{r\theta}}{r} + \rho B_\theta = 0 \tag{A-2.4}$$

$$\frac{\partial\tau_{rz}}{\partial r} + \frac{1}{r}\frac{\partial\tau_{\theta z}}{\partial\theta} + \frac{\partial\sigma_z}{\partial z} + \frac{\tau_{rz}}{r} + \rho B_z = 0$$

where $(\sigma_r, \sigma_\theta, \sigma_z, \tau_{r\theta}, \tau_{rz}, \tau_{\theta z})$ represent stress components defined relative to cylindrical coordinates (r, θ, z).

---

[2]A. E. H. Love, *Mathematical Theory of Elasticity*, 4th ed. (New York: Dover Publications, Inc., 1944), art. 5, p. 89.

(b) *Spherical coordinate system* (r, θ, ϕ). In Eqs. (A-2.1) we let $x = r$, $y = \theta$, $z = \phi$, where r is the radial coordinate, θ is the colatitude, and ϕ is the longitude. Since the differential length ds is defined by

$$ds^2 = dr^2 + r^2 \, d\theta^2 + r^2 \sin^2 \theta \, d\phi^2 \qquad (A-2.5)$$

comparison of Eqs. (A-1.5) and (A-2.5) yields

$$\alpha = 1, \qquad \beta = r, \qquad \gamma = r \sin \theta \qquad (A-2.6)$$

Substituting Eq. (A-2.6) into Eqs. (A-2.1), we obtain the equilibrium equations

$$\frac{\partial \sigma_r}{\partial r} + \frac{1}{r} \frac{\partial \tau_{r\theta}}{\partial \theta} + \frac{1}{r \sin \theta} \frac{\partial \tau_{r\phi}}{\partial \phi} + \frac{1}{r}(2\sigma_r - \sigma_\theta - \sigma_\phi + \tau_{r\theta} \cot \theta) + \rho B_r = 0$$

$$\frac{\partial \tau_{r\theta}}{\partial r} + \frac{1}{r} \frac{\partial \sigma_\theta}{\partial \theta} + \frac{1}{r \sin \theta} \frac{\partial \tau_{\theta\phi}}{\partial \phi} + \frac{1}{r}[(\sigma_\theta - \sigma_\phi) \cot \theta + 3\tau_{r\theta}] + \rho B_\theta = 0$$

$$\frac{\partial \tau_{r\phi}}{\partial r} + \frac{1}{r} \frac{\partial \tau_{\theta\phi}}{\partial \theta} + \frac{1}{r \sin \theta} \frac{\partial \sigma_\phi}{\partial \phi} + \frac{1}{r}(3\tau_{r\phi} + 2\tau_{\theta\phi} \cot \theta) + \rho B_\phi = 0$$

$$(A-2.7)$$

where $(\sigma_r, \sigma_\theta, \sigma_\phi, \tau_{r\theta}, \tau_{r\phi}, \tau_{\theta\phi})$ are defined relative to spherical coordinates (r, θ, ϕ).

(c) *Plane polar coordinate system* (r, θ). In plane-stress problems relative to (x, y) coordinates, $\sigma_z = \tau_{xz} = \tau_{yz} = 0$, and the remaining stress components are functions of (x, y) only (see Art. 5–2). Letting $x = r$, $y = \theta$, $z = z$ in Eqs. (A-2.4) and noting that $\sigma_z = \tau_{rz} = \tau_{\theta z} = (\partial/\partial z) = 0$, we obtain from Eq. (A-2.4)

$$\frac{\partial \sigma_r}{\partial r} + \frac{1}{r} \frac{\partial \tau_{r\theta}}{\partial \theta} + \frac{\sigma_r - \sigma_\theta}{r} + \rho B_r = 0$$

$$\frac{\partial \tau_{r\theta}}{\partial r} + \frac{1}{r} \frac{\partial \sigma_\theta}{\partial \theta} + 2\frac{\tau_{r\theta}}{r} + \rho B_\theta = 0 \qquad (A-2.8)$$

where $(\sigma_r, \sigma_\theta, \tau_{r\theta})$ are stress components defined relative to polar coordinates (r, θ). Equations (A-2.8) hold also for plane-strain problems (Art. 5–1), and they apply to generalized plane-stress problems, provided $(\sigma_r, \sigma_\theta, \tau_{r\theta})$ are defined as mean stress components relative to coordinate z (see Art. 5–2).

A-3 Strain-displacement Relations

Let (x, y, z) be orthogonal curvilinear coordinates relative to the unde-formed state of medium; that is, (x, y, z) are Lagrangian coordinates. Let (u, v, w) be the projections of the displacement vector of a point (x, y, z) in the medium on tangents to the coordinate lines at point (x, y, z). Then, since the unit tangents e_1, e_2, e_3 to the coordinate lines are defined by Eq. (A-1.7), the displacement vector of a particle initially located at point (x, y, z) defined by the position vector $\mathbf{r} = \mathbf{r}(x, y, z)$ is

$$\Delta\rho = \frac{u}{\alpha}\mathbf{r}_x + \frac{v}{\beta}\mathbf{r}_y + \frac{w}{\gamma}\mathbf{r}_z \tag{A-3.1}$$

After the deformation, the particle which initially lies at point (x, y, z) is located at the point (x^*, y^*, z^*) defined by the position vector $\mathbf{r}^*(x^*, y^*, z^*)$ $= \mathbf{r} + \Delta\rho$. Accordingly, with Eq. (A-3.1), the final position vector $\mathbf{r}^*$ of the particle that initially lies at point $\mathbf{r}$ is

$$\mathbf{r}^* = \mathbf{r} + \frac{u}{\alpha}\mathbf{r}_x + \frac{v}{\beta}\mathbf{r}_y + \frac{w}{\gamma}\mathbf{r}_z \tag{A-3.2}$$

The initial length of a line element ($\alpha\,dx$, $\beta\,dy$, $\gamma\,dz$) is determined by Eq. (A-1.5). The final length ds^* of the line element is determined by the relation (see Art. 3–3)

$$\left(\frac{ds^*}{ds}\right)^2 = \left(\frac{d\mathbf{r}^*}{ds}\right)^2 = \left(\mathbf{r}_x^*\frac{dx}{ds} + \mathbf{r}_y^*\frac{dy}{ds} + \mathbf{r}_z^*\frac{dz}{ds}\right)^2 \tag{A-3.3}$$

The derivatives ($\mathbf{r}_x^*$, $\mathbf{r}_y^*$, $\mathbf{r}_z^*$) may be evaluated by Eq. (A-3.2), with the aid of Eqs. (A-1.10); thus, we find

$$\mathbf{r}_x^* = \left(1 + \frac{u_x}{\alpha} + \frac{\alpha_y v}{\alpha\beta} + \frac{\alpha_z w}{\gamma\alpha}\right)\mathbf{r}_x + \left(\frac{v_x}{\beta} - \frac{\alpha_y u}{\beta^2}\right)\mathbf{r}_y + \left(\frac{w_x}{\gamma} - \frac{\alpha_z u}{\gamma^2}\right)\mathbf{r}_z$$

$$\mathbf{r}_y^* = \left(\frac{u_y}{\alpha} - \frac{\beta_x v}{\alpha^2}\right)\mathbf{r}_x + \left(1 + \frac{\beta_x u}{\alpha\beta} + \frac{v_y}{\beta} + \frac{\beta_z w}{\beta\gamma}\right)\mathbf{r}_y + \left(\frac{w_y}{\gamma} - \frac{\beta_z v}{\gamma^2}\right)\mathbf{r}_z \tag{A-3.4}$$

$$\mathbf{r}_z^* = \left(\frac{u_z}{\alpha} - \frac{\gamma_x w}{\alpha^2}\right)\mathbf{r}_x + \left(\frac{v_z}{\beta} - \frac{\gamma_y w}{\beta^2}\right)\mathbf{r}_y + \left(1 + \frac{\gamma_x u}{\gamma\alpha} + \frac{\gamma_y v}{\beta\gamma} + \frac{w_z}{\gamma}\right)\mathbf{r}_z$$

Furthermore, the derivatives dx/ds, dy/ds, dz/ds may be expressed in terms of the direction cosines (l, m, n) of the vector $d\mathbf{r}$ relative to local coordinate lines, since

$$l = \alpha\frac{dx}{ds}, \qquad m = \beta\frac{dy}{ds}, \qquad n = \gamma\frac{dz}{ds} \tag{A-3.5}$$

The strain components ϵ_x, ϵ_y, $\dots$, γ_{yz} are defined, as for rectangular coordinates, by Eq. (3–10). Hence, substitution of Eqs. (A-3.4) and (A-3.5) into Eq. (A-3.3) yields with Eqs. (A-1.4), (A-1.6), and (3–10)

$$\epsilon_x = \frac{1}{\alpha}\left[u_x + \frac{\alpha_y v}{\beta} + \frac{\alpha_z w}{\gamma} + \frac{1}{2\alpha}\left(u_x + \frac{\alpha_y v}{\beta} + \frac{\alpha_z w}{\gamma}\right)^2 \right.$$
$$\left. + \frac{1}{2\alpha}\left(v_x - \frac{\alpha_y u}{\beta}\right)^2 + \frac{1}{2\alpha}\left(w_x - \frac{\alpha_z u}{\gamma}\right)^2\right]$$

$$\epsilon_y = \frac{1}{\beta}\left[v_y + \frac{\beta_z w}{\gamma} + \frac{\beta_x u}{\alpha} + \frac{1}{2\beta}\left(v_y + \frac{\beta_z w}{\gamma} + \frac{\beta_x u}{\alpha}\right)^2 \right.$$
$$\left. + \frac{1}{2\beta}\left(w_y - \frac{\beta_z v}{\gamma}\right)^2 + \frac{1}{2\beta}\left(u_y - \frac{\beta_x v}{\alpha}\right)^2\right]$$

$$\epsilon_z = \frac{1}{\gamma}\left[w_z + \frac{\gamma_x u}{\alpha} + \frac{\gamma_y v}{\beta} + \frac{1}{2\gamma}\left(w_z + \frac{\gamma_x u}{\alpha} + \frac{\gamma_y v}{\beta}\right)^2 \right.$$
$$\left. + \frac{1}{2\gamma}\left(u_z - \frac{\gamma_x w}{\alpha}\right)^2 + \frac{1}{2\gamma}\left(v_z - \frac{\gamma_y w}{\beta}\right)^2\right]$$

$$\gamma_{xy} = \frac{u_y}{\beta} + \frac{v_x}{\alpha} - \frac{\beta_x v}{\alpha\beta} - \frac{\alpha_y u}{\alpha\beta} + \frac{1}{\alpha\beta}\left(u_x + \frac{\alpha_y v}{\beta} + \frac{\alpha_z w}{\gamma}\right)\left(u_y - \frac{\beta_x v}{\alpha}\right)$$

$$+ \frac{1}{\alpha\beta}\left(v_x - \frac{\alpha_y u}{\beta}\right)\left(v_y + \frac{\beta_x u}{\alpha} + \frac{\beta_z w}{\gamma}\right) \qquad\qquad (A\text{-}3.6)$$

$$+ \frac{1}{\alpha\beta}\left(w_x - \frac{\alpha_z u}{\gamma}\right)\left(w_y - \frac{\beta_z v}{\gamma}\right)$$

$$\gamma_{xz} = \frac{w_x}{\alpha} + \frac{u_z}{\gamma} - \frac{\alpha_z u}{\alpha\gamma} - \frac{\gamma_x w}{\alpha\gamma} + \frac{1}{\alpha\gamma}\left(w_z + \frac{\gamma_x u}{\alpha} + \frac{\gamma_y v}{\beta}\right)\left(w_x - \frac{\alpha_z u}{\gamma}\right)$$

$$+ \frac{1}{\alpha\gamma}\left(u_z - \frac{\gamma_x w}{\alpha}\right)\left(u_x + \frac{\alpha_z w}{\gamma} + \frac{\alpha_y v}{\beta}\right)$$

$$+ \frac{1}{\alpha\gamma}\left(v_z - \frac{\gamma_y w}{\beta}\right)\left(v_x - \frac{\alpha_y u}{\beta}\right)$$

$$\gamma_{yz} = \frac{v_z}{\gamma} + \frac{w_y}{\beta} - \frac{\gamma_y w}{\beta\gamma} - \frac{\beta_z v}{\beta\gamma} + \frac{1}{\beta\gamma}\left(v_y + \frac{\beta_z w}{\gamma} + \frac{\beta_x u}{\alpha}\right)\left(v_z - \frac{\gamma_y w}{\beta}\right)$$

$$+ \frac{1}{\beta\gamma}\left(w_y - \frac{\beta_z v}{\gamma}\right)\left(w_z + \frac{\gamma_y v}{\beta} + \frac{\gamma_x u}{\alpha}\right)$$

$$+ \frac{1}{\beta\gamma}\left(u_y - \frac{\beta_x v}{\alpha}\right)\left(u_z - \frac{\gamma_x w}{\alpha}\right)$$

Equations (A-3.6) are exact geometric expressions for the strain components; that is, they are not quadratic approximations. For small-displacement theory the quadratic terms in (u, v, w) are discarded. Then, Eqs. (A-3.6) reduce to linear relations between the strain components and the displacement components.

The strain-displacement relations may be specialized for particular orthogonal curvilinear coordinate systems. For example, $\alpha = \beta = \gamma = 1$ for rectangular cartesian coordinates, and then Eqs. (A-3.6) reduce to Eqs. (3-3.4).

For small-displacement theory the following specializations of Eqs. (A-3.6) are obtained:

Cylindrical coordinate system (r, θ, z):

$$\alpha = 1, \qquad \beta = r, \qquad \gamma = 1$$

$$\epsilon_r = \frac{\partial u}{\partial r}, \qquad \epsilon_\theta = \frac{u}{r} + \frac{1}{r}\frac{\partial v}{\partial \theta}, \qquad \epsilon_z = \frac{\partial w}{\partial z}$$

$$\gamma_{r\theta} = \frac{1}{r}\frac{\partial u}{\partial \theta} + \frac{\partial v}{\partial r} - \frac{v}{r}, \qquad \gamma_{rz} = \frac{\partial u}{\partial z} + \frac{\partial w}{\partial r} \qquad (A\text{-}3.7)$$

$$\gamma_{\theta z} = \frac{\partial v}{\partial z} + \frac{1}{r}\frac{\partial w}{\partial \theta}$$

Spherical coordinate system (r, θ, ϕ):

$$\alpha = 1, \qquad \beta = r, \qquad \gamma = r \sin \theta$$

$$\epsilon_r = \frac{\partial u}{\partial r}, \qquad \epsilon_\theta = \frac{u}{r} + \frac{1}{r}\frac{\partial v}{\partial \theta}, \qquad \epsilon_\phi = \frac{1}{r \sin \theta}\frac{\partial w}{\partial \phi} + \frac{u}{r} + \frac{v}{r} \cot \theta$$

$$\gamma_{r\theta} = \frac{1}{r}\frac{\partial u}{\partial \theta} + \frac{\partial v}{\partial r} - \frac{v}{r}, \qquad \gamma_{r\phi} = \frac{1}{r \sin \theta}\frac{\partial u}{\partial \phi} + \frac{\partial w}{\partial r} - \frac{w}{r} \qquad \text{(A-3.8)}$$

$$\gamma_{\theta\phi} = \frac{1}{r}\left(\frac{\partial w}{\partial \theta} - w \cot \theta\right) + \frac{1}{r \sin \theta}\frac{\partial v}{\partial \phi}$$

Plane polar coordinates (r, θ):

$$\alpha = 1, \quad \beta = r, \quad \gamma = 1, \quad w = \frac{\partial}{\partial z} = 0, \quad u = u(r, \theta), \quad v = v(r, \theta)$$

$$\text{(A-3.9)}$$

$$\epsilon_r = \frac{\partial u}{\partial r}, \qquad \epsilon_\theta = \frac{u}{r} + \frac{1}{r}\frac{\partial v}{\partial \theta}, \qquad \gamma_{r\theta} = \frac{1}{r}\frac{\partial u}{\partial \theta} + \frac{\partial v}{\partial r} - \frac{v}{r}$$

Similar results may be obtained for other orthogonal curvilinear coordinate systems by substitution of appropriate values for α, β, γ.

B

NUMERICAL APPROXIMATION
OF TORSION PROBLEM

B-1 Introduction

An engineer who wishes to solve an elasticity problem is often faced with the task of computing a number. In certain cases, such as the classical torsion problem of elasticity, exact solutions may be obtained for particular cross sections; in these cases the engineer may compute the number exactly. The existence of an exact solution also allows quick experimentation with the effect of various parameters of the problem. For many of the cross sections employed in practice, however, exact solutions are not readily obtainable, and then to calculate the number the engineer must often employ numerical techniques such as methods of finite differences, relaxation techniques, methods of successive approximations, energy methods (in conjunction with the Ritz method), and so on. Analogy methods are often used to obtain approximate results or to study the effects of certain parameters.

B-2 Finite Difference Approximations

Any linear partial differential equation may be studied by representing the derivatives of all orders in a sufficiently small range of the variables by a system of linear algebraic difference equations. For example, consider a function $f(x, y)$ of the variables (x, y). Let us assume initially that the variable y remains constant as the variable x is changed. The graphical representation of $f(x, y)$ is shown in Fig. B-2.1.

The curve which represents $f(x, y)$ may be approximated by a series of

straight-line segments AB, BC, ...
which connect points A, B, C, ... on
the curve, the abscissa of A, B, C,
... being x_0, x_1, x_2, ... For mathematical simplicity the intervals
(x_0, x_1), (x_1, x_2), ... are sometimes
taken to be equal. Then the slopes
of the line segments between points
A, B, C, ... are given by the expressions

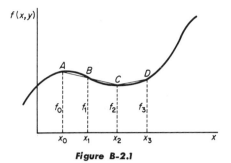

Figure B-2.1

$$\frac{f_1 - f_0}{x_1 - x_0}, \qquad \frac{f_2 - f_1}{x_2 - x_1}, \qquad \frac{f_3 - f_2}{x_3 - x_2}, \qquad \ldots \tag{B-2.1}$$

In the limit, we have

$$\left(\frac{\partial f}{\partial x}\right)_{AB} = \lim_{x_1 \to x_0} \frac{f_1 - f_0}{x_1 - x_0} \approx \frac{f_1 - f_0}{h}$$

$$\left(\frac{\partial f}{\partial x}\right)_{BC} = \lim_{x_2 \to x_1} \frac{f_2 - f_1}{x_2 - x_1} \approx \frac{f_2 - f_1}{h} \tag{B-2.2}$$

where h denotes the equal intervals $x_1 - x_0$, $x_2 - x_1$, ... The differences
$f_1 - f_0, f_2 - f_1, \ldots$ are called the *first differences* of f. The accuracy of the
approximation denoted by Eq. (B-2.2) is increased as $h \to 0$, that is, the
smaller the intervals $x_1 - x_0$, $x_2 - x_1$, ...

Similarly, the rate of change of slope of the line segment AC is defined by

$$\left(\frac{\partial^2 f}{\partial x^2}\right)_{AC} = \lim_{x_2 \to x_0} \frac{(\partial f/\partial x)_{BC} - (\partial f/\partial x)_{AB}}{(x_2 - x_0)/2} \approx \frac{f_2 - 2f_1 + f_0}{h^2} \tag{B-2.3}$$

The expression $f_2 - 2f_1 + f_0$ is called the *second difference* of f. Proceeding
in the above fashion, approximations for higher-order derivatives may be
obtained in terms of higher-order differences. Similarly, approximations for
$\partial f/\partial y$, $\partial^2 f/\partial y^2$, ... may be derived.

The above method of approximating the function $f(x, y)$ by straight-line
segments is the crudest finite difference approximation of f and its derivatives.
More refined approximations may be employed by approximating the
function f near a particular point x by a power-series expansion. For example,
we may let

$$f(x, y)_{y=\text{const.}} = a_0 + a_1(x - x_0) + a_2(x - x_0)(x - x_1)$$
$$+ a_3(x - x_0)(x - x_1)(x - x_3) + \cdots \tag{B-2.4}$$

The coefficients $a_0, a_1, a_2, \ldots$ of Eq. (B-2.4) are determined such that the
series is exact for a finite number of points $x_0, x_1, x_2, \ldots$, where $x_1 - x_0$
$= x_2 - x_1 = \ldots = x_n - x_{n-1} = h$.

Problem. In Eq. (B-2.4), retain the first three terms only. Evaluate the constants
a_0, a_1, a_2. Compare the results with Eqs. (B-2.2) and (B-2.3).

B-3 Application of Difference Equations to the Torsion Problem

The basic equations of the torsion problem of simply connected cross sections are

$$\nabla^2 \phi = -2G\theta \qquad \text{over region } R$$
$$\phi = 0 \qquad \text{on contour } C \tag{B–3.1}$$

where C is the bounding curve of region R (Fig. B-3.1).

To set up the torsion problem [Eqs. (B-3.1)] for solution by finite difference equations, we subdivide region R into regions $R_0, R_1, R_2, \ldots$ by a *mesh* (or *net*) formed by horizontal and vertical lines. The intersection points of these lines are called *interior nodal points* (Fig. B-3.1). The intersection points of the straight lines and the boundary curve C are called *boundary nodal points*. The line segment joining two adjacent nodal points is called a *string*. If region R is arbitrary, these strings will not in general form rectangular (square) regions with the boundary C. Hence, in general, the distance between any boundary nodal point and the adjacent interior nodal point or between any two adjacent boundary nodal points depends on the points considered.

For example, consider points 0, 1, 2, 3, 4, in Fig. B-3.1. It is apparent that the intervals between points (0, 1), (0, 2), (0, 3), (0, 4) are not equal. To take such situations into account, the original difference equations [Eqs. (B-2.2) and (B-2.3)] must be reformulated to allow for unequal intervals between nodal points. In theory, the inclusion of nonequal nodal point intervals in the finite difference equations is a simple matter, but in practice, nonequal nodal point intervals usually greatly increase the numerical work.

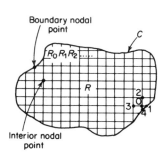

Boundary nodal point

Interior nodal point

Figure B-3.1

To account for nonequal nodal point intervals, we define the intervals $x_1 - x_0 = h_1$, $x_2 - x_1 = h_2, \ldots$, where now the constants $h_1, h_2, \ldots$ are no longer equal (Fig. B-2.1). Then Eq. (B-2.2) becomes

$$\left(\frac{\partial f}{\partial x}\right)_{AB} \approx \frac{f_1 - f_0}{h_1}, \qquad \left(\frac{\partial f}{\partial x}\right)_{BC} \approx \frac{f_2 - f_1}{h_2} \tag{B–3.2}$$

and Eq. (B-2.3) becomes

$$\left(\frac{\partial^2 f}{\partial x^2}\right)_{AC} \approx \left(\frac{2}{h_1 + h_2}\right)\left(\frac{f_2 - f_1}{h_2} - \frac{f_1 - f_0}{h_1}\right) \tag{B–3.3}$$

For the torsion problem of prismatic bars, Eq. (B-3.1) must be satisfied at each nodal point 0 of region R. Then, if the nodal points adjacent to point

0 are interior nodal points, we may approximate Eq. (B-3.1) by using Eq. (B-2.3).

Accordingly, we obtain

$$\frac{\partial^2 \phi}{\partial x^2} \approx \frac{1}{h^2}(\phi_3 - 2\phi_0 + \phi_1)$$

$$\frac{\partial^2 \phi}{\partial y^2} \approx \frac{1}{h^2}(\phi_4 - 2\phi_0 + \phi_2)$$

(B-3.4)

Equations (B-3.1) and (B-3.4) yield

$$\phi_1 + \phi_2 + \phi_3 + \phi_4 - 4\phi_0 \approx -2G\theta h^2 \qquad \text{(B-3.5)}$$

where $\phi_0, \phi_1, \ldots$ are the values of ϕ at nodal points $0, 1, 2, \ldots$.

Similar relations hold for every nodal point in R surrounded by interior nodal points. If one or more of the nodal points adjacent to point 0 are boundary nodal points, Eqs. (B-3.2) and (B-3.3) apply. Then Eq. (B-3.1) becomes (see Fig. B-3.1)

$$\left(\frac{2}{h_1 + h_2}\right)\left(\frac{\phi_3 - \phi_0}{h_3} - \frac{\phi_0 - \phi_1}{h_1}\right)$$

$$+ \left(\frac{2}{h_2 + h_4}\right)\left(\frac{\phi_2 - \phi_0}{h_2} - \frac{\phi_0 - \phi_4}{h_4}\right) \approx -2G\theta$$

(B-3.6)

where h_1, h_2, h_3, h_4 denote the intervals between nodal points $(0, 1)$, $(0, 2)$, $(0, 3)$, and $(0, 4)$, respectively, and where $\phi_0, \phi_1, \ldots$ are the values of ϕ at points $0, 1, 2, \ldots$.

By Eq. (B-3.1), $\phi = 0$ for all boundary nodal points (in this case, $\phi_1 = \phi_4 = 0$). When applied to the n nodal points in region R, Eqs. (B-3.5) and (B-3.6) yield a set of n linear algebraic equations. The solution of these n linear algebraic equations yields the values $\phi_0, \phi_1, \ldots, \phi_n$ of the stress function ϕ.

B-4 Higher-order Difference Approximations

In the above examples, ϕ was approximated by straight-line segments over intervals of length h. The accuracy of the approximation may be increased by decreasing the length of the interval, that is, by decreasing h. Alternatively, the accuracy of the approximation may be increased by including more terms in the power-series expansion of $f(x, y)$. For example, if we retain the first three terms in the series representation of $f(x, y)$ [Eq. (B-2.4)], we find that the resulting equation for $f(x, y)$ leads to Eqs. (B-2.2) and (B-2.3). If we retain the first five terms in Eq. (B-2.4), we obtain

$$\left(\frac{\partial^2 f}{\partial x^2}\right)_{x=x_2} = -\frac{1}{12h^2}(f_4 - 16f_3 + 30f_2 - 16f_1 + f_0) \qquad \text{(B-4.1)}$$

where $x = x_2$ is the midpoint of the interval $(0, 1, 2, 3, 4)$.

With Eq. (B-4.1), Eq. (B-3.1) becomes

$$\phi_5 + \phi_6 + \phi_7 + \phi_8 - 16(\phi_1 + \phi_2 + \phi_3 + \phi_4) + 60\phi_0 = 24G\theta h^2 \qquad \text{(B-4.2)}$$

Equation (B-4.2) shows that the value of ϕ_0 depends on the values of ϕ at eight neighboring nodal points 1, 2, . . ., 8 (Fig.B-4.1), whereas Eq. (B-3.5) indicates that the value of ϕ_0 is determined by the value of ϕ at four adjacent nodal points. Accordingly, Eq. (B-4.2) is said to be a *higher-order approximation* than Eq. (B-3.5). Although straightforward in theory, higher order approximations often lead to lengthy computations. The completion of such computations in a reasonable amount of time generally requires the use of high-speed electronic digital computers.

Symmetry considerations may often be used to reduce the number of calculations required. For example, for the torsion of bars with rectangular cross sections, only one-quarter of the cross section need be examined.

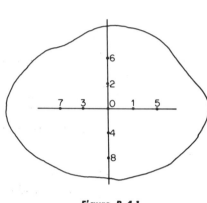

Figure B-4.1

B-5 Stress Components of Torsion Problem

With the values of ϕ known at all nodal points, the value of the stress components τ_{xz}, τ_{yz} may be computed by using Eqs. (B-2.2) and the relations

$$\tau_{xz} = \frac{\partial \phi}{\partial y}, \qquad \tau_{yz} = -\frac{\partial \phi}{\partial x} \tag{B-5.1}$$

Accordingly, by Eqs. (B-2.2) and (B-5.1),

$$(\tau_{xz})_{02} \approx \frac{\phi_2 - \phi_0}{h}, \qquad (\tau_{yz})_{01} \approx \frac{\phi_0 - \phi_1}{h} \tag{B-5.2}$$

If ϕ is approximated by straight-line segments, Eqs. (B-5.2) may serve to determine the stress components, provided the interval h is sufficiently small. If ϕ is determined by higher-order approximations, it is justifiable to fit smooth curves through x and y nodal points, by means of standard interpolation formulas[1] (Newton's interpolation formula, Stirling's central difference interpolation formula, etc.). Then by differentiating the resulting equation for ϕ, the stress components may be determined by means of Eqs. (B-5.1). Alternatively, in some cases, greater accuracy may be obtained by using values of ϕ, obtained by straight-line approximations, to approximate ϕ along nodal lines by a smooth curve given by standard interpolation formulas.

---

[1]W. E. Milne, *Numerical Solution of Differential Equations* (New York: John Wiley & Sons, Inc., 1960); F. B. Hildebrand, *Introduction to Numerical Analysis* (New York: McGraw-Hill Book Company, 1956).

Higher-order approximations of the stress components may also be obtained by using Eqs. (B-2.4) and (B-5.2).

B-6 Relaxation Technique

As noted in Eq. (B-3.5), the value of ϕ at nodal point 0 may be approximated by the relation

$$\phi_1 + \phi_2 + \phi_3 + \phi_4 - 4\phi_0 = -2G\theta h^2$$

Similar relations hold for each nodal point in the region R. Hence, the application of finite difference equations leads to the solution of large numbers of simultaneous linear algebraic equations.

An alternate approach to the determination of ϕ is to write Eq. (B-3.5) in the form

$$\phi_1 + \phi_2 + \phi_3 + \phi_4 - 4\phi_0 + 2G\theta h^2 = 0 \qquad \text{(B–6.1)}$$

If now values of ϕ_0, ϕ_1, ϕ_2, ... are selected arbitrarily, Eq. (B-6.1) will not be satisfied exactly. Then, Eq. (B-6.1) may be written

$$\phi_1 + \phi_2 + \phi_3 + \phi_4 - 4\phi_0 + 2G\theta h^2 = E \qquad \text{(B–6.2)}$$

where E denotes the error (or residual) in Eq. (B-6.1). The principal idea of the relaxation technique is to reduce the residual for each nodal point to zero. For example, if ϕ_1, ϕ_2, ϕ_3, and ϕ_4 are increased by 1, the value of E is increased by 4. Also, if ϕ_0 is increased by 1, the value of E is decreased by 4. Thus, by taking adjusted successive trial values of ϕ at the nodal points 1, 2, 3, 4, 0, the residual E in Eq. (B-6.2) may be reduced to zero. By extending this idea to all nodal points in the region R, all error terms may be reduced to zero (approximately). In general, it is not possible to reduce the residuals to zero for every nodal point. However, the computation is considered complete when the residuals are all "sufficiently" small.

In the relaxation method, values of $\phi(x, y)$ for each nodal point in the cross section are assumed. With these assumed values of ϕ, the corresponding residuals are computed for each nodal point. Beginning with the largest residual, E_{max}, new values of $\phi(x, y)$ are chosen to make E_{max} vanish. Then the process is repeated for a second nodal point. Depending on the number of nodal points and the relative magnitude of the errors, the process may converge more or less rapidly. To speed up the convergence of the calculations, several modifications of the basic method of relaxation have been invented. For example, the processes of over-relaxation, block relaxation, group relaxation, and multiplying factors are all designed to reduce the number of calculations required to obtain convergence.[2]

---

[2]Milne, *Numerical Solution of Differential Equations;* Hildebrand, *Introduction to Numerical Analysis.*

Review Problems

R-1 Derive Eqs. (B-4.1) and (B-4.2).

R-2 Apply the method of finite differences to the torsion problem of a bar with rectangular cross section.

R-3 Apply the technique of relaxation to the torsion problem of a bar with rectangular cross section.

INDEX

A

Acceleration field, 9
Acceleration vector, 8
Adiabatic deformation process, 104
Aeolotropic material, 110
Airy, G. B., 139
  stress function, 138–43
    solutions in polar coordinates, 155
    solutions in rectangular coordinates,
      140
Algebraic equations, theory of, 77–78
Angle of twist, 123, 164
Anisotropic material, 107, 110
Arrays, 23–24
  antisymmetric square, 23, 24
  characteristic equation, 33
  rectangular, 23
  skew-symmetric, 23
  square, 23
  stress, 39, 59
  symmetric square, 24
  typical element, 23
Averbach, B. L., 224
Axis of twist, 181, 182

B

Bar, prismatic, 162–215
  bending, 195–215
    elliptic cross section, 209–11
    circular cross section, 211

Bar, prismatic (*cont.*):
  bending (*cont.*):
    rectangular cross section, 211–15
  boundary conditions, 163
  Prandtl theory, 168–72
  St. Venant torsion theory, 164–68
  torsion, 164–95
    elliptic cross section, 172–75
    equilateral triangle, 176–77
    narrow rectangular cross section,
      189–90
    rectangular section, 190–94
    with tubular cavities, 179–81
Beams, thermal stress, 221–23
Beltrami-Michell compatibility relation,
  117, 164
Bending, pure, 133
  bar subjected to transverse end force
    195–215
  function, 199
Biharmonic equation, 139
  solutions of, 140
Biot, M. A., 217
Birkhoff, G., 97
Boley, B. A., 218
Boresi, A. P., 64
Boundary conditions, 118–19
  for multiply connected regions, 142–43,
    179–80
  for plane polar coordinates, 154–55
  in terms of Airy stress function, 140–
    42

Boundary conditions (*cont.*):
   for torsion of bars, 167–71
Boundary value problems of elasticity
   118–19
Brown, O. E., 7

C

Carslaw, H. S., 218
Cauchy-Riemann equations, 168, 231, 232
Center of shear (shear center) 206–8
Center of twist, 170
Chadwick, P., 217
Characteristic roots, 33, 34
Chasles' theorem, 64
Churchill, R. V., 168, 175, 192, 203
Compatibility:
   equation for plane elasticity in polar
      coordinates, 154–55
   small displacement, conditions of, 90–
      91
Complementary function (solution or in-
      tegral), 203
Complex variables, 147
Conservation of energy, law, 105
Continuous body, 63
   deformation, 63, 64–67
Continuous medium, 35
Contour map, 177
Coordinate line, curvilinear, 17, 241
Coordinate surfaces, 17, 240
Coordinate systems:
   cylindrical, 16
   Eulerian, 65
   Lagrangian, 61
   left-handed, 3
   orthogonal curvilinear, 16, 17, 240–42
   rectangular cartesian, 16
   right-handed, 3
   spherical, 17
Courant, R., 16, 48, 76, 99, 168, 181
Cross section:
   multiply connected, 179–81
   warping, 175, 177
Curl of a vector field, 9
Current density, 10, 11

D

Deformable body :
   definition, 63

Deformable body (*cont.*):
   differential equations of motion, 56–58
      61–62
Deformation:
   definition, 63
   condition for continuously possible, 67
   of a continuous body, 64–67
   zero state (zero configuration), 103
Del, 5
Determinants, notation for vector prod-
      uct, 3
Differential length in orthogonal curvilin-
      ear coordinates, 17, 18
Differential, total, 68, 105
Differentiation:
   of scalar field, 8, 9
   of vectors, 7
   of vector fields, 9
Diffusivity, 219
Direction cosines between two sets of
      rectangular Cartesian axes:
   determinant, 26
   orthogonality relations, 25, 26
   relations between 25–27
   table, 24
Directional derivative, 5, 182
   maximum value, 5, 182
Dirichlet boundary value problem, 168
Displacement:
   of cantilever beam subjected to trans-
      verse end force, 203–6
   components for plane elasticity, 148
   deformable body, 64–67
   particle, 63
   plane, 64
   potential, 232–36
   rigid-body, 63, 64, 74, 87
   vector, 66
Divergence, 10
   theorem 11–13
   in two dimensions, 13, 14
Duhamel, J. M. C., 216

E

Eigenvalues (*see* Characteristic roots)
Eigenvectors, 33, 34
   orthogonality, 33, 34
Eisenhart, C. P., 25, 33, 44
Elastic limit, 103
Elastic constants (stiffnesses), 106

Elastic constants (*cont.*):
for general anisotropic elastic material, 107, 130
Elasticity:
boundary value problems 118–19
bulk modulus, 112
concept, 102–3
perfect, 102
plane axially symmetric problem in polar coordinates, 155–57
plane problem, 131
plane strain, 131
plane theory, 131
polynomial solution of two-dimensional problems, 145–48
shear modulus, 113
strain energy density, 103–4
uniqueness theorem for equilibrium problem, 119–21
Emissivity, 220
relative, 220
Energy:
internal, 104–5, 128
kinetic, 106, 128
Equilibrium:
of cubic element, 39, 58
differential equations of, 58
in cylindrical coordinates, 224
in orthogonal curvilinear coordinates, 244
in plane polar coordinates, 152, 245
in spherical coordinates, 245
of infinitesimal tetrahedron, 40
of moments, 39
Eulerian coordinate method, 65
Eulerian coordinates, 65, 69
Euler's theorem, 64
Exact differential, 15, 16

F

Fields, 6
divergence, 10
nonstationary (unsteady) 6
steady 6, 11
vector lines, 6
Finite difference:
application to torsion problem, 251–54
approximations for derivatives, 249–50
expressions for stress components of torsion, 251

Finite difference (*cont.*):
first difference, 250
higher order differences, 250, 252
mesh (or net), 251
nodal points, 251
second difference, 250
Flexural function, 199
Fluids:
circulation, 14
Eulerian continuity equation for, 10–11
frictionless, 37
ideal, 37
incompressible, 11
irrotational flow, 11
steady flow, 12
unsteady flow, 11
viscous, 37
vorticity, 15
Forces:
body, 37, 56
conservative, 104
distributed, 35, 36
non-conservative, 104
normal, 36
point, 35
shearing, 36
statically equivalent systems, 119
surface, 37, 56
tractive, 56
Foster, R. M., 192, 193

G

Gibbs, 21
Goodier, J., 119, 143, 150, 151, 194, 233, 238
Goursat, E., 12
Gradient (grad), 5, 182
in orthogonal curvilinear coordinates, 18, 19
Green, A. E., 29, 147
Green's theorem, 13
of the plane, 14
Grossmann, G., 185
Günther, W., 176, 189

H

Heat conduction, differential equation, 218

Hilbert, D., 76, 168, 181
Hildebrand, F. B., 253, 254
Hill, R., 104
Hodge, P., Jr., 51
Homogeneous media, 109–10
Hysteresis, 103

I

Indexes:
  dummy, 22
  free, 22
  notation, 21–24
  repeated Greek index, 21
  repeated nonsummed, 22
  rule of substitution, 31
  summing, 22
Integral, particular, 203
Interpolation formulas, 253
Invariance, 15
  stress, 47
Isotropic media, 109–10

J

Jacobian, 66
Jaeger, J. C., 218
Jeffreys, H., 111

K

Kaplan, W., 68
Kellogg, O. D., 167, 168, 235
Kirchhoff, 119
Kronecker delta, 30, 31
  properties of, 31

L

Lagrangian coordinates 65, 245
Lagrangian multiplier method, 48, 99
Lamé coefficients, 18
Lamé elastic constants, 111
Lanczos, C., 76
Langhaar, H. L., 64, 242
Laplace, 11, 20, 175
Laplace equation, 11, 175
  in three-demensional orthogonal cur-
    vilinear coordinates, 20
Laplacian, in orthogonal curvilinear co-
  ordinates, 19, 20

Level surfaces, 5
Line element:
  final direction cosines of a deformed,
    72–74
  direction cosines, 69, 73
Line integral, 14
Lines of force, 6
Love, A. E. H., 87, 90, 104, 108, 112,
  143, 244
Ludwik, P., 72

M

Mc Dowell, E. L., 236
Maclane, S., 97
Magnification factor, 69, 71, 93
Matrix, 23
Maxwell, James Clerk, 140
Method of series:
  for bending, 211–15
  for torsion, 190–94
Metric tensor of space, 18
Michell, J. H., 155
Milne, W. E., 253, 254
Milne-Thomson, J., 147
Mindlin, R. D., 35
Mohr, O., 54
  circle of, 53–55
Moment:
  body, 39, 40, 41
  equilibrium of, 39
  twisting, 187
Momentum, time rate, change of, 56, 57,
  61
Morris, M., 7
Multiply connected region, 142–43, 179–
  81
Muskhelisvili, N. I., 119, 131, 143, 147

N

Nabla, 5
Necessary conditions:
  for compatible small displacement
    strain, 90
  for exact differential, 16, 33
  for rigid-body displacement, 70
  for single-valued Airy stress function,
    143

Neou, C. Y., method of, 146
Neumann, F. E., 216
Neumann boundary value problem, 167, 181
Newton, 220
Nonhomogeneous material, 110
Nonisotropic material, 110
Novozhilov, V. V., 58, 74, 102
Nowacki, W., 218
Nye, J. F. 108, 110

O

Octahedral planes, 52
Octahedral shearing stress, 51–52
directions, 51
Olmstead, J. M. H., 66

P

Parkus, H., 218
Particle:
displacement, 64
initial location, 65
Pestel, E., 185
Pierce, B. O., 192, 193
Pipes, L., 33
Pippard, A. B., 105
Planck, M., 108
Plane strain, 131–33
compatibility equation, 137
Plane stress, 135
compatibility equation, 137
generalized, 133–36
Plasticity, 103
Poisson equation, 202–3, 219
Poisson's ratio, 111, 113
Polar coordinates:
Airy stress function in, 155
equilibrium equations in, 152
plane compatibility equation in, 154
strain components in, 158, 159
stress components in, 154
Potential field, 7
Potential function, 7
Prager, W., 51
Prandtl, L., 168, 169
Prandtl membrane analogy 185–88
Prandtl torsion function, 169, 172
Pressure, 47
Principal planes, 44

Q

Quadratic forms, homogeneous, 32, 33

R

Real variables, theory, 66
Relaxation, 254
residual, 254
modification, 254
Rigid body:
definition, 63
displacement, 63–67, 74, 87
Rosenfeld, H. R., 224
Rotation, 64
of a volume element, 81–83
vector, 83

S

Saint-Venant principle, 119
Saint-Venant semi-inverse method, 121, 164
Saint-Venant solution of torsion, 164–68
Saint-Venant warping function, 165, 166, 172
Scalar, 27
Scalar field, 4
Scalar point functions, 4–6, 241
Scalar product of vectors, 2
application 14, 15
triple product of vectors, 3, 4
Schild, A. 18, 24, 29, 51, 55, 97
Semi-inverse method, 121, 164
Sen, B., 236
Sharma, B., 236
Shearing strain (see Strain, shearing)
Shearing stress (see Stress, shearing)
Shear modulus of elasticity, 113
Sneddon, I., 147
Sokolnikoff, E. S., 99
Sokolnikoff, I. S., 99, 131
Sokolovski, V. V., 51, 81
Solids, 37
plastic, 37
Special states of stress:
hydrostatic, 112, 113, 122
plane, 52
pure shear, 113
simple tension, 112–13
Specific heat, 218

Sternberg, E., 119, 236
Stevenson, A. C., 147
Stokes' Theorem, 15
Strain:
  components, 69, 70, 71, 72, 87
  components in cylindrical coordinates, 247
  components in orthogonal curvilinear coordinates, 246–47
  components in plane polar coordinates, 158–59, 248
  components in spherical coordinates, 248
  definition:
    large-deflection, 71, 93
    engineering, 71
    logarithmic, 71, 72
    natural or true, 71
  deviator, 79
  Eulerian components, 69, 94
  in index notation, 92–101
  invariants, 77, 78
  Lagrangian components, 69, 93
  of a line element, 67–72, 92–94
  mean, 79
  octahedral, 80–81
  octahedral shearing, 81
  plane, 131–33
  principal, 76, 97–101
  principal axes (directions) 77, 99, 100, 101
  principal values, 76, 97, 98
  shearing, 74–76, 94–96
    physical significance, 75
  special types, 87–89
    dilatation, 88
    homogeneous, 89
    simple shear, 88
  tensor, 75–76, 96–97
  in terms of rotation vector components, 83–86
  transformation of components, 76, 97
  volumetric, 78–79
    engineering, 79
    large deflection, 78
    logarithmic, 79
Strain energy density:
  for certain symmetry conditions, 108–9
  for elastically isotropic medium under adiabatic conditions 110–12
  function, 103–4

Strain energy density (cont.):
  for general anisotropic linearly elastic material, 107–8
  in index notation, 129
  relation to stress components, 104–6
  in terms of principal strains, 119
  for thermoelasticity, 115
Stream lines, 6
Stress:
  array, 39, 59
  boundary conditions, 41
  circle of, 53–55
  components, 39–40
    normal to a plane, 37, 38, 41, 59
    on oblique plane, 41
    relation to strain energy density, 104
    symmetric of, 40
    tangent to a plane, 37, 38, 41, 59
  definition, 35–37
  deviator tensor, 50, 51
  direction, 37
  extremum values, 47
  extremum values of shearing, 47–49
  invariants, 47
  mean tensor 50, 51
  normal, 36, 37, 59
  notation, 37, 38
    index form, 59
    summary, 38
  plane, 52–55
  plane components in terms of Airy stress function, 153–54
  at a point, 36
  principal, 44–47, 60, 61
  principal axes, 44, 46, 51, 60
  principal directions, 47, 60
  rectangular components in terms of Airy stress function, 139
  shearing, 36, 37, 59
    component, 38, 40, 41
    component in any direction, 182–85
    extreme values, 47–49
    octahedral, 51
  sign convention, 38
  tensor, 44, 59
  tensor character of, 43–56
  theory, 35–62
  thermal, 216–39
  tranformation of components, 43, 44, 60
  vector, 36, 40, 60

Stress couple, 35
Stress-strain relations, 106–15
  generalized Hooke's law, 106–9, 129–30
  in index notation, 128–30
  including temperature effects, 224–25, 227, 229
  for isotropic media, 110–11
  special states, 112–15
Sufficient conditions:
  for compatible small displacement strain, 90
  for exact differential, 16, 33
  for rigid-body displacement, 70
  for single-valued Airy stress function, 143
Summation convention, 21–24
Surface integral, 14, 15
Synge, J. L., 18, 24, 29, 51, 55, 97

T

Temperature, distribution:
  diffusivity, 219
  stationary, 219
  steady-state, 219
Tensors, 24–32
  antisymmetric parts of, 29–30
  conjugate, 29
  deviator strain, 79–80
  deviator stress, 50
  invariants, 80
  isotropic, 31
  mean strain, 79–80
  mean stress, 50
  nth order, 28–29
  second-order, 44
  special third-order (ϵ_{ijk}), 31
  stress, 44
  substitution, 31
  symmetric parts, 29–30
  tranformation under change of rectangular Cartesian coordinate system, 24
Thermal conductivity, 219
Thermal expansion coefficient, 220
  effect of stress, 224
Thermal stress, 216–39
  axially symmetric, 236–39
  Duhamel-Neumann theory, 217
  elementary approach, 220–23

Thermal stress (cont.):
  physical interpretation, 226–27
  plane theory, 229–36
  spherically symmetrical, 227–28
Thermoelasticity:
  axially symmetric case, 236–39
  compatibility equations in terms of stress, 115–17
  equations, 114–15
  plane theory, 229–36
Tiersten, H. F., 35
Timoshenko, S., 119, 140, 150, 151, 189, 194, 209, 238
Timpe, A., 155
Torsional rigidity, 173
Torsion of prismatic bars, 164–95
  displacement components, 170–72
  moment-angle of twist relation, 173
  Prandtl torsion-function, 168–72
  Saint-Venant's solution, 164–68
  shaft with constant circular cross section, 123–26
  warping function, 164–68
Transform methods, 147
Translation, of a mechanical system, 64
Twist:
  angle, 173
  axis, 181, 182
  transfer, 181, 182
  center, 170

U

Uniqueness theorem for equilibrium problem of elasticity, 119

V

Vector addition:
  associative law, 1
  commutative law, 1, 2
  in index notation, 21
Vector algebra, 1–4
Vector fields, 6, 7
  potential function of, 7
Vectors, 1–10, 27–28
  acceleration, 8
  body force, 56
  components of, 1
    Cartesian, 1
  differentiation (see Differentiation of vectors)

Vectors (*cont.*):
  displacement, 6, 57
  magnitude, 1, 2
  notation, 1
  operator, 5
  point function, 5
  product, 2–4
  projections, 1
  scalar product (*see* Scalar product of vectors)
  stress, 36, 40, 60
  sums (*see* Vector addition)
  traction, 57
  triple product, 4
  unit, 1, 241
  velocity, 6, 8,
  vorticity, 15
Velocity, 6
  field, 6, 8–12
Viscoelasticity, 103

Volumetric strain (*see* Strain, volumetic)
Von Mises, R., 119

W

Weber, C., 176
Weiner, J. H., 218
Whittaker, E., 64–88
Work:
  of body forces, 105, 128
  of external forces, 104, 128
  of surface forces, 105, 128

Y

Young's modulus, 111, 113
Warping function, St. Venant, 164–68

Z

Zerna, W., 29
Zero state (zero configuration), 103